Contents

CHAPTER 1

Why We Hope

IS THERE ANY HOPE?

The afternoon of December 17, 1927, was as gray as any winter's dawn. The waters of the Atlantic off Provincetown, Massachusetts, were rough and cold as United States submarine S-4 completed its test run under water and began to surface. Raking upward through the chill waves, the captain checked the periscope. Nothing on the surface.

Moments later the coast guard cutter *Paulding* rammed into the side of the S-4 as it surfaced immediately in front of the cutter. The force of the impact from the *Paulding,* cruising at 18 knots, tore two gaping holes in the hull of the S-4, and the sub dropped like a stone to the seabed.

The *Paulding* sent out a distress signal and waited for survivors. None surfaced. The S-4 lay in 100 feet of water, just 1,800 yards from shore.

Rescuers were slow to arrive at the scene and to locate the sunken sub. The first diver made it down some 22 hours after the accident. Working his way along the wreck, his lead-weighted boots banged on the metal hull. He heard a faint tapping from the torpedo room. Could it be that some of the crew had survived the disaster?

He banged on the hatch cover and received an answering tap. Using Morse code, he learned that six men had survived and were trapped in an air pocket.

"Is there any hope?" came the question. "Please hurry!"

Imprisoned in a steel shell at the bottom of the ocean, the men of the S-4 had only a short time until their air ran out. They were in total darkness without food or water. Their only thought: *Is there any hope?*

That's the question! Is there any hope? Faced with the inevitability of death, all look for some kind of hope—a way out, a means of escape. Yet like the six on the S-4, we have no way to save ourselves. Groping around in the dark, hungry, thirsty, cold, wet, and tired, the only thing that keeps us alive is hope itself.

With a storm brewing, the rescuers tried to refloat the submarine. But it was too badly damaged, and the air line was ineffective. They attached an oscillator to the hull so that the crewmen inside could communicate to the ship above by Morse code. Messages of comfort came from the men's relatives. Then a diver descended in atrocious weather to try to bring the suffocating men some air. He became trapped in the wreckage and had to be rescued himself. The divers had to postpone any further attempt.

The messages became infrequent as the air ran out. After 62 hours in their living coffin, the men sent their final message: "We understand." Their hope had turned to hopelessness as the rescue failed.

Three months later the Navy salvaged the S-4 and repaired it. It became the test submarine for experimental equipment like the Momsen Lung, designed to help submariners survive such an accident and escape to the surface. The vessel was a memorial to a hope that had died.

The tragedy of the sinking of the S-4 and its failed rescue illustrates in a graphic way the condition in which we find ourselves. It's a situation with no escape. We have no source of salvation in ourselves. In the darkness, as we feel cold, wet, hungry, and thirsty, we realize that our rescue can come only from outside.

The question is always: "Is there any hope?"

The failure to help the men of the S-4 also shows what can happen when we place our hope in human strength and ability. However well intentioned, however eager to assist, human hope is feeble and fallible.

For our situation, when we too ask, "Is there any hope?" the only response that has any real meaning is to place our hope in the God of hope.

That is why Christian hope defines who we are. Without it we are as doomed as the crew of the S-4. Yet with this wonderful hope we have the assurance of life with meaning now—and an eternity beyond. That is why Scripture can describe our anticipated future as "sure and certain," and why it is truly the "blessed hope." For it relies on the assurances of God Himself, the only one trustworthy and true.

WHY HOPE?

We all need hope to function, to live. Without hope, life becomes meaningless and pointless. We have nothing good to expect in the future, so we ignore the future. If we have no hope in our hearts, then life is simply one long grinding despair, the "monotonous moils of strained, hard-pressed humanity" (Thomas Hardy).

When hope ceases, life becomes nothing more than mere existence. For "if the mere delay of hope deferred makes the heart sick, what will the death of hope—its final and total disappointment—despair, do to it?" (W. Nevins).

Truly, "in all things it is better to hope than to despair" (Goethe).

That is why to hope is so vital, and to really live we need a dynamic hope. The future must always be part of our perspective, leading us on from where we are to where we wish to be:

"Hope, like the gleaming taper's light,
Adorns and cheers our way;
And still, as darker grows the night,
Emits a brighter ray" (Oliver Goldsmith).

We are creatures of hope. The need for hope is an essential part of who we are. As we look forward, we expect, we anticipate. The future we hope for determines the way we think and act in the present. When hope dies, we—for all meaningful purposes—also die. Without hope we are imprisoned in an existence of despair, a life that has no purpose and no goal. Hope is what makes us free—free to anticipate a future that is not just a continuation of the dreary present.

The capacity to see that life has meaning and purpose, that we can choose to make a difference, that we are *free to hope*—such vision makes us free. As Christians, that means the liberating power of God, so that whatever our circumstances, we know that both our present and our future are secure in Him.

Christian hope is the excitement of knowing God's intentions, of trusting His promises. That's expectation of the keenest kind. That's anticipation. And that's the freedom that the blessed hope brings—looking for a present and a future guaranteed by God Himself.

Why hope? The answer is that to abandon hope is not an option, not a possibility. Hope defines us, declares who we are. The Christian hope is the hope above all hopes, and without it we are immeasurably poorer. It is the future of God, and our participation in such a future.

HOPE IS THE WINDOW

"Eternity is the divine treasure house, and hope is the window, by means of which mortals are permitted to see, as through a glass darkly, the things which God is preparing" (William Mountford).

Hope is our window on life. The way in which we see what is around us, it defines the present and what we long for. Many people down through the ages have tried to describe the meaning of hope and its basis. Some of their attempts have been wise, some amusing, some plainly foolish. But such thoughts give us some idea of the contrast between humanity's hope and that of God:

"We must accept finite disappointment, but never lose infinite hope" (Martin Luther King, Jr.).

"We judge of man's wisdom by his hope" (Ralph Waldo Emerson).

"Great hopes make great men" (Thomas Fuller).

"He that lives upon hope will die fasting" (Benjamin Franklin).

"Hope is a waking dream" (Aristotle).

"The miserable have no other medicine but only hope" (William Shakespeare).

"Lord, save us all from . . . a hope tree that has lost the faculty of putting out blossoms" (Mark Twain).

"Hope is faith holding out its hand in the dark" (George Iles).

"If one truly has lost hope, one would not be on hand to say so" (Eric Bentley).

"Take hope from the heart of man, and you make him a beast of prey" (Ouida).

"Hope never abandons you, you abandon it" (George Weinberg).

"Hope is patience with the lamp lit" (Tertullian).

"Hope is the poor man's bread" (Gary Herbert).

"Hope is the word which God has written on the brow of every man" (Victor Hugo).

"Everything that is done in the world is done by hope" (Martin Luther).

"True hope responds to the real world, to real life; it is an active effort" (Walter Anderson).

"Hope is itself a species of happiness, and, perhaps, the chief happiness which this world affords" (Samuel Johnson).

"Hope is the pillar that holds up the world" (Pliny).

Yet what do *we* see as we look out through hope's window? Is it just a dream or a vain expectation? Is hope "the universal liar" (R. G. Ingersoll)? What is hope?

ANY HOPE? THE ANSWER OF THE ONLY HOPE

The basis for the Christian hope is not vague or insubstantial. Jesus, the Son of God, is the promise-maker and the promise-keeper:

" 'Do not be worried and upset,' Jesus told them. 'Believe in God and believe also in me. There are many rooms in my Father's house, and I am going to prepare a place for you. I would not tell you this if it were not so. And after I go and prepare a place for you, I will come back and take you to myself, so that you will be where I am' " (John 14:1-3, TEV).

Such exciting words to thrill the heart! And "he is faithful that promised" (Heb. 10:23). Here we have the true foundation of hope, the assurance of the God who not only knows the future but invites us to be there with Him. That is why "we have placed our hope in the living God, who is the Savior of all" (1 Tim. 4:10, TEV).

Sometimes the days seem dark and dreary, and it is easy to fall into depression and despair and demand "Is there any hope?" That's when God comes close once again as we search for meaning and purpose, and reminds us of the implications of our hope. Hope is everything to us—the source of our being, our destiny, our very lives. To live without hope is not to live at all. In fact, it denies our very system of belief, for "where there is no hope, there is no faith" (William Gouge).

It is God who intervenes to bring hope. For us even to exist, we must believe in a future, whatever we may think that future may bring. It *has* to be there, as a part of our inner life. And it is the God of hope who brings hope. "We have placed our hope in the living God, who is the Savior of all" (1 Tim. 4:10, TEV).

Our hope is based on God—and on Him alone. It has no confidence in anything or anyone else. And it is a divine hope, based on the assurance of God Himself. In the words of Adoniram Judson: "My future is as bright as the promises of God."

This is the only hope that is truly meaningful. We may hope in many things, extend our hopes in many directions, and have many vain hopes. But the only true hope is God Himself, for there is no future without Him. That is why we need to continue to be "looking for that blessed hope, and the glorious appearing of the great God and our Saviour Jesus Christ" (Titus 2:13). That's where we need to focus the eyes of hope, for "we have placed our hope in him" (2 Cor. 1:10, TEV). Ultimately, "we will always be with the Lord. So then, encourage one another with these words" (1 Thess. 4:17, 18, TEV).

What do we hope for? To be with Jesus. To be home with God. To begin an eternal life in the presence of our loving Lord.

Is that really what we are hoping for? The true goal of hope is not in feelings or even in the Second Advent as an event itself. The meaning of the Second Advent is that God comes for His friends to take them to be with Him for all eternity. Now, if we are not really looking forward to such a time, then our reaction to the Advent hope may be less than positive. Much depends on our understanding of who God is—do we want to spend all eternity in the presence of one we do not love, trust, and admire? What is our own personal hope, really and truly? Whom are we hoping for?

SAVED BY HOPE

"For it is by hope that we were saved; but if we see what we hope for, then it is not really hope. For who of us hopes for something we see? But if we hope for what we do not see, we wait for it with patience" (Rom. 8:24, 25, TEV).

Saved by hope! Instead of pointing to a legal definition of salvation, Paul in Romans affirms that God's salvation rests in the hope that He provides. Instead of the many other hopes of our world, here we catch a glimpse of the vastness of hope when God is its underwriter. Our reaction can only be, "What, then, can I hope for, Lord? I put my hope in you" (Ps. 39:7, TEV).

At those times when hope seems dim, we need to remember this fact. Our salvation is intimately bound up with this divinely given hope, as sure as the promises of God Himself:

"Let us hold on firmly to the hope we profess, because we can trust God to keep his promise" (Heb. 10:23, TEV).

We can sum up our response in the words of Psalm 130:1-7:

"Out of the depths I cry to you, O Lord; O Lord, hear my voice. Let your ears be attentive to my cry for mercy. If you, O Lord, kept a record of sins, O Lord, who could stand? But with you there is forgiveness; therefore you are feared. I wait for the Lord, my soul waits, and in his word I put my hope. My soul waits for the Lord more than watchmen wait for the morning, more than watchmen wait for the morning. O Israel, put your hope in the Lord, for with the Lord is unfailing love and with him is full redemption" (NIV).

THE GOD OF HOPE LEADS US INTO HIS FUTURE

One of my earliest memories is of a picture that hung in my parents' bedroom. It was a simple countryside scene of a bright woodland clearing covered with bluebells. I remember gazing into that picture for hours when I was really sick with chickenpox. I loved the bending of the tree boughs, the patterned bright green of the new leaves, the shafts of sunlight slanting bright against the dark trunks. In the foreground the bluebells shone with an intense reflected brilliance, flowers like a living carpet spread across the glade.

But what intrigued me most, though, was the path that led my eyes into the distance.

There, in the center of the scene, the path disappeared into a fascinating haze, a misty blur of possibilities. For me, that beautifully captured blend of mist and light became the substance of the future hope. A hazy shimmering on the borders of reality, a symbol of the arrival of time into the present. I can still feel that chilling, thrilling, exciting sense of wonderment.

I strained to make out something in that misty light. But the future symbolized there remained distant and insubstantial. I wanted to throw myself into the picture and run up that path to find what that haziness hid.

The vision remains—the substance of things hoped for, the evidence of things not seen. The future of God's hope makes a reality of this present. God's promised future is more real, more meaningful, than "this insubstantial pageant."

The future leads us on in hope. To God.

CHAPTER 2

Hope Alive!

RESURRECTION HOPE

Anne was a sad girl that time I visited. Her sunken eyes were ringed with dark circles and smoldered with a dying fire. Her mouth turned down, her hollow cheeks were pale, her hair rough and ragged.

Anne was anorexic. A friend concerned for her—for the girl's survival—had introduced me to her in her hospital room in southern England. She weighed maybe 70 pounds, and yet every time she looked at herself in the mirror she saw herself as grossly obese.

Her thin arms rested limp on the bedspread as she wearily turned to me.

"Yes. What do you want?"

"I called to see how you were. Someone told me about you. Do you want to talk?" I explained that I was a pastor and that a mutual friend had suggested I visit.

"If you like."

"Tell me about yourself."

"Nothing much to say. I don't eat. I suppose I'm going to die. I don't care." The hopelessness of her situation hung heavy in the air. "Now I'm losing my teeth. They say I don't get enough nutrition. But I eat so much. I just wish I wasn't so fat."

I wanted to respond sharply and tell her she was lying to

herself. But the doctors had explained enough to make me keep quiet. Since she lived in denial, she wasn't about to believe what some stranger told her.

I asked her what she believed in.

"I don't know. Nothing, really. Once you're dead, you're dead. Least that's what it seems. Who knows? At any rate I should find out soon enough. If it's different I'll come back and let you know." She laughed—a hollow, mirthless laugh.

I began explaining what I believed. I spoke of the hope of eternal life—that death is not the end, that God has promised an incredible future for those who choose Him, that at His coming He will change us, and all our pain and problems will be healed—forever.

Anne was silent for a long time. Then she shook her head, and a tear trickled down her face.

"No, it can't be true. It can't be as good as that. It's a vain hope."

I said nothing.

"And how do you know it's true? No one knows! Just a fable, a fairy tale." Her eyes burned with anger. "Don't you give me all this religious claptrap. Bunch of nonsense. Get out of here!"

With a nod I left.

The next week she turned her face away as I came into the room.

"Hello, Anne. How is it today?"

She said nothing at first, then in a low voice muttered, "They're sticking more tubes into me." An IV unit stood beside the bed. "They say it's the only way to get nutrition into me. They just want to make me fat."

"Anne, they just want to help you go on living."

"Why? What's the point? I have nothing to hope for. Why go on living?"

Some of the saddest words I've ever heard echoed around that cold and clinical hospital room.

Picking up my Bible, I just started reading. Psalm 23. John 3. John 14. First Thessalonians 4. Revelation 22.

Messages of assurance, promises of hope, reasons for living.

I read for what seemed a long time. She said nothing. The anger had gone. At the end she sighed.

"You didn't make that up, did you? What you were reading, it's true, isn't it?"

I smiled and nodded. "It's the Bible."

"I'd like to read it myself. Could I?"

Giving her the Bible, I suggested some places to read. She held it against her chest.

"I'll see you next week," I said as I left.

The next week Anne had many questions. The first surprised me.

"So who wrote this Bible? I mean, it says it was printed in 1988. So it's quite recent."

Of all the people I've ever met, Anne knew the least about the Bible. She even thought that someone had just written it. It took a lot of explaining to help her understand what it was and what it taught. But after many weeks she began to take hold of the truth.

But not without setbacks. One day I arrived to find that she had tried to run away and had made it onto a bus before collapsing. But slowly progress came.

And as hope returned, so did her appetite and her self-image. She began to recognize exactly what she had been doing to herself.

What made the difference? Not me, that's for sure. It was God Himself who intervened—the God of hope. For that is what she needed most of all—a sense of meaning and purpose in a future together with the loving Lord. Slowly she recovered her health as she regained her hope and assurance—that God was her best friend and would walk with her on her way.

Eventually she was strong enough to leave the hospital. She went home, taking the Bible I had given her. Before I moved away to a new pastoral district she was doing fine, strong in her hope. At our last meeting she told me how she felt about what had happened.

"It was like experiencing the resurrection," she smiled shyly. "It was as if I were already dead. Then God came in and called me back to life, just as He did with Lazarus. I know that soon I would have been gone—the doctors told me so. But God wasn't going to let me go, was He?"

I shook my head. "He wanted you to live again, to find your eternal hope in Him, not just now, but for all eternity."

"Yes," she said, looking straight into my eyes, "and it's hope that we all need most. Hope that we have a future, hope that God will remake and heal us, hope that He will bring us back to life. That's why hope is really blessed. Because I am saved by hope—God's hope."

HOPE ALIVE—INDIVIDUALLY

That's how hope comes alive in our individual lives. As we understand the incredible graciousness of God in confirming hope beyond our pointless existence without Him, then the confidence of a future with Him becomes a reality in our experience. Each of us comes to the point at which we can say with Micah: "But as for me, I watch in hope for the Lord, I wait for God my Savior" (Micah 7:7, NIV).

Our world today often misuses and misunderstands the idea of hope. As a word, it is so overused and undervalued that we give it too many worthless meanings.

"I hope so" all too often means "I don't really expect it." It's a faint, vague wish that we "hope" something will happen, but do not really anticipate it. It just would be nice, but who could really believe in such a hope.

The truth is that God's hope is not some insubstantial carrot to lure us on into an insecure future. It is the solid answer to our hopelessness, that hopelessness that hangs over us like a gray mist and chills any confident anticipation of a wonderful future. Hope is what gives meaning to the present and makes the troubles and trials worthwhile as we look for the fulfillment of promise.

Too many people hope in things that cannot provide assurance. They hope in money, or in possessions of any kind; hope in a cure; hope in fallible human beings—none of these are worth trusting with your treasure of hope. "Hope without an object cannot live" (Samuel Taylor Coleridge), and the object of our hope must be in the nature and character of God Himself.

For hope is essential—and without it we cannot survive. Hope is close to the fundamental essence of living—to motivation, to meaning, to purpose. It is a vital part of our creativity that says that life is more than just what we see now.

Thus hope is the antidote to the fearfulness permeating our world and assaulting each of us. Our consumer society gives us what we think we want, then we find material things don't really help us at all. As a result, we become frustrated and dissatisfied. All our grasping after this world's elusive answers only leads us to despair. But God's hope, in contrast to our supposed "answers," gives direction to our lives and fills them with meaning and purpose.

THE LIFE OF HOPE

As not just an aspect of belief, but as life's destination and goal, Christian hope points us to God in the present and assures us of Him at the end of our journey. That's why living the hope does make such a difference, especially as we face the hard questions that confront us in this existence. It's when crises come that hope really can make the absolute difference.

When others around us notice a different attitude in us, a refusal to fall into the way the world thinks, then we are truly representing our Lord. Jesus called for His followers to be distinctive. In expressing hope at all times, whether in tragedy or in success, we truly show that we are Christians eagerly anticipating the return of our Lord:

"We want each of you to show this same diligence to the very end, in order to make your hope sure. . . . God did this so that, by two unchangeable things in which it is impossible for God to lie, we who have fled to take hold of the hope offered to us may be greatly encouraged. We have this hope as an anchor for the soul, firm and secure" (Heb. 6:11-19, NIV).

"Hope is brightest when it dawns from fears," Sir Walter Scott observed, and truly when the night is at its darkest, hope shines the most brightly. It is in the hardest times that God's promises are the most precious and the most meaningful. While crises and tragedies may tempt us to give up on God, it is at these times we need Him most.

God's message of hope is today more necessary than ever. The stress of modern life, the increasing problems and challenges, the rising tide of evil—all indicate the vital importance of holding on to the God of hope. To live the hope means not only that we believe in the soon return of Jesus, but that the belief makes itself real in our daily lives.

MAKING HOPE REAL

Sarajevo, May 27, 1992, 4:00 p.m. A mortar shell lands on a line of people waiting to buy bread in the market. Twenty-two men, women, and children die. As he sees this act of violent destruction, Vedran Smailovic, the principal cellist of the Sarajevo Opera Orchestra, decides to fight back. Not with bombs or bullets or mortar shells, but with his cello.

Every evening in full evening dress he goes to the cratered market square and plays. Performing a rebuke to those who kill indiscriminately, he presents music of hope in a time of abandonment. He plays for a future amid the chaos and rubble of the present.

What Smailovic does symbolizes the practical kind of hope that we all need to share. Hope has to become real and individual for all of us. It needs to be part of who we are, the motivator and inspirer of our lives.

We may say that we hope, that we believe in Jesus' return as one of the fundamental beliefs. But do we passionately look forward to that day, eagerly wanting it to come? Can we say that we are longing for Jesus to come back for us? That we look up to heaven with anticipation, waiting for the day when we can say, "Lo, this is our God; . . . he will save us"?

We have to live the hope.

Pastor H is more than 70 and from a country in eastern Asia, where he dedicated his whole life to helping those around him, regardless of religion or ethnicity. He has seen many changes in his homeland—ranging from foreign overlords to atheistic ideologists to military tyrants to ruthless secularist exploiters.

Yet he survived. In a small village with a Christian community in the remote countryside, Pastor H continued to share his faith and to help with the practical needs of others—food, clothing, and shelter. He married and had children. Down by the river he laboriously built a wooden house as the family home beside the church.

In the twilight of his years he continued his ministry, working for the good of others. Then came more troubles, as if he had not seen enough of violence and death. Yet this came not from the rulers, as in the past, but from the community. Though of different faiths, the villagers had lived together in harmony whatever the situation. But now it was different.

"I do not understand it," he says. "I do not want to understand it. For so many years we lived together, side by side. But then came religious leaders who told those of their faith in the village that we were the enemy. Armed men came to the village and forced us out of the village. They set fire to the church; then they went to our homes and burned them, too. I saw the home I had built destroyed before my eyes. It was very hard."

After a while Pastor H and his family returned to his home. The local religious leaders said they wanted peace. "They promised us it would be like before," says Pastor H. "That is what we wanted. To live in peace. So we came back. And I used all my savings to buy timber to make another church and another house."

After rebuilding the church, Pastor H slowly constructed a new house for himself and his family. But just months later the village leader announced that no Christians would be allowed to remain. "This has to be a pure village," he told them. "All Christians must leave."

And so the pastor and his family picked up what belongings they could and left to become part of another tragic refugee crowd, slowly trailing out of the country.

They now live in exile, strangers in a land far from home. At the end of his life, Pastor H is sad his village forced him out. "It is incredible what has happened," he says. "To be evicted from your home by those of another religion who claim to be lovers of peace is bitterly disappointing. After all we endured together, to be thrown out now, and all because of religion—that is hard to bear. I often think of those we left behind and wonder what has happened to them, and who remains to tell God's good news."

A tragic story of rejection and loss. But what of his own convictions?

"Oh, my trust in God is as strong as ever. Despite all that has happened, and that we had to flee all that we called our home, we continue to hope in the power of God. We know that God holds this world like a pebble in His hand, and that our future is secure with Him. One day—and soon—we will see Him coming back for His own people, and we shall be together with Him forever. I long for that day even more, and that is why it is rightly called the blessed hope."

"I heard a loud voice speaking from the throne: 'Now God's home is with people! He will live with them, and they shall be his people. God himself will be with them, and he will be their God. He will wipe away all tears from their eyes. There will be no more death, no more grief or crying or pain. The old things have disappeared" (Rev. 21:3, 4, TEV).

CHAPTER 3

The Jesus Hope

THE FIRM FOUNDATION OF HOPE

Just a month before he died, noted atheist and humanist writer Jean-Paul Sartre spoke of what he was anticipating. "The world seems ugly, bad and without hope. There, that's the cry of despair of an old man who'll die in despair. But that's exactly what I resist, and I know I shall die in hope. But that hope needs a foundation" (cited in Stephen H. Travis, *I Believe in the Second Coming of Jesus* [London: Hodder and Stoughton, 1982], p. 227).

Sartre's tragedy, as he himself recognized, was that he did not have a firm foundation for any kind of hope, least of all to be able to die in hope. We can find such a hope only in God, whom Sartre had rejected. When God is not part of our hope, then any kind of hope is futile. For we are mortal, and all our hopes and dreams turn to dust unless we place them in the hands of our loving Lord.

The truth is that we define our hope as Jesus. It is based on the promise of Jesus Himself, and it centers in the sure and certain expectation of His return. Our hope is guaranteed by the words of Jesus, and confirmed by His resurrection from the dead. The only foundation for a realistic hope is in Jesus, the one whom John in his Gospel terms the eternal Word. The Word, who is God, became flesh and dwelt among us, living and dying so we could live forever with Him. It is *this same Jesus* who will return—the Jesus we know in our daily experience here and now: "This same Jesus, who has been taken from you into heaven, will come back in the same way you have seen him go into heaven" (Acts 1:11, NIV).

In proclaiming the Advent hope we must always remember that it centers on Jesus. We are not preaching a message of gloom and doom, or a Hollywood-like disaster scenario, but the great news of Jesus' return. Our message is clear: it is the *Jesus hope!*

We need to focus on His personal promise, on how it brings us assurance in life. Our hope is credible, sure, and certain—it is not a misguided hope. We can hope with confidence because we hope in *the Jesus we know.*

The blessed hope is of the return of our loving Lord to keep His promise to take us to be with Him forever. The hope is

based on the promises of Jesus,
made possible by the victory of Jesus,
accomplished by the will of Jesus,
achieved by the power of Jesus,
completed in being with Jesus.

For it is God Himself who draws us into His future. The hope He shares with us means that we do not need to consider the present as wasted effort and time when we cannot accomplish all that we wish. God tells us we have a future assured with Him, so that even if we see no results in what we do, our work is not in vain. Because God is the source of the hope, we look forward to Him. "Lo, this is our God; we have waited for him, and he will save us: this is the Lord; we have waited for him, we will be glad and rejoice in his salvation" (Isa. 25:9).

THE JESUS HOPE: HOW IT WILL BE

Many Christians have unusual ideas about the fulfillment of

the Jesus hope. Some talk about rapture and secret comings and spiritual advents. But Jesus could not have made it clearer: "For the Son of Man will come like the lightning which flashes across the whole sky from the east to the west" (Matt. 24:27, TEV).

"Then the sign of the Son of Man will appear in the sky; and all the peoples of earth will weep as they see the Son of Man coming on the clouds of heaven with power and great glory" (verse 30, TEV).

"Look, he is coming on the clouds! Everyone will see him" (Rev. 1:7, TEV).

"There will be the shout of command, the archangel's voice, the sound of God's trumpet, and the Lord himself will come down from heaven" (1 Thess. 4:16, TEV).

The coming is like lightning. Everyone will see it, and everyone will see Him. The Lord arrives with a shout of command, the archangel's voice, the sound of God's trumpet. It will be dramatically visible and audible! No one will miss this event. Christ will not return in some secret rapture or invisible or spiritualized advent recognized by only a few.

When Jesus gave His promise, He was absolutely sure that His advent would be a literal return. As He left, so will He come again—but with infinitely greater majesty and glory. Anyone who says His coming will be invisible or secret or hidden completely contradicts the clear descriptions of Jesus and the Bible.

ANCHORED!

"So we who have found safety with him are greatly encouraged to hold firmly to the hope placed before us. We have this hope as an anchor for our lives. It is safe and sure" (Heb. 6:18, 19, TEV).

Just as a ship is safe and secure when firmly anchored, so will we be when we trust in the Jesus hope. Even though winds of false doctrine may blow or storms of persecution may rage against us, we can rest secure in this anchoring hope. Placing our confidence in Jesus, we can "hope firm unto the end" (Heb. 3:6; see also Heb. 6:11).

Human beings need conviction. Conviction that existence has meaning, that life has importance, and that there exists a future. The hope that God gives us assures us of all that—and more! As sure as God Himself, the Jesus hope is even more solid than the ground underneath our feet.

Many religions and philosophies attempt to answer humanity's questions about existence and to provide some kind of hope. Without being arrogant, the Christian hope presented in the Bible outclasses them all. We have a "better hope," according to Hebrews 7:19.

Why? Because it assures us of a future together with Him. Able to give motivation and purpose to the present, such a conviction is far more meaningful than the materialistic hopes of the present age. And Jesus guaranteed it through His own resurrection.

"The human being is only to be defined in terms of his whither, not of his whence," wrote theologian Helmut Thielicke. In other words, it's where we're going that is important, not where we came from. What God sees as potential in us is what He wants to make reality in His kingdom of the future—which is why He waits for us to respond to His glorious offer of salvation.

As a consequence, "hope does not disappoint us, because God has poured out his love into our hearts by the Holy Spirit, whom he has given us" (Rom. 5:5, NIV).

ONLY JESUS

The simple motto of those who look to God's future is "Christ Jesus our hope" (1 Tim. 1:1, TEV). Should the temptation come to become anxious and to despair, then this simple phrase sums up the Christian response. Christ is our hope—hope that gives assurance in our present and enables us to look forward to a fuller experience in the God-made future.

The prayer for all of us is this: "May God, the source of hope, fill you with all joy and peace by means of your faith in him, so that your hope will continue to grow by the power of the Holy Spirit" (Rom. 15:13, TEV).

Sometimes we worry over what happens to us in the present. We look around, and like David, ask, "Why do the wicked prosper?" It all seems so unfair at times, and we become disturbed about God and His involvement in our lives. Surely it should somehow be different.

But God reminds us that we are part of the ongoing great controversy over His nature and character. The present is the "time between," the era of demonstration that will fully vindicate truth and right and prove the charges of the devil false. So because of this, Scripture urges us, "Do not fret because of evil men or be envious of the wicked, for the evil man has no future hope" (Prov. 24:19, 20, NIV).

No future hope—that is why so many focus on the immediate present, on instant pleasure and satisfaction. Because they have no future to anticipate, no Jesus in whom to place their hope.

For in reality, we really do have no hope apart from God. We may try to fool ourselves, but any other hope will in the end prove to be nothing more than an illusion. Some, for example, hope that science will find a cure for all diseases, even to the point of having their bodies cryogenically frozen in the faint chance that one day medical science will be able to bring them back to life when it has conquered their particular disease. But such hopes will be in vain, and such people are "without hope and without God in the world" (Eph. 2:12, NIV). While many may not admit it, they have no real hope, and as a result look just to the things of this world to satisfy them—money, power, drugs . . . the list is endless.

But when the end comes, they will have nothing. They will grieve as "the rest of men, who have no hope" (1 Thess. 4:13, NIV). In an agony of despair, the hopeless try to blot out their pain by any means they can. They have sadly discovered that all other hopes are futile and worthless.

A PARABLE OF MISGUIDED HOPES AND CREATIVE LOSS

It was unusual to have months of snow and ice covering the ground around my childhood home in southern England. But not wishing to let such an opportunity slip by, that winter I began my greatest construction program ever.

A 9-year-old does not worry about such problems as below-freezing temperatures, exposure, and frostbite. Nor is time a factor when it comes to realizing dreams, of bringing one's hopes into hard reality.

Very hard reality, in fact. Ice hard as iron, water turned to stone.

The ground at the back of our house sloped up the hill. Right beside the house, on the northern side, was a steeper bank, separated from the house wall by a narrow ditch. It was there that the dream became reality. Hour after freezing hour I would stand in that ditch, crafting an ice village on the side of that bank. I had great hopes for my creation!

After the first week my mother gave up calling me to come in from the bitter cold. A man with a mission does not care about such trifles as hot chocolate and toasted muffins. Slowly my miniature village rose from in its frosty construction site.

First a one-lane road wound its way along the bank, circuitously avoiding humps of snow and the crevasses of the glacier down by the drain. That was hard enough, pounding away at ice as hard as rock to make something like a flat surface that toy cars could drive along. After many hours of backbreaking work, I discovered that warm water could do the job much more easily and produce some interesting shapes as I smoothed the road while it refroze. Developing my technology, I made rapid progress using mother's hair dryer attached to an extension cord until she objected (rather unreasonably, I thought) to its somewhat unorthodox use.

Once the roadway was in (complete with a terrifying section more like a bobsled run), I turned to architecture. Building with snow is not an easy task. For example, just try making square bricks while wearing mittens. Then there's the question of crumbling. Snow bricks have the annoying tendency to fall apart right at the critical stage of construction.

The first few houses were hardly recognizable, resembling mounds of small snowballs. But as I developed my technique, something more recognizable as human habitations took shape. Then office blocks. The skyscraper attempt ended in ignominious failure and required some heavy repair work to the residential area it had crashed down on. (I began to see the impact of human mistakes. A lot of ice people would have died in that terrible tragedy.)

I even attempted a church, and with the newly discovered process of spraying the construction with water from Mom's flower mister, it even held together, though the spire was decidedly skewed.

Eventually, after what must have been hundreds of hours of work in the fearsome cold, the village covered the whole length of the bank, with post office, bank, general store, gas station, and all the rest. (The skating rink idea admittedly did not work too well. Pouring gallons of hot water onto the snow only melted a large hole, and the end result looked more like a volcano.)

I would like to have said that people came from all around to admire my creation, but at least I convinced Mom and Dad and brother and sister to come outside and make the appropriate expressions of wonder. (They also wondered about the volcano.)

Next I began to lay plans to extend my village up the slope above the bank. Soon I would create a huge metropolis—a whole ice planet, maybe! Great hopes!

But that very morning my great schemes turned to dust. Or more correctly, slush. The temperature rose, and I watched in anguished horror as all my labor melted away before my eyes. The office block slid down the bank and wiped out the fire station. The church collapsed (with what effect on its ice-worshipers, who can tell?). The ice rink/volcano became a lake. And before long, everything slid down into the ditch and melted down the drain. All gone, swept away.

Hardly able to speak, I dragged my mother outside and just pointed. Where there had once stood a proud ice village was just the old familiar grass bank.

If I'd known the words, I would have quoted Solomon about everything being vanity and there being no profit for any work under the sun (which by now had come out and was melting all the snow away). All gone. And not even a picture for the record. Only what remained in our memories.

It was a hard lesson on the lack of permanence in this life, on building without a sure foundation. All that work—for what? At this time of loss I saw with crystal vision that everything here is temporary. Just as with my ice village, all melts, fades, dies. We search for permanency in a world that does not know the concept. Our dreams and hopes seem so insubstantial.

But one day our God, in whom we place our hope and trust, will open up far more than an ice bank to our creativity. We will have worlds upon worlds, and ideas beyond imagination. On that day we will have vastly more than short-lived ice villages that melt in the morning sun.

One bright morning God will be here, and His people will be with Him in His eternal city. I just want to be there, experiencing God's total creative permanence. What about you?

CHAPTER 4

Hope Makes a Difference

WHEN HOPE DROWNS

According to a poll in the Houston *Post* of January 15, 1995, one out of every five people in America feels life is meaningless.

As Charles Sawyer noted: "Of all the forces that make for a better world, none is so indispensable, none so powerful, as hope. Without hope men are only half alive."

Half alive—or not even alive at all. For without hope in the future, the present has no meaning.

On March 24, 1950, the town of Flagstaff, Maine, drowned. A vast hydroelectric project dammed the waters of the aptly named Dead River, and it rose to engulf the town. But the town was already dead. During the months before the inevitable end, the townspeople gave up on their community, since it had no future.

No hope.

If it is true that where there's life, there's hope, then the opposite is also true. Where there's no hope, there's no life.

The buildings became run-down. No one bothered to repaint their homes. The streets went unrepaired. What was the point in doing anything? Soon the town would cease to exist, its name erased from maps. In its place a vast lake spread across the valley.

The town decayed long before the water rose, because hope had died. As someone said at the time, recognizing the impending abandonment of the town and its lack of a future, "where there's no hope for the future, there is no power in the present."

No future hope, no present power. We all see that. In our own life experience, when the future hope dies, present power vanishes, for it is the future that gives power to the present. Hope really does make the difference!

THE HOPING KIND OF PEOPLE

So if that is true, what is the result in those who hope? Peter asks that very question—as we come to know this Christian hope, what kind of people are we to be? His answer: "You ought to live holy and godly lives as you look forward to the day of God and speed its coming" (2 Peter 3:11, 12, NIV).

Though we should take it seriously, this is not a message of doom and disaster to the hoping Christian. Nor is it a process of beating ourselves into submission and making ourselves right, but rather of accepting the results of hope—the transforming power of God's grace in the present. Remember that we are to rejoice in this hope. Holiness and godliness are not incompatible with joy and happiness—they are aspects of the whole. What God looks for is a people who will live rightly for Him, representing the truth that He came at such tremendous cost to share eternal life with us. As we live in hope we consequently become clearly identifiable Christians.

For, as Paul reminds us, "we have been made a spectacle to the whole universe, to angels as well as to men" (1 Cor. 4:9, NIV). Each of us becomes a display, an exhibition of hope. It is not an act but a living of the life of hope so that others can look and understand and want that same motivational hope in their own lives.

Since we are to be a spectacle to a watching world, we need to ask ourselves, "What do they see in relation to our hope? Do they see us as Christ's friends and followers, ever hoping, ever looking for the completion of salvation, and living honest, truthful, and joyful lives?"

God is waiting for a people who truly follow Him, who believe His truth as opposed to the devil's lies; who, despite all kinds of attacks, remain true to their Lord. This end-time generation refuses to let any assault on their faith shake them, and they truly live their lives in harmony with God. Nor should they be surprised or taken unawares by the fulfillment of their hope.

"But you, friends, are not in the darkness, and the Day should not take you by surprise like a thief. All of you are people who belong to the light, who belong to the day. We do not belong to the night or to the darkness. So then, we should not be sleeping like the others; we should be awake and sober" (1 Thess. 5:4-6, TEV).

SPEEDING THE HOPE—WITHOUT BECOMING EXTREME

Peter talks about our speeding the hope, or hastening the day (see 2 Peter 3:12). How is this possible? Doesn't God already know the time of His coming? So how can we "hasten" it?

Yes, God does know the time. And yes, He will come when He chooses. But He comes for those who wait. This gives us a clue to understanding our part in the return of the Lord. We can "hasten" it by being part of the process.

God comes "in the fullness of time." That "fullness" refers to conditions on earth. Our part consists of outreach and witness, of living our lives for God. Then when the fullness of time matures, Jesus will return. Until that time, though, we are to share our hope, rightly represent God, preach the gospel, stand for the right, live the truth in our lives, and speed the hope.

Those who claim to live the hope must wake up and realize the implications of this life-changing, world-altering hope:

"The time has come for you to wake up from your sleep. For

the moment when we will be saved is closer now than it was when we first believed. The night is nearly over, day is almost here. Let us stop doing the things that belong to the dark, and let us take up weapons for fighting in the light" (Rom. 13:11, 12, TEV).

Wake up! Our role is to be alert, ready to share the good news of hope as we await its fulfillment! Not in a condition of overexcitement, but in the assurance of our trust in the One who has promised to return. Jesus Himself reminded His followers that the timing rests in the hands of the Lord, and that we should not overstress the imminence.

"While the people were listening to this, Jesus continued and told them a parable. He was now almost at Jerusalem, and they supposed that the Kingdom of God was just about to appear. So he said, 'There was once a man of high rank who was going to a country far away to be made king' " (Luke 19:11, 12, TEV).

The problem Jesus addressed here is an overemphasis on the *soonness* of the coming. So Jesus related the parable about the nobleman journeying to a far country. The implication here is that the nobleman's journey will take some time. People should not expect him to return immediately.

Although Jesus earnestly desired to return instantly—and why He says in Revelation that He is coming quickly—Scripture recognizes the need for time for people to respond. God is patient, "not willing that any should perish, but that all should come to repentance" (2 Peter 3:9).

His people can become extreme in other ways. Some go well beyond Scripture in their expectations. They can distort even good into evil. But Scripture urges us to "put all things to the test: keep what is good and avoid every kind of evil. May the God who gives us peace make you holy in every way and keep your whole being—spirit, soul, and body—free from every fault at the coming of our Lord Jesus Christ" (1 Thess. 5:21-23, TEV).

OUR ROLE AS HOPE-SHARERS

Our role is not to indulge in speculation as to when we expect the Lord will arrive. Rather, we are to "be ready at all times to answer anyone who asks you to explain the hope you have in you" (1 Peter 3:15, TEV). As we speak to others about the hope within us, we are to tell them what Jesus means to us, and about our anticipation of meeting Him at His return and being together with Him for all eternity. Christian hope needs to be personal and real. We must think it through, then explain our reason for cherishing such a hope.

It is a privilege to be part of God's plan to share His hope to a world that, like Flagstaff, Maine, is drowning in all its hopelessness!

Why does God invite us to participate with Him? Isn't it because we can give the best testimony of what it is like to find hope after being hopeless, to discover it when we thought all hope was lost? As His children, He invites us to be part of His wonderful plan of salvation for humanity and to demonstrate the truth about God to the whole universe. Hope is an essential part of that plan, and not just the "frosting on the cake," as someone once called Christian hope. Hope is far more substantial than that—in fact, it's the main course! Our perspective is this: "Keep alert and set your hope completely on the blessing which will be given you when Jesus Christ is revealed" (1 Peter 1:13, TEV).

Jesus tells us to lay up treasure in heaven—for that is where our hope will be realized (Col. 1:5). Our focus will not be on ourselves, but on others and the true values that God endorses.

Nor are we to dismiss anyone or anything as beyond hope. As Charles L. Allen said: "When you say a situation or a person is hopeless, you are slamming the door in the face of God." We are to recognize in all those around us the same potential that God sees for the restored and redeemed children of the kingdom of hope.

Our hope in seeing Jesus soon really does make a difference. It has an effect in all areas of life and work and in our relationships and behavior. Coloring our attitude to the things of this world, it identifies true values and affects our approach to life itself. Even when the outlook may seem dim in human terms, God's hope gives meaning and purpose to those "who against hope believed in hope" (Rom. 4:18). Such hope shapes family relationships, the use of money, the desire for possessions, our ambitions, career perspectives, and our plans for the future. If hope does not have such an impact, then it really has no power in our lives. We all need to be able to say, "The Lord is good to those whose hope is in him, to the one who seeks him" (Lam. 3:25, NIV).

Though in the eagerness of pursuing our lives, we may become impatient—for what we want, even for the Second Coming itself—we need to remember that we must wait on God's time, and not on our own plans so that "we through patience . . . might have hope" (Rom. 15:4). Consequently we need to wake up to our responsibilities, and act "like men and women who believe" this hope!

PARABLE: HOPE ON THE BEACH OF THIS WORLD

On the beach in the gray-splashed coldness of a winter's day stands a man. A vast bank of shingle stretches away to an infinity hidden by the mist, a huge ocean of white-washed silver spumes against the shore beneath a sky of tarnished metal scraped bare of clouds. The stranger stands staring at the point where earth and sea and sky meet. He is a lonely man under a lonely sky on a lonely beach.

The beach is not the fun-filled one of summer, crowded with people swimming, surfing, windsailing, waterskiing, paddling, sailing, picnicking, sunning, and building sand castles. Instead of an idyllic dream, the world he sees is reality in all its harshness:

the bitter cold, the threatening surf, the utter loneliness. Wrapping his coat tighter, he walks on and on down the beach.

It seemed another time, another place, another planet. The empty desolation reflected the man's mood, and he symbolized and represented all the human race. Stranded on the edge of an immense, uncrossable ocean, he walked the shoreline in the hope of finding something, but heard only the crunch of shingle underfoot. The man bent down, bowed low by troubles, then picked up a stone and rose. With a shout, a cry of desperation, he flung the pebble with all his might into the broken surface of the tossing sea. A splash, a few ripples, and it vanished. The cry itself went unheard among the crashing waves of eternity. Alone and unnoticed, he struggled on down the beach.

Finding a tiny stretch of sand, he crouched down and began to write with his finger, recording all his complaints, his hopes and fears, his need to know why he existed. In all his meaningless words he presented his tale in a passionate outpouring of his innermost thoughts. At the bottom he signed his name, and stood back to admire his beautiful creation, satisfied that he had at least recorded his protest. Moments later a massive breaker crashed in, sweeping over all his words. Then rushing back, the water left bare, unmarked sand. All was if it had never been. With sea-soaked shoes he sat and sobbed, his sighs swirling in the splashing spray drenching the beach.

Bravely he battled on until he discovered the flotsam on the shoreline, the relics of others who had gone before: the cans and bottles, the plastic cups and cigarette wrappers. Carefully he sifted this treasure in the vain hope of finding answers to his questions, something of value in all the trash. He searched for hours, collecting together all the trivial castoffs scattered along the shore. But in the end he had nothing, no joy in possessing, no answers among all the rusting cans and soggy papers, no hope in any of his pieces of collected junk that stood piled up beside him like a memorial on the beach.

In his hopelessness he lay down, just another piece of flotsam thrown up by the tide, a dark shape abandoned in the midst of all this emptiness. Lost, lonely, helpless, hopeless, he waited as the light grew dim. It was the evening of the world, and as the cold bit deeper, he wondered if it was his last. Hungry, frightened, shivering, and intensely alone, he waited. He stared out over the bitter sea of separation and felt his own emptiness. Unable to do anything more, unable to help himself, unable to leave, he remained stranded on the beach.

But as he watched the far horizon, over the sea, another Man walked toward him. From the other side, impossibly heading toward the beach, arms outstretched as the waves subsided and the wind died to a gentle whisper. He came to embrace, to enfold hopelessness in eternal hope. The Man now arrived to save, to rescue, to transform. To remake hope from human hopelessness for the man on the beach.

The Son appeared in blazing splendor, a brilliant demonstration of absolute majesty clothed in the humblest love. Suddenly the whole scene changed. The sea glowed like molten lava, the sky shone with surrealist colors of green and blue and red—like emeralds, sapphires, and rubies rolling across the floor of heaven. The transformation was the work of a moment, a twinkling of an eye. Leaping to his feet, the man stood and shouted and sang. Caught up into all this glory, he himself altered—from the inside out. He saw, and as he did so, he now understood. As he repented and claimed the promise, he was redeemed. Hope made a difference now, as he recognized the truth of salvation. Then as the vision faded, he stood in silence with an overpowering sense of awe. The darkness approached, but in the twilight the man smiled, his heart full of endless hope, looking forward to the time he would be together forever with the Man—on the beach that edged the sea of glass.

CHAPTER 5

Hope: Motivation for Mission

HOPE IS THE KEY

English crime writer Agatha Christie entitled one of her books *Fear Is the Key.* Some may see in her title a symbol of life, but for the Christian surely the opposite is true: *Hope is the key.*

For the Jesus hope is not only a belief that we assent to, but a motivation for life itself, an energizer that leads to action. It truly is the motivation for mission. The hope that we find encompassed in the gospel makes us want to share such glorious good news with others. For "we do not preach ourselves, but Jesus Christ as Lord" (2 Cor. 4:5, NIV). Our mission is to illuminate the whole world with the saving hope of Jesus.

We can sum up the life of our message and mission in this blessed hope. Without such hope the gospel is meaningless—an empty promise, a worthless philosophy. For if there is no future together with God, then the present loses its value and, as Paul commented, without the hope of resurrection, all is in vain.

But because we have this transforming, incredible hope in being part of God's glorious future, then we have all the reason in the world to want to share that same hope with those we meet. Hope is indeed the motivation for mission, because it is the key to a saving relationship with God, both now and eternally.

HOPE FOR A FRIGHTENED JOURNEY

"Is it supposed to do that?"

It was an urgent voice—the first sign I was sitting on a plane next to a passenger with a fear of flying. A set of white knuckles on the armrest accompanied the anxious question.

"Do what?" I asked. *A strange opening move in a conversation,* I thought.

"That noise. Is that normal?"

All I could hear were the engines at full throttle.

"Yes. Of course. This is takeoff," I responded.

"Oh." A rather faint and plaintive "oh."

The rest of the flight involved me filling in the gaps of conversation when my fellow passenger obsessed on the aircraft noises again.

She (and it could just as easily have been a he, since flying still scares me some) admitted that she was on the plane only because she wanted to get to her dying grandmother. But every bank and turn made her gasp; every little bit of turbulence produced panic.

So we talked. About anything and everything. About what she did (a student and a nanny) and what I did (a newswriter and a pastor). About her family and mine, about life and death and meaning and purpose and . . .

And hope.

At that moment hope meant more to her than anything else. Hope that she would see her grandmother before the woman died. Hope that the plane would not fall out of the sky. Hope that she would arrive safely.

More than such immediate hopes, she sought hope beyond—a hope that inevitably means God's hope.

She did believe in God, she conceded. Recently, in fact, she had begun to pray again. At that moment she was praying especially hard, she told me with a nervous smile.

Her grandmother's terminal illness was really affecting her. An only child, she had grown up with Mom and Grandma, and Grandma meant much to her. But now, at 90, Grandma's life was ebbing away. My fellow passenger was aching for hope.

Only God's blessed hope meets such needs. Only the promise of God, who never lies, can ease the pain of our own passing mortality. And only the power of God can make such hopes reality.

So we talked—about what this God of hope is really like, how Jesus shows us this God who saves and heals, and how He gives us life now, and eternally, as we choose His way.

As we bumped down to the runway, she clutched my arm. Safe on the runway, she expressed her happy relief, as the hope of the journey became the reality of solid ground.

She left—I believe—with more than just hope to survive a frightening plane flight. God gives wonderful, glorious, amazing hope that transforms a frightened journey through life into a new existence of meaning and purpose, joy and confidence.

We have this hope, we share this hope—hope that flies beyond death into an eternity together with the God of the blessed hope.

HOPE MAKES US BOLD

"Because we have this hope, we are very bold" (2 Cor. 3:12, TEV).

A holy boldness comes from the hope we hold in Jesus. It is a hope that gives us conviction and assurance for whatever challenges we face. Most of all, it encourages us to share the promise of an eternal future with the God we love and adore.

Sometimes we see witnessing as a burden, or as an activity we need to perform as part of our Christian duty. We may even dread having to go out and "evangelize." But such an attitude misses the point completely. Our role is not to perform some duty or complete some requirement. Rather, our joy is to let others know the wonderful hope and the delight of God's salvation. We are not preaching ourselves, but Jesus as Lord, and the wonder of knowing Him as our closest friend, the one who both saves us now and returns to take us to be with Him for all eternity. The gospel is no somber religion, but a hope-filled message of assurance in a loving, saving God.

"We put our hope in the Lord; he is our protector and our help. We are glad because of him; we trust in his holy name. May your constant love be with us, Lord, as we put our hope in you" (Ps. 33:20-22, TEV).

Our responsibility is to let this joy-filled hope shine through us, so that those around us recognize the incredible value of what we have. "For it is not ourselves that we preach; we preach Jesus Christ as Lord, and ourselves as your servants for Jesus' sake. The God who said, 'Out of darkness the light shall shine!' is the same God who made his light shine in our hearts, to bring us the knowledge of God's glory shining in the face of Christ" (2 Cor. 4:5, 6, TEV).

As a result of this wonderful divine treasure we possess, God's saving light of hope illuminates the world. Our hope-motivated mission is to help everyone in our dying world see how much they need Jesus. "And this gospel of the kingdom will be preached in the whole world as a testimony to all nations, and then the end will come" (Matt. 24:14, NIV).

The conviction we share in the hope of soon seeing Jesus at His return is what gives our outreach activities their drive and power. The slogan "the gospel message to all the world in this generation" is simply a summary of the results of sharing the gospel of hope. The Second Coming hope component of the Advent message gives it urgency and power, and assures us of an eternal future at home with our loving Lord.

The church today operates from a number of motivations, all relevant. We wish to alleviate hunger and misery and to improve people's education and life prospects. Each of us is committed to helping others have a healthy lifestyle. Yet the truly Advent part of our beliefs is what makes us the church of hope, the ones looking for Jesus' soon return.

A COMMUNITY OF HOPE

Of all people, we are the ones who wish to claim the future in the present. The future hope is what makes us a community in the present. Why? Because "the future belongs to those who belong to God. This is hope" (W. T. Purkiser).

In the words of Zechariah 9:12 we are "prisoners of hope." Now, does that mean prisoners who hope, or those imprisoned by hope?

Both meanings are appropriate. We are strangers and pilgrims (Heb. 11:13) on this earth who hope for a better land. And we are also "imprisoned" by hope. As hope fills us as a people, we are both contained by hope and a community of hope.

Once we lived our lives in rebellion. But now, saved by hope, we have become heirs of the promise—the promise of God and the hope of eternal life. "At one time we too were foolish, disobedient, deceived and enslaved by all kinds of passions and pleasures. We lived in malice and envy, being hated and hating one another. But when the kindness and love of God our Savior appeared, he saved us, not because of righteous things we had done, but because of his mercy. He saved us through the washing of rebirth and renewal by the Holy Spirit, whom he poured out on us generously through Jesus Christ our Savior, so that, having been justified by his grace, we might become heirs having the hope of eternal life" (Titus 3:3-7, NIV).

Since we are truly a community of hope, we must recognize where we came from and what our future is. But we cannot be proud of ourselves, since we cannot save ourselves—it is all of God. As a result of all that God has done, we have "become heirs having the hope of eternal life."

Consequently, the message we have to share is very simple. It is the same message that has given us hope, and which we pass on: "A faith and knowledge resting on the hope of eternal life, which God, who does not lie, promised before the beginning of time, and at his appointed season he brought his word to light through the preaching entrusted to me by the command of God our Savior" (Titus 1:2, 3, NIV).

"A faith and knowledge resting on the hope of eternal life." The church of hope could have no better motto. It's worth just pausing and contemplating the phrase, because it sums up our message, our theology, and our motivation. It captures the foundation, the basis for all that we do, think, and say. Our faith, and the knowledge we gain, rests solidly on the God-given hope of eternal life.

As we follow the Lord's command to make disciples, we pattern ourselves after His example and point people both to a better life here and now, and to the wonders of the hope of eternal life with Jesus when He returns.

HOPE RENEWS STRENGTH

Hoping in God gives us not only strength to live but also power to share His glorious good news. Trusting in God as our source of hope brings assurance and conviction. And preaching in God enables us to transmit to others that same hope to live for the God-filled present and for the God-promised future. As a result, "those who hope in the Lord will renew their strength. They will soar on wings like eagles; they will run and not grow weary, they will walk and not be faint" (Isa. 40:31, NIV).

That's why it is important to hope in the Lord. It's our only source of spiritual strength, because we have none of our own. Our hope's foundation rests in God and His eternal majesty and power, expressed in the humility and love of Christ.

If your hope grows dim, go back to the Bible and restudy

the "hope promises," then pray for the restrengthening power of God's hope. Hope recovered brings restored motivation and drives us to share that hope with those around us. As we celebrate that hope, "we hold on to our courage and the hope of which we boast" (Heb. 3:6, NIV).

While we may express ourselves in different ways, the heart of the message of hope remains the same. Our boldness and courage lie in our conviction of its reality. We boast not in ourselves, but in the God we preach and teach, the God of that exciting future together with Him that makes such a difference in the way we experience the present.

As a people we need that revitalizing strength of hope as we proclaim God's salvation. But as we tell others, it also strengthens us. As Bible translator J. B. Phillips wrote: "The gospel is nothing but a frozen asset unless it is communicated." We need to recognize that truth and get busy communicating hope!

HERALD OF HOPE

Patrick, the missionary to Ireland in the fifth century, is one of the best examples of a "herald of hope" as he brought the goodness of the God of hope to a pagan society lost in the darkness of evil. Almost single-handedly this man of God totally transformed Irish society in a single generation. He was born into a Christian family on the west coast of Britain. During his youth pirates captured him, taking him to Ireland, where he became a slave-shepherd at the age of 16. With little food or clothing, his experience was truly one of harsh and brutal treatment. After six years he escaped and returned home. But the image of his former captors and masters living without the hope of Christianity led him to return, much against his family's will.

His father was a deacon, his grandfather a priest. But after his experience as a slave, Patrick had learned the really vital aspects of the gospel, and he now lived the hope. Daily he expected death because of his preaching, but he determined to continue whatever the threats and dangers, so that the Irish might come to know the Lord as a loving and compassionate Father.

In his "Confession" Patrick writes of his experience of having known the love of God for him as a father for his son, of discovering the meaning and purpose of life, and of being thrilled by the resurrection hope. He quotes only the Bible, and bases his life on scriptural principles. His was a simple and uncomplicated faith that preached hope to the hopeless.

His witness produced an Ireland that changed from dark despair and human sacrifice to a land that glorified Jesus as Savior and Lord, the living hope and returning King.

In his prayer, known as the "Breastplate of Patrick," he affirms his hope: "I arise today . . . in the hope of the resurrection to meet with reward" (translation by Kuno Meyer; http://elvis.rowan.edu/~kilroy/JEK/03/17.html). And in his "Confession" he looks forward to the fulfillment of his hope at the second coming of Jesus:

"He [Jesus] was made man, and, having defeated death, was received into heaven by the Father; and He hath given Him all power over all names in heaven, on earth, and under the earth, and every tongue shall confess to Him that Jesus Christ is Lord and God, in whom we believe, and whose advent we expect soon to be, judge of the living and of the dead" (translation by Ludwig Bieler; http://www.ccel.org/p/patrick/confession/confession.html).

The consequence of such a dynamic hope-filled life was a nation turned to God, a whole society transformed, and a new Christian community living by the Bible and looking forward in hope to the return of their newly discovered Savior. It is a powerful illustration of the motivation of hope in a committed Christian, leading us to share God's good news of salvation and an eternal future.

CHAPTER 6

Hope: Too Much or Not Enough?

MISPLACED HOPES

On our first visit to the United States back in 1980 we decided we needed to buy a car in order to get around. We paid a visit to the local car auction and successfully bid for a Chevy station wagon. The auctioneer made the car appear the best buy since the United States had bought Alaska! (Oh, and don't ask me the model; as far as I was concerned, it was just a car!) Not knowing much about American cars, I looked under the bonnet (sorry, hood) and checked to see that there was an engine present, then made sure that it had a spare tyre (sorry, tire) in the boot (sorry, trunk). (And you're telling me we speak the same language?)

Anyway, we drove off, more than pleased with our purchase. I had high hopes for this wonderful product of American engineering. It really did look good, and on the surface I couldn't see anything wrong. I was willing to trust the claims of the auctioneer.

You have to have hope, right? You want to hope, to believe, to have faith. I was sure we had found the car we had been hoping for.

However, during the next few days we discovered a few

idiosyncrasies. The air conditioning would occasionally start up for no apparent reason and begin wailing like a banshee. The first time it happened I nearly drove off the road. But after a while it became almost an accepted example of car eccentricity, and it was fun to see how unsuspecting passengers reacted.

It did seem to be running a bit rough at times too, and I wasn't sure that flames normally came out of the end of the tail-pipe. But it still ran. On very smooth tires, which I suspected were a special American adaptation of Formula 1 slicks to help you drive faster. After having plowed into a snowbank, however, I discovered that they were just worn bald.

But the really scary aspect of my misplaced hopes and blind trust hit even me as we returned from picking someone up at the airport in Chicago. We drove the 90 miles back home, sailing along the freeway until we exited. As we slowed down on the off-ramp I heard a strange jangling sound. Stopping, I looked under the car. Nothing. I opened the windows and drove a few feet. It was as if someone were rattling stones in a can. Then I remembered an old prank from English weddings of putting gravel inside the hubcaps of the "Just Married" car.

I took off a hubcap. Instead of gravel, I found three nuts and bolts that held the wheel onto the axle totally sheared off. Only one still held the wheel in place! And that was well worn through too. Shuddering, I checked the other front wheel. Same problem, with just two nuts still in place.

We drove the few miles home at five miles an hour. Thankfully we made it safely. Then I checked with a mechanically minded neighbor. He shook his head in amazement, and then told me I'd been driving a car all that time with the wrong-sized wheels on the front. Someone had removed the right wheels and replaced them with the wrong ones—maybe just before taking it to the auction.

How important it is to know your vehicle. Hope without a

sure foundation is futile. I had hoped too much, and misplaced my hope in the assurances of those who obviously could not deliver. To trust the words of an auctioneer—"Great car! Just serviced! Like new!"—is foolishness. You need to know for yourself that you're traveling safe. The only way you can really be sure is to check it all out for yourself—and have a definite idea of what you're looking for.

The same applies in the spiritual world. You have to examine all the evidence and not just trust mere claims. To believe just what anyone tells you is as foolish as my driving that Chevy death trap. I learned fast.

In the material world you must read the owner's manual. Check out the manufacturer's advice. And don't you owe it to yourself and your eternal destiny to do the same in the spiritual realm? Make sure your hopes are properly grounded in the sure and certain promises of the God who does not lie.

TOO MUCH HOPE?

Is it possible to have too much hope? Some may say no. But as one proverb says, "too much hope deceives," and we can encounter danger in overanticipation. For example, it is possible to overstress the timing of hope, to say that its fulfillment is absolutely imminent. This can set believers up for disappointment and despair.

Paul addresses this particular problem of "overhoping," of making expectation so intense that some Christians were even saying that Jesus had already returned. "Concerning the coming of our Lord Jesus Christ and our being gathered to him, we ask you, brothers, not to become easily unsettled or alarmed by some prophecy, report or letter supposed to have come from us, saying that the day of the Lord has already come" (2 Thess. 2:1, 2, NIV).

The apostle says that we must reject that kind of over-expectation, especially any time-related prophecy that says the Advent hope is going to be fulfilled next week, next month, next year—or whenever.

The trouble is that disappointment and doubt often surface once the vividness of too much hope dies away. After we have preached an extreme position we face the other danger of giving up on hope altogether, or pushing it so far into the background that it no longer makes any impact on our lives. In truth, for most Christians today, the greater problem is not one of overhoping, but of not hoping enough.

NOT ENOUGH HOPE?

The biblical call is to have an enduring hope—not one that flares up for a while, only to cool down and die. The hope given by God is not temporary, like all things human. It is absolutely sure and certain, and will endure until its fulfillment. The Lord summons us to "hope to the end for the grace that is to be brought unto you at the revelation of Jesus Christ" (1 Peter 1:13).

Hoping to the end! While it may not be the easiest part of Christian life, it is essential nevertheless. Though the excitement of our first love of the Lord may mature to a sure certainty as we live with Him, that should not mean a dimming of our greatest hope. Quite the opposite: as time continues on, and we grow older in hope, it should blaze brighter.

Surely this is no time for giving up on hope. Sadly, many believers in the blessed hope seem to feel let down, as if what they had hoped for so earnestly has not been fulfilled as they had expected. We need to remember that we are to wait for the Lord according to His timetable, not ours.

The Bible reminds us that we are to look forward to Jesus, the author and finisher of our faith (Heb. 12:2). Hope does not depend on us and what we can fulfill—it is anchored in the rock-solid assurance of God Himself. That is why this hope can bring such joy to the present.

DAMAGED HOPE

For many reasons, hope can become damaged. Sometimes we equate hope with our feelings, and when we do not feel happy, we assume we are losing hope. But the hope we should have is confidence not in how we may feel, but in the assurance of God Himself. The next time you feel less than hopeful, remind yourself of these words from the Psalms: "Why are you downcast, O my soul? Why so disturbed within me? Put your hope in God, for I will yet praise him, my Savior and my God" (Ps. 43:5, NIV).

Put your hope in God! Always remember that it does not come from us but rather from God.

The disciples on the road to Emmaus (see Luke 24:13-35) expressed some of the saddest words of dashed and disappointed hope. They told Jesus, whom they did not recognize, "we had hoped." Although they were actually walking with Christ, journeying in the presence of divine hope Himself, they could not see any reason to go on hoping. In fact, they spoke of hope in the past tense: "we had hoped that he was the one who was going to redeem Israel" (verse 21, NIV).

But as Jesus, the very source of hope, then explained to them all the scriptures concerning Himself, their eyes were opened—finally they saw! Hope blazed bright again. "When he was at the table with them, he took bread, gave thanks, broke it and began to give it to them. Then their eyes were opened and they recognized him, and he disappeared from their sight. They asked each other, 'Were not our hearts burning within us while he talked with us on the road and opened the Scriptures to us?' " (verses 30-32, NIV).

AN UNSURPRISED HOPE

Of all people, we should be constantly aware of the coming of what we hope for! "But you, brothers, are not in darkness so that this day should surprise you like a thief. You are all sons of the light and sons of the day. We do not belong to the night or to the darkness. So then, let us not be like others, who are asleep, but let us be alert and self-controlled" (1 Thess. 5:4-6, NIV).

As the community of hope that looks forward to the return of our loving Lord, we are "sons of the light and sons of the day." We must be people who recognize the light God has given us, and then live in that light, because we have come "out of darkness into his marvellous light" (1 Peter 2:9).

Consequently, nothing should catch us unaware when the Lord does return and completes His promise, fulfilling the blessed hope. We should not be asleep, living our lives unmindful of what God has promised, but "alert and self-controlled." Our actions should reflect that we are a faith community of hope, and that individually we are *awake* to the working of hope in our own lives.

DESPERATE HOPES

Sometimes the reason for hope is a desperate one. People feel compelled to hope, for if they do not they fear being overwhelmed with thoughts of doom and judgment. If you decide to hope because of the terrors of the alternatives, that too can lead to a crisis of hope.

The myth of a resurrected national hero is common to many cultures. Whether it is King Arthur returning to his court at Camelot to answer the summons to free England, or Joan of Arc fighting once more for French freedom, or King Vaclav riding forth again at the head of the Knights of Blanik to save Bohemia, the legends point to a national hope in past glories.

The latter legend became embroidered during the dark

days of the Second World War. Writer Frantisek Langer tells a story of how some Czechs refound the sword of their hero Vaclav or Wenceslas—a symbol of national pride and hope—during the Nazi occupation of the city of Prague in 1939. The legend had related how King Wenceslas (of the Christmas carol's fame) had possessed a magical sword, and that it had been hidden in the stones of the Charles Bridge that crosses the river Vltava in the center of Prague.

The sword was supposedly rediscovered in the middle of the bridge by a group of children as they walked home on a snowy Christmas Eve. There before them glowed and flashed the sword, and one of the boys picked it up and hid it under his coat. Wondering what to do, the children tried to unsheathe the sword, but could not. Eventually they decided to keep their sword of hope hidden, ready for Wenceslas when he returned.

And they still wait. History marches on; the Nazi occupation ended. No Wenceslas came to the rescue, then or during the time of the Communist oppression—or now. It was a story of hope for a time of trouble. But in the end, it was a misguided hope as people waited for a mythical hero to be resurrected and to come to the aid of his former land.

And it is also sad, because what is the point of waiting for Arthur or Joan of Arc or Wenceslas to return from the dead when the Savior of the world is already resurrected?

In the words of the *Rubáiyát of Omar Khayyám:*

"The Worldly Hope men set their Hearts upon
Turns Ashes—or it prospers; and anon,
Like Snow upon the Desert's dusty Face,
Lighting a little hour or two—is gone."

—Edward FitzGerald

God's hope is not a passing and inconsequential one. Nor is

it a hope that vanishes like snow in the sun—as useless as a hidden sword or as insubstantial as mythical Camelot. God offers hope sure and certain—the sure and certain hope not of resurrected legendary heroes but of *the Resurrection*—of Jesus and you and me. It is a hope based on one who is already resurrected and returned, the Lord of the universe, risen with healing in His wings and soon to reclaim His kingdom for all eternity.

For example, if your reason for embracing the blessed hope is nothing more than fear of punishment, then it may certainly be true that you hope "too much." As life seems to get better, you may then end up hoping "not enough."

BALANCED HOPE

We all need to ask ourselves why we hope. Our answer should not first and foremost be just to escape the horrors of judgment, or the disaster scenarios of the end-time. No, the reason for hope is not a negative one—but the ultimately positive reason of wanting to be with Jesus. All such fearful hopes need to be replaced by the hope that God alone gives, since "perfect love drives out fear, because fear has to do with punishment. The one who fears is not made perfect in love" (1 John 4:18, NIV).

God draws us, never forces us. With a loving, compassionate heart, He holds out hope to us, and does not compel us to hope "or else." God's perfect love drives out our fear and replaces it with the desire to hope based not on threats, but on our wanting to be with the Lord who loves us.

Ours is to be a balanced hope, avoiding any extremism and resting its confidence in God, the source of our hope. We may still have questions, but we can remain confident in the trustworthiness of our Lord, who has already proved Himself completely worthy and reliable.

Our evangelistic message is not one of repentance based on

threats of doom and disaster, but an invitation to come to love God before we miss out on the privilege. Such hope is not "fire insurance" against the horrors of hell or end-time destruction—for that is mere self-preservation and self-centeredness. Rather our hope is a longing to be with the One who saves and heals and loves—God Himself.

We are the ones who long for his appearing (2 Tim. 4:8). That longing is our intense desire to be with God, not an attempt to use this hope to escape punishment. Hope is not self-serving, but a natural reaction of the reborn child of God. We eagerly desire the time when "God's home is with people! He will live with them, and they shall be his people. God himself will be with them, and he will be their God. He will wipe away all tears from their eyes. There will be no more death, no more grief or crying or pain. The old things have disappeared" (Rev. 21:3, 4, TEV).

CHAPTER 7

Practical Hope

ON STACKING WOOD

Today we stacked wood. All of us, the whole family. Now tired, but satisfied, we relax inside. Daughter Rebekah snuggles close. "Now we'll be nice and warm and cuddly for the whole winter." She wriggles comfortably at the thought.

The late-afternoon sun caught the sugar maples as we'd worked, turning the red-orange leaves into miniature flaming sunsets down the street. As we stacked the slabs of wood the air chilled and our breath turned white in the stillness. It was evening, a time of ending.

Yet it was an activity of hope, of expectation, because we hoped to see the winter through.

Ana picked up the splinters and chippings. "Good kindling for starting the fire," she told herself. My son Paul carried one log at a time. "He won't die of stress," Ana commented. Rebekah hopped, skipped, jumped—never content simply to walk carrying the wood. I piled it up methodically, building for the future.

As the woodpile grew, so did my happiness. Preparation. Ready for the cold. Comfort and assurance. But most of all, hope.

Hope for warmth in the death of the year, when all outside is fading and ending. Hope for the future, a little permanence in a world full of change. Hope for the chance to see another spring, to witness again new birth.

Stacking wood. That's what we're doing now in the present. For the winter comes, and the end, and death.

But in the stacking of wood we state our hope to live again, not cramped and confined by the snows of winter but free in the warm meadows of forever. Our hope focuses not in the woodpile itself, but in preparing for an eternity with the One who comes to end our winter.

Time to start stacking.

HOPE IS LIVING

George Iles defines Christian hope as "faith holding out its hands in the dark." More than anything else, hope has to be practical and functional. It has to work. In the same way as you hold out your hands in the dark when you cannot see, hope does just that, actively walking and expecting, not just sitting still and waiting.

Hope is living, both in the sense that it is the way we live, and that hope itself is alive! As Peter reminds us: "Let us give thanks to the God and Father of our Lord Jesus Christ! Because of his great mercy he gave us new life by raising Jesus Christ from death. This fills us with a living hope" (1 Peter 1:3, TEV).

This is not "pie in the sky by and by." We need to understand that what we hope for affects how we act and relate not just in the future but here in the present. In grief or in joy, in good times or bad, hope has a major part to play. Most of all, it is intensely practical.

Our hope is not some dim and vague longing for something better, but of knowing God and His salvation now and of having an assured place in His kingdom forever.

That is the hope we are *born* into. Notice the word. Not a hope we pick up casually or one we work out for ourselves. We enter the living hope because Jesus gives us new birth into it. In a sense, the whole process of the new birth is based on hope—the hope that God can do as He has promised, that His salvation is secure, and that one day all this world with its evil and sadness and death will be swallowed up in God's ultimate victory.

Notice what this new birth of hope brings: "And so we look forward to possessing the rich blessings that God keeps for his people. He keeps them for you in heaven, where they cannot decay or spoil or fade away. They are for you, who through faith are kept safe by God's power for the salvation which is ready to be revealed at the end of time" (1 Peter 1:4, 5, TEV).

Here is where hope really makes a practical difference. If our hope is in an immortal inheritance with God, what do the things of this world matter? As Jesus told His hearers, we're not to store up treasure here where the corrupting rust of evil and the invading moths of loss will take it all from us. No, our storehouse is safe with God, and it contains all that is good and right and pure and best. Forget the drive for material possessions that just satisfy the physical. Look for the spiritual investment!

HOPE WHATEVER HAPPENS

The problems and troubles of life may seem overwhelming. Fears about job security, financial worries, family crises, lawsuits, damaged relationships, health worries, bereavement—all can lead to so many kinds of grief. But that's when we should live the hope no matter what is happening to us (see 1 Peter 1:6, 7).

Not that we should think that the troubles are deliberate tests sent by an investigating God. Difficulties afflict everyone—it is our response to them that is important. In the story of Job the tests came from the evil one, and God permitted them as a way of revealing the depth of the patriarch's commitment to God. We need to remain firm to the hope we have committed ourselves to. Once again, this is why our hope is truly living—we live it out in the fabric of our lives, whether times are good or bad.

See how Job clung to his hope in his Redeemer: "I know that my Redeemer lives, and that in the end he will stand upon the earth. And after my skin has been destroyed, yet in my flesh I will see God; I myself will see him with my own eyes—I, and not another. How my heart yearns within me!" (Job 19:25-27, NIV).

Though such words of hope may be easy to read and to say during times of peace, they are far harder to hang on to when you are in a crisis. In times of trouble people may vent very harsh feelings. Some may even want to follow the advice of Job's wife: "Curse God and die." It's easy to understand the depths of pain that lead to such angry attacks on God and His wisdom.

We also remember that some attempts at showing sympathy can appear trite and unthoughtful. Telling someone who is suffering that they have only themselves to blame, as did Job's friends, is hardly helpful. Nor is it particularly wise to express some pious comment about God when you refuse to offer practical help yourself. The hope we have means that we are messengers of hope and will do whatever is in our power to demonstrate that our hope is *practical.*

Most of all, our living of the hope brings the joy and salvation of God: "You love him, although you have not seen him, and you believe in him, although you do not now see him. So you rejoice with a great and glorious joy which words cannot express, because you are receiving the salvation of your souls, which is the purpose of your faith in him" (1 Peter 1:8, 9, TEV).

Why can we rejoice? Because of salvation! The joy we experience comes from recognizing that God is saving us, that He is right now fulfilling His promises, and that the blessed hope will be that glorious reality.

This is not some passing excitement or foolish sense of fun. Rather it is the deep-seated joy that is totally sure of hope's objective. The joy of the Christian is wrapped up in the definite purposes of God, who will bring to pass all that He has promised. From this point of view, hope is more than human yearning—it is absolute conviction. Because we know our Lord, and He has told us what He will do, we find ourselves "filled with an inexpressible and glorious joy" (verse 8, NIV).

Of course, we are not beings that can be always joyful in an outward sense. However, the joy that God gives us is similar to the "peace that passes understanding" and the attitude of "pray without ceasing." It is an inner attitude, a sure conviction that we can safely rest our lives upon. No one can steal that kind of joy away.

HOPE MEANS SETTING YOUR MIND ON GOD

"Keep alert and set your hope completely on the blessing which will be given you when Jesus Christ is revealed" (1 Peter 1:13, TEV).

Great words. But what do they mean? It's back to the gospel and the fact that every part of our lives must express God's grace. That means unlearning our self-righteousness, denying ourselves anger, restraining our sinful appetites, filling our days with prayer and praise to the God of grace.

It is through God's graciousness—the free gifts that He gives us—that we even exist, that we receive His salvation, and that we have an eternal life to look forward to. When Jesus returns at His second coming, then grace will become complete as He transforms us from mortal to immortal, from perishable to imperishable (see 1 Cor. 15).

In case we should be focusing on our own works—that is, attempting to make ourselves righteous—Scripture reminds us that everything depends on the grace that God gives. Our hope itself is just as much grace as any other element in God's plan of salvation.

But we too must act in order to hope. In fact, as Peter says in this same verse, "So then, have your minds ready for action" (1 Peter 1:13, TEV).

Ready for action! That's the command given here. We are to prepare our minds for doing. One thing a Christian cannot be is inactive. God calls us to a busy life lived in hope, one sharing the truth He has committed to us. More than that, we are to be "self-controlled"—in other words, not hasty or overzealous or foolish. And should we think that any of this is of our own doing, the rest of the verse makes it clear where our focus needs to be.

Because our hope is not of this world, we should "be obedient to God, and do not allow your lives to be shaped by those desires you had when you were still ignorant. Instead, be holy in all that you do, just as God who called you is holy" (verses 14, 15, TEV).

Hope means rejecting the principles that many others so easily seem to accept. Without being "pretentiously pious," God's people are called to be holy. Holiness is allowing God's character to reflect in our characters. We acknowledge that His ways and His principles are just and right. Our hope points to the same objective: "Know also that wisdom is sweet to your soul; if you find it, there is a future hope for you, and your hope will not be cut off" (Prov. 24:14, NIV).

The hope of the wise is God's hope—because they hope in God! Knowing God as He truly is gives us the greatest confidence, not because of what He has promised but because of who is doing the promising. In the same way as salvation must come from outside ourselves, so must our hope. That is the only hope worth trusting. Anything else only leads to disappointment and failure. "When a wicked man dies, his hope perishes; all he expected from his power comes to nothing" (Prov. 11:7, NIV).

God wants us to demonstrate our hope in the most practical way we can, revealing that we have set our minds on the God of hope and that we live our lives through Him.

JOHNNY BARNES: THE PRACTICAL FACE OF HOPE

Every weekday morning Johnny Barnes stands by the side of the road in Hamilton, Bermuda, and waves and calls to passing traffic. A seemingly pointless activity. Yet because of his smiling ministry, he has become a national institution in Bermuda. He even has a statue to prove it.

Johnny began his unique witness more than 30 years ago. Now he's Bermuda's official greeter, receiving media attention from around the globe. I had the privilege of meeting him just recently.

"I get calls from all over the world," he says, smiling. "Last week it was a lady from the BBC in England, who told me mine was one of a very few pictures that had gone all around the world. Many people call and write, and I'm happy to hear from them."

Why does he do it? Because "when you accept Jesus Christ as your Savior, you have to let your light shine any way you can," Johnny replies. Besides, "my mother used to tell me, 'Don't let me hear that you saw someone and didn't say hello to them.' I like to let people know, and tell them, 'Someone cares for you, someone loves you.' "

Johnny Barnes is the face of hope to more than three quarters of all Bermudan workers, since they all have to pass his roadside spot every morning on their commute. But is that all it is? I wonder. Just a smile and a greeting on the way to work?

"Sometimes I can have a longer conversation," he adds. "One person told me last week I was doing a wonderful thing that gives people a lift in the mornings. One man couldn't sleep, and when I arrived at 4.30 a.m. he was waiting for me. I talked with him for about an hour and prayed for him. He felt so much better and could go back home. Another man came, and

I prayed for him. I heard later he was thinking about suicide, and because I cared and told him I loved him and God did too, he didn't do it."

He says that what he does is one of God's ways of sharing hope and love. "God is using it in a mighty way. I'm just a little instrument in His hand to use as He may choose. I'm not here for the fame or the honor or the glory. I'm here to be used in any way the Lord sees fit. At the foot of the cross, nothing belongs to me."

He has to get to bed early so he can get up by 2:30 a.m. He has breakfast at 3:30 before he sets out. "I enjoy what I'm doing," he comments. "When I get up, I thank the Lord for another day. When people aren't happy, I tell them it takes more muscles to frown than to smile. So why not use those smiling muscles all the time? I'm always smiling."

How much longer does he intend to be Bermuda's face of hope? "This year I'll be 78. I will keep going as long as the good Lord gives me strength. When they asked me who would take over from me, I said the good Lord would take care of that. It's not up to me."

And what about that statue? "They promised they'll put up a statue of me after I die." He smiles again, more wryly this time. "I told them, 'Why wait until I die? I'd enjoy it more while I'm alive!'"

He gives a wide arms-open greeting. People honk their horns, stop to chat. It seems that he knows everybody. "They're happy for a bit of spiritual uplift," Johnny comments. "We all need hope and love in our lives. Too often people say 'I love you' for selfish reasons. I ask God to make sure that when I say it, it is godly love."

He's still smiling as I leave. The face of hope—God's hope smiling through a human face.

CHAPTER 8

Hope on the Inside

SONG OF HOPE IN WINTER'S COLD

The snow had come, unlooked for and unwanted. Despite the white beauty all around, I had much to do, and here was another unwelcome delay to the day. I left the safe warmth of the house and trudged out to the car as the snowstorm swirled around me. Thick it came, and fast, wrapping me in its fierce coldness like a mantle of ice.

No, not today. Not any day like this. Why now? I just don't need this. I have so much to do it's not funny. I'm too busy. Enough already!

Errands to run. People to see. Meetings to attend. Work to do. Life to live.

Just as I reached for the car door to wrench it open in annoyance and frustration that became worse as I realized I'd have to clean off the windows before I could leave, something stopped me in my snowy tracks.

A pure, lilting birdsong like tinkling crystals descended with the snowflakes.

I could hardly see anything in the blizzard. Why on earth would a bird be singing today of all days? If I were a bird, I'd be hidden deep inside some welcoming evergreen, shivering and puffing up my feathers against the freezing cold. But no, this brave bird was singing in the snowstorm, challenging the elements with its melody.

Peering through the onrushing ice missiles, I tried to catch a glimpse of this winter songster at the top of the cherry tree, holding on to a bare twig against the whirling gale as if daring it to blow him from his perch. A goldfinch, singing his heart out as he whistled against the wind. It was an unseasonal song, but one that challenged me every bit as much as the elements.

Why should the creature be singing? I could think of no reason, for no bird nests in January snows. He had no territory to defend, no rivals to fight, no mate to lure. Instead he had just a delight in song—a snowsong to remind me that life is more than all my daily cares and burdens.

Like Thomas Hardy's "Darkling Thrush" who sang for him in winter, "when Frost was spectre-grey"—

"In a full-hearted evensong
Of joy illimited;
An aged thrush, frail, gaunt, and small,
In blast-beruffled plume,
Had chosen thus to fling his soul
Upon the growing gloom."

Just a bird singing. Just notes on a scale. Just music on the wind. And for what?

My hand outstretched toward the door handle, I stopped, frozen not by cold but by enchantment and realization. A dawning that seeped into my thoughts of a reality beyond all this fussing and fighting, all this running to and fro, all this getting and spending and laying waste our powers. The world *is* too much with us.

Now I stood and listened, the only audience in this winter concert hall, the only ears to hear this unique masterpiece. And I thought of what it meant, on such a bitter day as this.

Like Hardy again:

"So little cause for carolings

Of such ecstatic sound
Was written on terrestrial things
Afar or nigh around . . . "

Nothing in this bleak midwinter gave any indication of happy expectation, offered no reason for such delightful, joyful music. And then I thought of how Hardy ends his poem of praise to his singer:

"That I could think there trembled through
His happy good-night air
Some blessed Hope, whereof he knew
And I was unaware."

I shook my head. No! I was not unaware. For I did know of the blessed hope, the reason for any such singing for joy. This blessed hope "trembles through" all our existence here, a reminder that this world is not everything, and that nothing in this life can ever compare to the future we anticipate, the sure hope that is as certain as the promises of God Himself.

As the song concluded, as the bird took flight and disappeared into the snow-filled air, the silence of winter descended as heavy as the blanket of white all around me. It was as if it had never been.

But in my heart I carried the memory of that song—a reminder of joy in the blessed hope that makes all the monotony and trouble of our life here as nothing in comparison to our God-filled future. Days may be filled with busyness, but our eternity is assured.

HOPE ON THE INSIDE

Hope can only exist on the inside. Intensely personal and internal, it is "Christ in you, the hope of glory" (Col. 1:27).

Jesus' appeal to you and to me is to take His promised hope and make it personal. In your mind see yourself there eagerly awaiting as Jesus comes. Look toward your own eternal life together with Jesus. And because of that blessed hope, you can then walk with Jesus day by day, living the life He gives until He returns to fulfill His wondrous promise (see Mal. 4:2).

Make hope real for yourself—on the inside!

God promises that "the faith and love that spring from the hope that is stored up for you in heaven and that you have already heard about in the word of truth, the gospel" (Col. 1:5, NIV) will indeed come to pass.

Faith and love spring from hope! Thus they are just as much gifts of our gracious God of hope as any other aspect of salvation. And that hope is the secure hope stored up by God in heaven for all those who trust in Him. And what will heaven be like? "No eye has seen, no ear has heard, no mind has conceived what God has prepared for those who love him" (1 Cor. 2:9, NIV).

You want to know about hope on the inside? Reflect on God and His promises, and how that can keep you assured and trusting despite whatever life may bring. This is the message of the gospel—not one that makes us proud or arrogant, but does produce loyalty and conviction. The promise comes from God, who "cannot lie" (see Heb. 6:18).

Our assurance is that "we have this hope as an anchor for the soul, firm and secure" (verse 19, NIV). Anchored! That's the rock-solid attitude of hope, a perspective that looks beyond the things of this world to the vital realities of God's kingdom.

In the words of the English proverb: "If fortune torments me, hope contents me." Such hope is not some bland and unsubstantial wish that may or may not come to pass, but a certain and definite future. Each one of us needs to believe in what God has said, then take Him at His word. Although we must avoid obsessively dwelling on the future blessings, we must still acknowledge the reality of that hope God has stored up for each one who has accepted Jesus.

God says to each of us, personally and individually, "There

is surely a future hope for you, and your hope will not be cut off" (Prov. 23:18, NIV). "'For I know the plans I have for you,' declares the Lord, 'plans to prosper you and not to harm you, plans to give you hope and a future'" (Jer. 29:11, NIV).

As a result, "by faith we eagerly await through the Spirit the righteousness for which we hope" (Gal. 5:5, NIV).

RED BIKE

I was 5 years old and wanted a real bike. I'd had toy bikes, and a tricycle that was fun for a while and had been stable enough to keep me from crashing too much. But now I longed for one like the bigger boys had. Besides constantly mentioning it to my parents, I thought about it almost every moment and even dreamed about it. My hope was strong and enduring—I would one day have a bike of my own. Soon.

Of course I dreamed of what my new bike would be like. But the exact specification was not the most important thing. As long as it worked. I could see myself flying down the street, the wind rushing past my face, my heart pounding with the thrill of speed.

But for my parents I offered a slightly different set of reasons. It would be a good thing to learn how to ride a bike, I assured them—everyone ought to know such an important life skill. And I could ride it to school. And run errands. And so on.

But in my dreams, I just wanted to be free, to ride, to fly across the world on my new bike. I held on to my hope, trusting it would come true.

Then eventually, after an eternity of weeks, my birthday arrived. Could it be the time . . . ? My hope was high, vibrant.

All through the family present-giving ceremony my parents were smiling. We were hardly rich, yet I always had good birthdays. But as I looked around that day, I didn't see anything that even vaguely looked like a bike. My hope sank like a stone. I had wanted it so badly that now I blinked back tears. But still my parents smiled.

Then, in the end, they led me out to the back of the house. There, leaning against the wall, was a bright-red bike with a red ribbon tied to the handlebars! I could hardly believe my eyes. My hope had come true, fulfilled, achieved.

I shouted for joy and jumped on the bike—and promptly fell off again. My parents laughed as they picked me up, telling me that I had time to learn. Then my dad explained about the bike. It wasn't exactly new. In fact, it was quite old and had been severely damaged.

But my father had taken the broken bike and had welded it back together. You could see the weld as a swelling where the crossbar met the fork. The paint job was a bit rough—the brushstrokes stood out. And the handlebars were a little off from straight. But it didn't matter to me—it was my bike. Painted bright red, the wheels cleaned up, the brakes and tires all brand-new.

My hope had come completely true. Although at first I fell many times, before long I was riding, flying free with the wind against my face. I saw the world from a whole new viewpoint. Liberated, I went places I'd never been before as I explored a whole new universe on my red bike. It was the best thing that I had ever had.

From that point on I realized that it was not wanting some physical possession that mattered, but that hope is what leads us on. The gift was not the bike—not even the red bike I treasured so much—but hope alive, the personal hope that sets us free.

That bike lasted me several years. Eventually I outgrew it. I have no idea what happened to that bike I had hoped for so much. The physical passes, breaks, rusts—and even if we fix it up for a while, it breaks again and finally becomes useless.

Yet from that gift of my long-expected red bike I learned

personally the meaning of living in hope, a hope that opens doors, that gives meaning and purpose in the present and an anticipation of the future. Hope on the inside.

HOPE PERSONALLY ASSURED

God gives us this personal hope—hope on the inside—so that we will have total confidence in His assured promise. He tells us to "continue in your faith, established and firm, not moved from the hope held out in the gospel" (Col. 1:23, NIV).

Many varieties of hope exist in the world today. But the gospel holds out only one hope—and that is the Jesus hope. The hope of Jesus is both hope *in* Jesus, and the hope *of* Jesus, that is, the hope that He also held.

If there is one thing the devil wants to take from Jesus' followers it is their hope. Once Satan can dim the bright flame of hope, if not even extinguish it, then he can raise fear, doubt, and despair to attack the Christian. But if we let nothing move us from the hope of the gospel, then we remain secure. In fact, such a hope is so real it seems as if we almost have what we are hoping for, because it is so secure. Hope so real that we already have it!

The appeal is to "put your hope in the Lord both now and forevermore" (Ps. 131:3, NIV).

We must not conclude that we should never take personal responsibility for making sure our hope is real and active. Each of us still needs to exercise our decisions of choice. But we are strengthened by knowing that when we are in union with Jesus it allows Him to change and remake us into His image day by day. This is our hope, one that grows throughout our lives and looks for its final fulfillment in glory. Our hope of glory is only through Christ in us—it is not of ourselves. Glory comes from God, the same source as our hope!

HOPE INSIDE YOU

Jeremiah describes this internal hope in Lamentations—a part of Scripture often considered as rather depressing. On the contrary, here is Jeremiah's testimony to his hope on the inside:

"Yet this I call to mind and therefore I have hope: Because of the Lord's great love we are not consumed, for his compassions never fail. They are new every morning; great is your faithfulness. I say to myself, 'The Lord is my portion; therefore I will wait for him.' The Lord is good to those whose hope is in him, to the one who seeks him; it is good to wait quietly for the salvation of the Lord. It is good for a man to bear the yoke while he is young. Let him sit alone in silence, for the Lord has laid it on him. Let him bury his face in the dust—there may yet be hope" (Lam. 3:21-29, NIV).

What is involved here? Memory, recognition of God's love and trustworthiness, action in seeking God. And while it may not be the easiest thing to do, hope demands much waiting. But the most important aspect of such a "confession of hope" is that it is real and personal. Notice how the preceding passage expresses the close relationship between the "I" and the Lord. Hope without such a personal and practical aspect is pointless.

Similarly, Paul, when brought to trial before Felix, could give his personal testimony to his hope: "I have the same hope in God, . . . that there will be a resurrection of both the righteous and the wicked" (Acts 24:15, NIV).

Hope takes account of such essential realities. God's hope is based on salvation, justice, judgment, vindication, and completion. Such hope keeps us going, with our faces looking upward, ready to welcome the hoped-for One and to enter into God's eternal kingdom.

THE PERSONAL HOPE

Let us return to the goldfinch's song in the middle of a winter snowstorm. For me at least, the song we shall sing of victory when hope is completed, the promise realized, and joy fulfilled, will have the same elements of melody that made my own heart sing that winter morning.

Like the bird, we live in a time of winter desolation, longing for summer. Just as the bird singing in the snow, we share our joy of our hope even when the situation seems hopeless. Because we know that our hope will be fulfilled, we will always be able to sing.

As Emily Dickinson wrote:

"'Hope' is the thing with feathers—
That perches in the soul—
And sings the tune without the words—
And never stops—at all."

Or in the words of Shakespeare: "True hope is swift, and flies with swallow's wings."

May it truly be soon, our Lord, and may our true personal hope in You be fulfilled swiftly.

CHAPTER 9

Hope and the Position of Suspense

HOPE AND WAITING

As I write this I am staying near Geneva, Switzerland. My nephew Imanuel is due to arrive from Frankfurt, Germany. We have planned this meeting. Knowing that he is coming and trusting his promises, I have a definite hope of seeing him soon.

But I don't know exactly when.

He knows where I will be and expects me to be here. So I wait, trying to be patient. But it is not the easiest of situations. What if I want to go somewhere else, even for a short while? He may come while I'm gone and not find me. I wouldn't want that. So I keep an eye out the window to see if he approaches. At the same time I keep on working (on this!) and look forward to seeing him arrive.

Yet it is a "position of suspense." Activities other than "occupying till he comes" (see Luke 19:13) are not practicable or possible, for otherwise I might miss him. I find my mind wondering when he may appear. Soon, I hope, because it will be great to see him again, after so long. Waiting, I find, is not an activity I most enjoy. But it is an active waiting as I continue with what needs to be done, but always ready to drop whatever I might be doing and to meet him in happiness when he does get here.

It is a small and imperfect image of the time in which we find ourselves, as we too wait for our hope to be realized, wait for the coming of our Lord and Friend.

Hope means keeping alert and ready whatever the time. "Therefore keep watch, because you do not know the day or the hour" (Matt. 25:13, NIV).

A LONG TIME COMING?

A sleek space rocket sits on its launch pad. After years of preparation scientists have all its mechanisms ready. All systems are go! In the control room the computers make their constant checks and tests, the controllers wait anxiously, and the clock on the wall shows the time remaining. With rhythmic precision a voice counts out the last seconds of time.

"T minus 30 and counting. We are go for launch. Automatic firing sequence initiated. T minus 20. Looking good. T minus 10 . . . . 9 . . . . 8 . . . . 7 Main engine ignition . . . . 4 . . . . 3 . . . . 2 . . . . 1 . . . . Zero. Lift off, we have lift off!"

And the gleaming silver arrow hurtles heavenward in a cloud of smoke and fire.

Soon we too will be traveling heavenward. Soon Jesus will return to take us home with Him. And soon the end will arrive.

But when exactly? comes the insistent question.

That's the $64,000 question. We always want to know how much time we've got! It is human nature to want to plan ahead. As a result, we demand a definite date, because we just can't stand having to wait without knowing exactly when! So if Jesus is returning to our planet, when is this dramatic event going to take place?

People all through history have tried to pinpoint the date of Jesus' return. And all have failed. Why? Because Jesus Himself said: "No one knows, however, when that day and hour will come—neither the angels in heaven nor the Son; the Father alone knows" (Matt. 24:36, TEV).

No one will be able to work it out by mathematics or with computers. It's something we cannot know. In fact, Jesus went on to say: "You do not know what day your Lord will come" (verse 42, TEV) and "the Son of Man will come at an hour when you are not expecting him" (verse 44, TEV).

The problem, though, is that we always want to know when. We want to determine the time, not so much so that we can be ready, but so we can concentrate on the fulfillment of our hope when and only when we really need to!

God knows our fallible humanity only too well, which is why He does not give us a specific date. In the words of Augustine: "The last day is hidden so that every day may be regarded."

But in our waiting, it may seem that the realization of our hope is a long time coming. Living in suspense is not easy as we constantly wonder, "When?" That is why Jesus told a story to illustrate what should be our response. "The bridegroom was a long time in coming, and they all became drowsy and fell asleep" (Matt. 25:5, NIV).

As we study His parable, we should remember that it immediately follows Jesus' answer to the disciples' question about the signs of the end. So when we read Matthew 25, we need to understand what Christ's illustrations describe. Jesus is speaking about the hope of the Second Coming—and our relationship to this dramatic and conclusive event. He had just finished explaining all about His return. But like most of us, the disciples needed some help understanding what He meant. So Jesus illustrated His explanation with a parable.

We should look carefully at this picture of the Second Coming. In doing so, we must try to imagine that we are in that very situation. Think of what it means to us. Work out in our minds what Jesus was attempting to say.

We find 10 young women categorized into two classifications. "Five of them were foolish and five were wise" (verse 2, NIV). The emphasis here involves separation and preparation. All were waiting—in fact, all fell asleep—but they had different attitudes and levels of preparedness. They all went through the waiting time, becoming weary and tired. But the wise were ultimately ready—they held on to their hope, symbolized by their keeping a supply of oil on hand.

The wise were ready to act on the fulfillment of their hope. When the bridegroom arrived, they were prepared despite the passing of time.

THE CRY AT MIDNIGHT

Finally the announcement of the bridegroom rings forth. Hope is fulfilled. "Here's the bridegroom! Come out to meet him!" (verse 6, NIV).

They have no more time for preparation. No more time for hope—for the object of hope is here!

The midnight cry is the announcement of the fulfillment of hope. All that they have anticipated is now completed in the arrival of the bridegroom. The anxieties along the way, the troubles of life, all the concerns, find themselves swept away in the glorious arrival of the King of kings and Lord of lords. The time of waiting has ended, the position of suspense over.

Our preparation time is now. This is why time continues: so that those who choose may get ready—now! Then "there will be the shout of command, the archangel's voice, the sound of God's trumpet, and the Lord himself shall come down from heaven" (1 Thess. 4:16, TEV).

All the women woke up. But the difference between them now becomes obvious. While they all waited in hope, five had done something about their hope—they had prepared. The five foolish women had been waiting, but they had not done anything about their hope. "The ten young women woke up and trimmed their lamps. Then the foolish ones said to the wise ones, 'Let us have some of your oil, because our lamps are going out.' 'No, indeed,' the wise ones answered, 'there is not enough for you and us. Go to the shop and buy some for yourselves.' So the foolish ones went off to buy some oil; and while they were gone, the bridegroom arrived" (Matt. 25:7-10, TEV).

The result of being ready is plain for all to see: "The five who were ready went in with him to the wedding feast" (verse 10, TEV).

That's the reward—just being there! Being with Jesus is the prize—not the streets of gold or the pearly gates. Commencing an eternity in the presence of our gracious God—that is the glorious objective of our blessed hope.

Once the bridegroom arrives, hope is fulfilled and the door of opportunity closes. "And the door was shut. Later the others also came. 'Sir! Sir!' they said. 'Open the door for us!' "But he replied, 'I tell you the truth, I don't know you' " (verses 10-12, NIV).

Somehow his statement sounds harsh. But we should more likely read the reply of the bridegroom as a voice tinged with sadness and regret. Clearly the foolish women had made no preparation, and did not really know the person they were waiting for. The response from the bridegroom is a factual comment: there was no relationship.

Once the door of hope closes, hope ends. To be excluded from eternity because of lack of readiness to be with our Lord is a tragedy. In response we should look far more seriously at how we use our time and our talents. Readiness is not in making sure we legalistically obey requirements, but in developing a saving relationship with the God of hope.

THEREFORE KEEP WATCH

As Jesus concludes His illustration of how to live in the time-between, in the position of suspense, He urges: "Therefore keep watch, because you do not know the day or the hour" (verse 13, NIV).

Watch! That's the key. Again and again in Jesus' words on hope and preparation He emphasizes the need to watch.

So as we think of ourselves and our relationship to Jesus and His return, what is our attitude going to be? What is the basic motivation in our lives? Are we concerned about ourselves and making sure we do plenty of good things so we'll get a good reward? Or are we simply living as close to God as possible so that He can transform us, and then when He comes we will be surprised at the commendation we'll receive?

In His parable Jesus wasn't so concerned to establish the doctrine of the Second Advent as to answer the important question: How do I relate to such a hope?

"Watch, then, because you do not know when the master of the house is coming—it might be in the evening or at midnight or before dawn or at sunrise. If he comes suddenly, he must not find you asleep. What I say to you, then, I say to all: Watch!" (Mark 13:35-37, TEV).

As a teenager, I was returning from a long trip away from home. Some kind person had given me a ride, and I felt obliged to sit up front and make conversation. But I was so terribly tired that I just could not keep my eyes open. Whatever I did, I just could not keep watch. My eyelids kept closing. Although I bit my lip and pinched myself, I just could not stay awake.

Right then I recognized the situation of the disciples in Gethsemane. Jesus had asked His closest friends to do one thing for Him—to stay awake with Him, to keep watch. And they failed Him in His hour of greatest need.

For all our sakes, we need to stay awake to what is happening around us, to hold on to our living hope, to keep watch.

God says to each of us:

"Choose for yourselves *this day* whom you will serve" (Joshua 24:15, NIV).

"*Today,* if you hear his voice, do not harden your hearts" (Heb. 3:15, NIV).

"*Now* he commands all people everywhere to repent" (Acts 17:30, NIV).

"*Now* is the time of God's favor, *now* is the day of salvation" (2 Cor. 6:2, NIV).

This is the reason Jesus wants to tell us about His soon coming—so that we can be ready. Not at some time in the future, but now—which is all the time we really have.

The vital question is not "when?" What does matter is what we're doing about Jesus' promise *right now.* For when the trumpet sounds and the lightning flashes and the voice of God rings out, nobody will be worrying about the timing. All that will matter is whether we have followed Jesus' advice: Be ready! Watch and pray! Be on your guard! We measure our lives not in seconds and minutes, hours or days, months or years, but in heartbeats.

So as we watch in hope, let us make sure that hope fills our lives, and that hope prepares us for our meeting with our loving Lord. As Shakespeare says: "Journeys end in lovers meeting."

May we all be there with the One we love the most at hope's journey's end.

WATCHING IN HOPE OR FOLLOWING FATAL HOPES?

We need to have the true hope and not follow foolish and false ones. Most of all, we must watch in hope.

On October 22, 1707, an admiral of the English fleet by the unlikely name of Sir Cloudesley Shovell had a decision to make.

He was returning from a successful campaign fighting the French, and his flagship, the *Association,* together with others in his 21-strong fleet, bulged with captured treasure. But bad weather had made the trip north a difficult one. Not having seen the sun for days, they were navigating by dead reckoning. Shovell and the other captains believed they were off the coast of Ushant at the mouth of the English Channel. The course home lay northeast, they believed.

Or at least so they hoped.

The only dissenting voice was a man identified in some accounts as a pilot from the Isles of Scilly. He told the admiral and his advisers that they were wrong, and that the planned course would shipwreck them on his home islands.

But the commanders ignored him, and the fleet continued in the direction they hoped was right. It was a vain hope. An uninformed hope. And, eventually, a fatal hope.

For the pilot was right. Their dead-reckoning calculations were wrong. The charts on which they placed their trust were also wrong, placing the islands in the wrong spot. Disregarding the one man who did know where they were was the last wrong step on their way to disaster.

Sir Cloudesley sent three ships on ahead. They soon found they were way off their expected course and in great danger among the rocks of the Scilly Isles. Two made their way through, but a rock holed the *Phoenix,* and its crew had to beach it.

Going ahead in their hope—their blind faith in their rightness—during a gale, more ships sailed full speed into the treacherous western rocks of the Scillies, with a total loss of five vessels, including the *Association* herself. Sir Cloudesley also paid the price for his mistaken hope—he too perished during the wreck. Nearly 2,000 men died with him as the ships *Eagle, Romney,* and *Firebrand* faithfully followed the *Association* despite the firing of warning signal guns. Jagged rocks tore them to pieces.

It was a tragic lesson in how misguided hope turns deadly and shows how events can expose a false basis for hope as worthless. Clearly it is dangerous for a fleet to go on in poor visibility and at night. Most of all, we wonder why they did not listen to the one who knew, who advised a different course.

The English fleet followed a worthless hope that parallels the kinds of decisions we may also make. We may believe we are in the right place, that we can work out where we're going, and that we know the way ahead. But all too often we're wrong. Thinking we can trust our own hopes based on our own calculations, we plow right on, just like H.M.S. *Association*—straight into the rocks of Scilly's Gilstone Ledges, and make a shipwreck of our faith, our hopes, and our lives.

Watch in hope!

CHAPTER 10

Too Busy Occupying? On Making Hope Relevant

THE WORLD IS TOO MUCH WITH US

"The world is too much with us," wrote William Wordsworth. "Late and soon, getting and spending, we lay waste our powers."

The world truly invades our lives and our minds to the extent that we are preoccupied with occupying—so busy living our lives that we have no time for anything else. So busy that we forget what it is all for—what to live means, and why hope is so vital and relevant.

Entering a small village shop in England one time, I found the shopkeeper in conversation with a local friend. As I waited I immediately became struck by their conversation. It went something like this:

"How's the job, then, John?" the shopkeeper asked.

"Really dull and boring. What's the point of it all, anyway? Seventy years and that's it. Makes you sick, doesn't it, Andy?"

"Well, at least you're not working down at the poultry farm, John. Mean to say, you have it easy. So what if we all snuff it? We've all got to go sometime. Just enjoy life, take what you can, and have fun—that's my motto."

"I dunno, Andy. Must be more to it than that."

Deep down, people see that they're missing out on something. Too often life is just vanity, a "chasing after the wind." So what can they do about it?

If I were to characterize the way that people live I'd say that they're trying to find happiness. All the world wants to be happy, to get happy, to stay happy. "Come on, get happy" goes the song. Of course, people try different ways to find happiness, but in the end all that we do is dedicated to making ourselves happy. But what really works? Everyone has ideas, but so many are false. Where do we find true happiness? When earthly pleasures fade, what are we left with?

I had a friend who was once a Christian. He was also, I believe, very happy. At the time he had a simple job and made enough to live on. Then he went into business, doing first one thing and then the next until eventually he was a millionaire with a large number of profitable companies under his control. He was able to indulge himself and his family, buying expensive cars—later, even a helicopter. Purchasing an even larger place to live way out in the country, he lived an expensive and pleasure-filled life. But he was no longer a Christian. And from what he said to me once, I just wonder how happy he was.

For all the wealth of the world cannot compare to the joy of knowing we are right with God. Money, possessions, and ambitions have their place. But when they lead you away from God, then they can become terrible curses. My former friend's marriage broke up and he lost all his fortune in bad business deals. Today he lives alone—and has no hope.

I had another clever friend whom I worked with in the aerospace industry. The son of a clergyman, he entered space technology, and through his expertise he rapidly rose up the ladder of success. Soon he was project manager, works manager, and then general manager. By all appearances he had a most successful career, yet he was an unhappy man. He increasingly drank. One day someone asked me to talk with him. At the end of a long conversation about very deep things—on the meaning of life, the reason for being, hope, salvation, and all the rest—he said to me, "I wish I could have hope. I know you have hope, and I just wish I could have hope too."

JUST OCCUPYING

God clearly identifies the character of those preoccupied with occupying: "You say, 'I am rich and well off; I have all I need.' But you do not know how miserable and pitiful you are! You are poor, naked, and blind" (Rev. 3:17, TEV).

This clear rebuke should make us reconsider carefully what it is that we should be doing, what the really vital values are, and what is our true motivation. Here the Advent hope can help us by reordering our priorities and turning our vision away from all the busy things of this life back to eternal truths.

While Jesus in His parable did speak about occupying, it was occupying "till He comes" (see Luke 19:13). Sometimes it seems we are just occupying to no real purpose, thus losing sight of our objective. In all we do—in all that the church does—we must not be satisfied with working toward permanence here. Our future is with God, our home is with Him, and our values must be His. Instead of seeking a place in this world, let's remember that our goal is a city whose builder and maker is God, and that our citizenship is heaven (see Phil. 3:20).

It is important to analyze what we are doing and to see who we really are. We need to ask ourselves, "What is our primary motivation, what are our first priorities?" God reminds us that "I know what you have done; I know that you are neither cold nor hot. How I wish you were either one or the other!" (Rev. 3:15, TEV).

Neither cold nor hot. What does God mean? As we look at the kind of people we are, the greatest challenge is to do *some-*

thing. The modern curse is not first of all mistaken theological views of one extreme or another, nor of misguided programs or interpretations or positions. Rather it is that so few really seem to care at all. Apathy is the spiritual nerve gas that paralyzes the church, preventing it from achieving God's goals. That is why it offends Him so much, and He would prefer any other temperature than lukewarmness!

The double tragedy is that so many fail to see their situation. We need to include ourselves here, and not use the passage to point accusatory fingers at others. The general condition of the church, God declares, is one of widespread apathy, of a failure to see our spiritual condition. "But because you are lukewarm, neither hot nor cold, I am going to spit you out of my mouth!" (verse 16, TEV).

Like tasteless food that is all of one tepid temperature, God rejects our own self-centered deeds. And like soup that has cooled down, or ice cream that has warmed up, our apathetic deeds are an offense to a God who wants to come and fulfill the promises of the Advent hope.

HOPE FOR THE "WRETCHED 'RICH' "

As we occupy ourselves, all too often it is just that. We are just occupying ourselves. The tragedy is that we value that which does not truly satisfy—we run after the treasures of this world and of the passing moment.

God tells us we are not really rich, even though we may believe ourselves to be. Jesus concluded His parable of the rich fool in the same way: "This is how it is with those who pile up riches for themselves but are not rich in God's sight" (Luke 12:21, TEV).

"Not rich in God's sight!" is a tragic epitaph for those who believed themselves to be very rich. What about ourselves? Don't we need to reconsider what we are doing and why? We may think we are rich, but God tells us something different.

Here again our focus on hope can help. It reminds us not to become too involved in the affairs of this world. We are not to be self-focused either. Our hope-focus points to the true values God desires, and it gives us motivation to share the faith we have with others. Our riches come not from what we have achieved for ourselves, but in sharing of God's gracious gifts.

That is why God counsels us to "buy" from Him—not that we have anything "worth" the trade: "I advise you, then, to buy gold from me, pure gold, in order to be rich. But also white clothing to dress yourself and cover up your shameful nakedness. But also some ointment to put on your eyes, so that you may see" (Rev. 3:18, TEV).

Such gold is not wealth or material benefit but rather faith refined in the fire. It is true gold that lasts, not the fool's gold that will perish at the end.

The white clothes are those that God provides, such as the wedding garments in Jesus' parable (see Matt. 22:1-14). Our righteousness is as filthy rags, and God wants to take it from us and clothe us in His garments.

The eye ointment heals the blindness of sin, enabling us to truly see—see spiritually, see the truth. The god of this world blinds us from seeing the truth about God (see 2 Cor. 4:4), and we most of all need this spiritual sight to see reality for what it truly is.

God tells us to buy these essential qualities "without money and without cost":

"Come, all you who are thirsty, come to the waters; and you who have no money, come, buy and eat! Come, buy wine and milk without money and without cost. Why spend money on what is not bread, and your labor on what does not satisfy? Listen, listen to me, and eat what is good, and your soul will delight in the richest of fare" (Isa. 55:1, 2, NIV).

Without money and without cost—we have no currency to buy anything from God anyway. Nor can we trade with Him for the things He offers. We only "buy" by making a commitment, by demonstrating that we are giving ourselves.

Where does hope come into all of this? Again it is the motivator for action. Because we hope, we recognize our needs. We could identify the gold of hope, the white clothes of hope, and the eyesalve of hope—for hope gives us this spiritual richness, this spiritual clothing, and this spiritual sight.

JESUS THE DOOR OF HOPE

Jesus tells us that hope is here, because He is right outside the door: "Here I am! I stand at the door and knock. If anyone hears my voice and opens the door, I will come in and eat with him, and he with me" (Rev. 3:20, NIV).

When Jesus spoke about His coming, He said the same thing:

"And he will send his angels with a loud trumpet call, and they will gather his elect from the four winds, from one end of the heavens to the other. Now learn this lesson from the fig tree: As soon as its twigs get tender and its leaves come out, you know that summer is near. Even so, when you see all these things, you know that it is near, right at the door" (Matt. 24:31-33, NIV).

Right at the door—that's how close Jesus and His hope really is. Instead of ignoring the divine visitor who knocks at the door, saying we're too busy to answer, we need to run and open up the door!

Our response as we recognize that we have become too self-absorbed, too busy with all our occupying, must be a rush to unlatch the door to our loving Lord of hope. In the same way that we would run to fling open the door to someone we love, we will want to open the door to God and let Him enter. His offer is not to come in and rearrange the furniture, or to evict us, but to sit down and eat with us. In the same way as we share with others over a meal, God wants to talk with us, to be our truest friend. What an incredible offer from the God of hope!

Trouble is, we often see the Advent hope as interfering in what we want to do, as something disrupting our lives. We may even be self-satisfied and see no reason to change. Yet if we are honest with ourselves, we need to look again and understand what is truly valuable and important, what has real meaning and purpose.

When Jesus explained the values of His kingdom, the way He turned their value systems upside down, He shocked His listeners.

In Matthew 5 Jesus delivered His sermon on the mount. During it Jesus reversed the perceived wisdom of His time. That is how the Advent hope also affects us—for it points to a different goal and emphasizes a different attitude to life.

HOPE IS A MIRROR

Jesus turns our value systems around—what the world sees as important God's kingdom reverses. Priorities get inverted and "reality" becomes back-to-front. In this "mirrorland" we recognize that what we may think is important should be reversed, perhaps even turned upside down!

Jesus spoke of those who are blessed. They are blessed (happy) . . . because God will reverse their present state. His sermon reveals the world as a mirror image—backwards—of the true nature of God's kingdom.

Think of Jesus' other "reversal" sayings: The first shall be last, the last first. The proud abased, the humble exalted. Those who seek to save their lives will lose them, while those who lose their lives will save them. Again and again Jesus gives a perspective that is the opposite of popular views, especially in the realm of religion. He shows that popularity—achievement in the world's eyes—is not significant in His kingdom, for example, the story of the Pharisee and the publican. In the parable of the good Samaritan Jesus portrays an "enemy" as being the true friend, the one who follows the values of God's kingdom. Jesus is at odds with the way the world views things. "My kingdom is not of this world" (John 18:36).

In the Sermon on the Mount Jesus frequently uses the phrase "you have heard it said, but I say to you" to extend and expand on previous commands, demonstrating the real meaning behind them. He calls on us to "seek first the kingdom of God." We are to get our priorities straight according to the divine mirrorland.

And in His call for hope in His return, He makes His values and priorities clear. We are to follow His way, His commands, and His kingdom. Hope is a mirror that shows us who we are and where we're going. The arrival of Jesus fulfills this hope, and His kingdom of glory will reflect all that He came to live and die for.

The world remains "too much with us." But the mirror of hope reflects us to ourselves, helping us to see who we really are and what is truly important.

So what do you see in hope's mirror? While we are to stay occupied with the work we have to do, this must never blind us to the centrality of our hope, our present and future perspective.

The tragic words of the English poet Thomas Hardy in "In Tenebris" reveal a life without hope, an existence that is futile and meaningless:

"One who, past doubtings all,
Waits in unhope."

Waiting in unhope? Is that us? Has our hope turned into unhope?

No, God calls us to leave our busyness and preoccupation with things of this world and to make sure that in all we do we maintain our perspective.

For in this, as in all things, we are to be "looking unto Jesus the author and finisher of our faith" (Heb. 12:2). Both now in the present and in the future for all eternity.

CHAPTER 11

Dealing With the Delay of Hope

THE TROUBLE WITH THE FUTURE

The problem with hope in the future is that the present overwhelms us. We just can't seem to see beyond what we already know. So to think of what the future may hold troubles us.

When the Berlin Wall collapsed in 1989, who knew what would happen next? Many pundits made predictions. But on the tenth anniversary of that momentous event, a journalist looked back to see who had been right about what would happen after the Wall collapsed. He discovered that no one had had it right. No one predicted the rapid collapse of European Communism and the demise of the Soviet Union.

Instead they made predictions that were way off base.

The end of Communism will be a long time coming. Wrong. If the Warsaw Pact goes, so does NATO. Wrong. Germany will not be allowed to reunite. Wrong. A united Germany will become a nuclear power before the end of the millennium. Wrong. Gorbachev will long continue in power. Wrong.

In terms of foretelling the future, even over the brief time span of 10 years, the experts could not get it right. Why not? Because "the problem with trying to see the future is the present. What we know usually overpowers our ability to see what might be coming. What is, is; it has the advantage of tangible existence. This makes the present hard to shake, no matter how smart you are" (Robert G. Kaiser of the Washington Post service in *International Herald Tribune,* Nov. 10, 1999).

Does what we *know* overpower our ability to see what's coming? Is the present hard to shake? Most of all, what about the *timing* of the future?

We may think we have the answers. But the present can fool us too, unless we're open to the thought that it is not the dominant factor. That's why we may see a delay in our hope. Because we so strongly want our hope to be fulfilled and time goes on, we begin to wonder if the promise is being deferred.

Christians have been waiting in hope for almost two millennia. Questions disturb us: "Are we right to go on preaching such a message? Have the passing years given the lie to Christ's promise? Is it time to give up and to forget about any return of the Messiah?"

WHERE IS THE HOPED-FOR PROMISE?

To not doubt hope is a very real challenge for the church. While many would not want to put doubting thoughts into words, the questions are insistent as the shadows of pessimism lengthen and doubt invades the church. Read the following and see if it does not fit an attitude that you have heard yourself, or may even echo thoughts you may have had:

"Where is the promised return of the Savior who can put an end to all this? Why does time continue on? When will Jesus come? The Christian church has been waiting for almost two millennia. Were the early Christians right in affirming the soon coming? Were the Adventist 'pioneers' mistaken? Are we right to go on preaching such a message? Is it not time to give up, to forget about hope?"

This is the situation Peter answers:

"First of all, you must understand that in the last days scoffers will come, scoffing and following their own evil desires. They will say, 'Where is this "coming" he promised? Ever since our fathers died, everything goes on as it has since the beginning of creation'" (2 Peter 3:3, 4, NIV).

While scoffing certainly differs from genuine doubt, the question is the same: "Where is this 'coming' He promised?"

The Bible's answer is one that points to God's compassion and "long-suffering" nature. He certainly is not reluctant to return—in fact, He is eager to do so. But His advent also brings the tragedy of the loss of those who have not accepted Him, and He seeks to lead everyone that He can to repentance: "The Lord is not slow in keeping his promise, as some understand slowness. He is patient with you, not wanting anyone to perish, but everyone to come to repentance" (verse 9, NIV).

IS THERE A DELAY?

"Delay" is an unfortunate word. It suggests mistake and imperfection. We see delays caused by unexpected situations, breakdowns, or technical problems. As human beings we delay because we do not wish to be on time to do whatever we would prefer to avoid. But is this a useful term to describe the way some view the timing of the Second Coming?

Can we really term God's actions as delayed? If He is eternal and outside of time, how can He "delay"? How can one who knows the end from the beginning "postpone" His plans? What of God's all-knowing aspect?

It is from our perspective that we speak of the concept of delay. The trouble lies with us, with our finite understanding. We may think that Christ's return should have occurred before now. As human beings we see 2,000 years between the giving of the promise and our own time.

Christ made the gospel to the world (see Mark 13:10) a necessary precondition for the Advent. Through 2 Peter 3 we witness God's desire to save all humanity. Various earthly events and situations must precede the coming of the Son of man. The emergence of the antichrist, the climax of the attack against God (2 Thess. 2), and the filling of the cup of iniquity (see Rev. 17:4; 18:6) form part of the "time" that must first reach its fullness. However, we cannot take the world's condition as the primary reason for the delay. God is not waiting for total destruction before He saves His people. He is still in control of our planet. His angels hold back the winds of strife. The Lord is not sitting idly by, waiting for sin to multiply in its own time.

Two divine principles operate here: God's unchanging purpose, and His patience. The first involves His sovereign will and purpose that expresses itself in the certainty of Christ's second coming: "I will come again." To the all-knowing God, the time is also known (see Matt. 24: 36). In the same way as the Flood came (note verse 37), as the Israelites entered the Promised Land, as Christ appeared on the first occasion in "the fullness of time," so He will return again at His specific time (1 Tim. 6:14, 15; see also Luke 17:24, 30). God is in no way subject to or dependent on humanity in His fundamental decisions. The Second Advent will happen, and "will not tarry" (Heb. 10:37). In terms of God's absolute power and authority, Christ's second coming is an unconditional event. The promise has been made in divine omnipotence. He cannot fail, He cannot change, and He cannot "delay."

The other principle relates to God's patience—His mercy and "long-suffering" nature. This perspective sees God as allowing further time so that people may accept His promises and enter into a covenant relation with Him based on love. God is ultimately patient, "not willing that any should perish, but that all should come to repentance" (2 Peter 3:9).

The continuation of time is for our benefit. Yet we cannot

make God's compassion an excuse that allows sin, pain, and death to continue forever. The end must come, because permitting eternal evil is not the action of a loving God. Despite all this talk of delay, we must remember that it was the wicked servant who began saying "My Lord delays his coming"!

HOPE DEFERRED

Yet despite all this, we may still feel that our hope is being deferred. In the words of Proverbs: "Hope deferred makes the heart sick" (Prov. 13:12, NIV).

It's a natural reaction. Waiting, as we have seen before, is not the most comfortable of times. We find ourselves in between the promise and its fulfillment, and as time continues, we feel that it is not happening as fast as we want. Like Daniel, who saw the vision taking a long time, we feel exhausted and fall ill (see Dan. 8:27).

Unlike the case with Daniel, God does not inform us about the time for the fulfillment of our hope. But when we become discouraged, we need to remember that "hope does not disappoint us, because God has poured out his love into our hearts by the Holy Spirit, whom he has given us" (Rom. 5:5, NIV).

In the end, those saved out of the world are "they that are Christ's at his coming" (1 Cor. 15:23), the wheat ripened by God through the latter rain (Matt. 3:12; Matt. 13:30; James 5:7). God will gather His people, those with whom He has a special relationship (see 1 Peter 2:9), those who have trusted only in the divine demonstration and provision of Jesus and the Lord's promises.

The Lord provides the answer, the means, and the methods. We respond and act accordingly. God never told His people to calculate the time of the Advent, to concern themselves with whether all the preconditions had been met, or to worry about explaining the delay. All He asked them to do was to "Watch!"

to "Be ready!" and to "Look up!" Redemption is drawing near, and is nearer than when we first believed (Luke 21:28; Rom. 13:11).

It *is* going to happen. Doubt in the time can lead to doubt in the event. But no, says Peter, it is absolutely certain. The Lord will come. And as a result we should be looking forward to that new heaven and new earth, *"the home of righteousness"* (2 Peter 3:13, NIV).

The challenge is not to see hope as something being deferred. The goal is to keep hope very much alive, and not to tie it in our minds to time limits. As the verse in Proverbs concludes: "Hope deferred makes the heart sick, but a longing fulfilled is a tree of life" (Prov. 13:12, NIV).

We need to continue to look forward to hope's fulfillment, thus allowing God's tree of life to heal our heart-sickness.

PATIENCE MEANS SALVATION

As we wait for hope's fulfillment, we must "bear in mind that our Lord's patience means salvation" (2 Peter 3:15, NIV). Consequently, "hope does not disappoint us, because God has poured out his love into our hearts by the Holy Spirit, whom he has given us" (Rom. 5:5, NIV).

Impatience and over-expectation can leads us to speculate that the Second Coming is "not more than a few years away." Others may see just about any development as some sign of the times. This can set people up for terrible disappointment and discouragement.

It's interesting to see the various kinds of things people have considered as "signs" of the times.

One book on prophecy from the early 1900s regarded the development of rapid steam train transportation as fulfilling the prediction that "many shall rush to and fro." Under a picture of two early biplanes appeared the caption "the nations' airy navies"—again seen as an amazing development that "proved" the end was near.

Other past "signs" have included telegraphy, the "wireless" radio, the automobile, the typewriter, and the movies.

Yet the truth is that to "read your newspaper as dating the end" (as one person once advised) can lead to false assumptions and expectations. Not *everything* is a sign of the times.

For example, people often cite wars and military conflicts as evidence for the approaching end. But in Matthew 24 Jesus takes great pains to point out that though there may be wars and rumors of wars, *the end is not yet.* It is instructive to go through this "signs" chapter and realize how many events that we normally interpret as signs Jesus clearly excluded as such.

A quick check of the Internet shows predictions of the end of the world for nearly every day for the next few years, based on Mayan legends or measurements of the pyramids or mystic visions from extraterrestrials. The trouble with such false prophets—and any form of date-setting—is that they bring the whole future perspective into disrepute.

Some equate urging that "Jesus will be here in just a very few short years" to preaching fire and brimstone. The "selfish" desire to avoid the negative aspects of the judgment they regard as the equivalent of taking out "fire insurance."

We need to ask ourselves, What is most important here? Is it the time of the Advent, or the certainty of the Advent? Is it our message to preach dates in the immediate future (whether we give exact dates, or simply say within x years), or to preach the "sure and certain" hope that is fulfilled in the return of "this same Jesus"?

At a ministerial meeting one pastor expressed his disappointed feelings. "Here I am, on the verge of retirement," he told his fellow ministers. "I have been preaching the Advent message for more than 40 years. I argued with the brethren about the need for going to college before entering the ministry, because I believed I would not have time to complete the course before Jesus returned. Now I am old—and disappointed. Why hasn't Jesus come?"

WAITING ON THE LORD

If we are preaching a "within x years" doctrine, disappointment will be inevitable this side of the coming. Such an approach focuses on the timing, not on the meaning and purpose of the event. It speaks to our human nature, which wants to prepare for a specific event at a specific time. The unspecified time of the Advent thus leaves us unsettled.

But Jesus says, "Be ready. Always!" Not in the sense of trying to make ourselves fit for translation, but having such a relationship with our loving Lord that we can happily meet Him whenever He shows up. "Journeys end in lovers meeting," Shakespeare observed, and if we truly love Jesus, then His arrival will not be a dreaded event or an intrusion into our lives, but the day when our best Friend returns.

We don't need to date the Advent, but we do need to know "this same Jesus" now! His return is "the blessed hope" only if He is blessed to us in the patient present. That means despite our realization of all our faults and failings, we can still pray with John, "Even so, come, Lord Jesus" (Rev. 22:20) and mean it today and every day until He appears in the sky.

"For I am bound with fleshly bands,
Joy, beauty, lie beyond my scope;
I strain my heart, I stretch my hands,
And catch at hope."

—Christina Rossetti, "De Profundis"

Despite the world thinking us foolish, we catch at hope. We hold on to the blessedness of hope, knowing that we will not be disappointed in the end. While times of patience can be trying, we can have confidence in the God who promises. Each of us must learn to "wait on the Lord" in all things, and let the Lord work it all out in His good time: "Wait for the Lord; be strong and take heart and wait for the Lord" (Ps. 27:14, NIV).

"We wait in hope for the Lord; he is our help and our shield" (Ps. 33:20, NIV).

"I wait for the Lord, my soul waits, and in his word I put my hope" (Ps. 130:5, NIV).

CHAPTER 12

Called to One Hope

SAILING HOME—TOGETHER

The two teenage boys who escort me down to the waiting boat seem excited. We're on our way to a rendezvous offshore. The plan is to meet our friend who skippers a fishing boat, and for me to see for myself the evening seabird spectacle.

Erik, Steinthor, and I launch the inflatable boat from the tiny rocky cove that passes for a harbor and head straight out to sea. We sail out in hope.

I inquire cautiously as to how they know where to meet the fishing boat, and how they know the way. After all, the ocean has no signposts.

"Oh, we know where to meet him, and we know the way," Erik responds confidently. Out we go.

Now, I'm not the best boat passenger at the best of times, and the waves we're headed into look threatening to me.

We crash into the first big roller. Sitting in the stern of the inflatable, I fly up in the air and then drop down heavily on the plank of wood that passes for a seat.

The two young men laugh gleefully, and then quickly stop themselves as they decide it would be inappropriate to enjoy a guest's discomfort.

Next wave. *Crash*. Again. And again. My rear complains as I reconcile myself to a painful trip. Trying to brace my arms against the plank to reduce the impact, I smile thinly at the boys. They grin back.

"How far?" I inquire.

"Not far," Erik responds.

On reflection I should have asked, "How long?" I'm petrified that this little rubber craft will flip over any moment and we all will drown.

Crash. Crash. Crash.

Painfully and slowly we make our way out into the unknown, leaving comfort and security behind us. I think mournfully of soft beds and warm homes.

"So, do you usually venture out when it's this rough?" Just making conversation.

The boys grin again. "No; normally we'd never go out with waves this rough, but we didn't want to disappoint you, so we decided to go anyway."

Great! So now I'm the one to blame. I watch the waves and feel the wind blow hard against my face. Sensing my faith shrinking, I want to call out, "Lord, save me!"

I really believe I'm about to drown. How foolish this journey! Do I really think I can make it? Do I think I'm superhuman? Do I think I can walk on water?

Somehow it seemed like a parable of life itself—surrounded by huge waves of death, sitting painfully in a tiny boat, trying to make headway, and getting nowhere.

I can tell my friends are as worried as I am, though they keep their grins in place. No chance of turning back—the waves will swamp us immediately if we turn broadside to them.

"Lord, save us!" my mind shouts out of desperation.

The next wave crashes by.

Then, suddenly—nothing. I'm bracing for the next one, but . . .

Flat calm! When I look around I find no wind, no waves.

What happened? Where did the storm go?

We stare in stunned amazement, sitting in a little boat that is just gently rocking on the light swell, for all the world as if we were crossing the Sea of Galilee.

Eventually we move on, slicing through the still water, to meet our friend.

There, in the dramatic golden glow of the midnight sun low in the horizon, I watch entranced as shearwaters glide past and auks flutter close by while gulls mew and terns chatter. All around us wheel gannets, their white plumage gleaming golden in the unearthly light. Again and again they plunge into the sea, sending spray showering and glittering in fountains upon fountains. In the feeding melee wings touch wings in a swirling snowstorm of feathers, as if the hosts of heaven danced above my head.

All too soon I forced myself to drag my eyes away from the scene.

"We have to go," Steinthor says, pleased with my delight. Glancing back, I watch the birds still swirling and gliding above the sea as we sail home in a white cloud of spray over a sea like glass, journey almost done.

Through the voyage we've seen the waves at their roughest. Yet we've also witnessed the power of the One whom even the winds and waves obey. Catching a glimpse of heaven even in the brokenness of earth, we're homeward bound. For a better Friend, always there but seldom looked for, travels with us on the way.

THE HOPE THAT MAKES US ONE

Our shared hope makes us one—one in the blessed hope. All of us in the same boat, we hold on to the same hope, "the hope of eternal life, which God, who does not lie, promised before the beginning of time" (Titus 1:2, NIV).

Even our physical and spiritual unity is linked to our one hope: "There is one body and one Spirit—just as you were called to one hope when you were called" (Eph. 4:4, NIV).

It is far more than an attitude of hopeful expectancy, because we actually are *called* to *one* hope. Note both those words. We are *called*. God summons us as a people to hope. It is our special responsibility to which we have been formed. And if we fail to maintain such hope, then we fail in our God-given responsibility.

Our focus must remain clear: Our hope is in God and in His promised salvation. Specifically, we must center our hope on the arrival of the blessed hope, the glorious appearing of our Lord and Savior Jesus Christ. There can be no other hope for us. It is also one hope in the sense it is the hope that makes us one—uniting us in a common experience.

THE UNITY OF GOD

The one hope comes from the one God: "One Lord, one faith, one baptism; one God and Father of all, who is over all and through all and in all" (verses 5, 6, NIV).

It is hardly surprising that such hope should be unifying, since it has its origin in the God who is one, who seeks to make us one: "Yet for us there is but one God, the Father, from whom all things came and for whom we live; and there is but one Lord, Jesus Christ, through whom all things came and through whom we live" (1 Cor. 8:6, NIV).

This is the same oneness for which Jesus prayed for His disciples—and all who would follow later. "My prayer is not for them alone. I pray also for those who will believe in me through their message, that all of them may be one, Father, just as you are in me and I am in you. May they also be in us so that the world may believe that you have sent me. I have given them the glory that you gave me, that they may be one as we are one: I in them and you in me. May they be brought to complete unity to let the world know that you sent me and have loved them even as you have loved me" (John 17:20-23, NIV).

It is the unity to which God calls us, in the same way as He summons us to the one hope. In fact, they are aspects of one and the same belief and hope. "We have put our hope in the living God, who is the Savior of all men, and especially of those who believe" (1 Tim. 4:10, NIV).

THE UNITY OF THE FAITH

"Where there is no hope, there is no faith" (William Gouge).

Without hope we cannot identify ourselves as a community of faith. We have to have hope "so that the body of Christ may be built up until we all reach unity in the faith and in the knowledge of the Son of God and become mature, attaining to the whole measure of the fullness of Christ" (Eph. 4:12, 13, NIV).

By avoiding the extremes of speculation and by remaining totally committed to the Word of God we become united. As we demonstrate love for one another, recognizing the grace of God to each of us, then we grow together in oneness. Each of us should remember that Jesus' test for discipleship was that others would see that we love one another. Problems come when we want to enforce our own ideas and promote ourselves.

Such unity of the faith does not come about by accident. It requires that we make our hope and faith a priority and actively work to bring each other together.

A WORTHY LIFE

As a result, God wants our lives to reflect our calling, our hope. Paul declared: "As a prisoner for the Lord, then, I urge you to live a life worthy of the calling you have received. Be completely humble and gentle; be patient, bearing with one another in love" (verses 1, 2, NIV).

An unexamined life is a waste. So in leading up to his statement on the unity of the one hope, the apostle urges us to look at our lives and make sure they are "worthy of the calling."

One dominant form of hope motivates those who play the lottery. People dream that by matching numbers they will make themselves rich. But it is a vain hope, based on the premise of a very few getting rich at the expense of everyone else. Still it is a hope that many cling to.

Yet even the winners seem to find such a hope meaningless. How many times do you read of lottery winners losing everything, of being worse off than before? Family dispute, divorce, even death destroys everything. It is certainly not a hope that makes us one—rather the opposite.

One man spent his millions within months and went bankrupt. A woman winner now hides in her apartment, too afraid to go out. One family of winners are no longer speaking to each other, and two of them have become alcoholics.

God does not call us to judge others and their worthiness. Yet it is clear from our own personal experience that we are all deficient in some way. We need to grow in God's grace and hope as we become more like the Lord and His matchless character. Notice, however, what Scripture spells out as being a life worthy of the calling: one completely humble, gentle, patient, and bearing with others in love. Sometimes we have the idea that God summons us to some staggering task or overwhelming achievement. On the contrary, what God is looking for is on the inside, attitudes that reflect the way we treat one another. Only then can He invite us to the work He wishes us to do.

The source of our strength is God and His hope: "Even youths grow tired and weary, and young men stumble and fall; but those who hope in the Lord will renew their strength. They will soar on wings like eagles; they will run and not grow weary, they will walk and not be faint" (Isa. 40:30, 31, NIV).

Hoping in the Lord is our source of spiritual strength. Such hope means renewal, a reinvigorating supply of spiritual energy. Soaring like eagles, running without becoming tired, walking and not being exhausted: we are spiritually recharged by hoping in the Lord.

OUR WITNESS: HELPING OTHERS HOPE

In our hope we find ourselves observed by the whole world. As Paul put it, "It seems to me that God has put us apostles on display at the end of the procession, like men condemned to die in the arena. We have been made a spectacle to the whole universe, to angels as well as to men" (1 Cor. 4:9, NIV).

We are God's exhibition to the universe. The whole cosmos sees the witness we make to the Advent hope as we demonstrate our complete confidence in the God of promise.

In our Christian lives we can put into living reality the words of the proverb: "If fortune torments me, hope contents me." Why? Because we know the "good hope": "May our Lord Jesus Christ himself and God our Father, who loved us and by his grace gave us eternal encouragement and good hope, encourage your hearts and strengthen you in every good deed and word" (2 Thess. 2:16, 17, NIV).

HAPPILY EVER AFTER?

". . . and they all lived happily ever after."

The best stories finish with a final statement of comfort and satisfaction, the necessary conclusion to the tale.

But think again.

Happily ever after?

What in this world is ever "happily ever after"? To think that such a thing is possible in this life is an illusion. Situations change, accidents happen, people die. The neat ending is unreal, and is why the truth differs so greatly from fiction.

Now, I do not want to be a killjoy or to throw a bucket of cold water over such positive dreams, but maybe we end up believing such stories too much.

People look for the illusory happily-ever-after where it doesn't exist. They become offended when life doesn't work out as they fantasize. Sometimes they may even try to deny reality to preserve their illusion.

The people of this world watch the movies, read the romances, hear the songs—and, despite themselves, still believe them. In between the "Once upon a time . . . " and the ". . . happily ever after" they exercise a willing suspension of disbelief. They become entranced with the thought that instead of the reality of pain, sadness, and eventual death, in some way heroism and love and virtue will conquer all.

Then, when reality crowds in, so do cynicism and bitterness. As the dream dies, so do hope and meaning and destiny. Life, if there is no happy ever after, seems to be a nothing, a joke, a pointless existence.

Either way, what is there? Is it just a choice between a mirage, however desirable, or the bleak desolation of meaninglessness?

On our own, that's all there is—foolish dreams or cynical nightmares.

But that's where God steps in. His appeal is not to illusion or to the rejection of meaning and purpose in this life. God is not in denial. Rather, based in the reality that He alone controls, He offers to create real meaning in life now.

How can you be sure? By choosing what He offers. Do you want a baseless promise as insubstantial as a nursery story? An empty nothingness that aches like a void? Or a life of real purpose and meaning?

Only with God can there be any security, any reality to such promises.

The odd thing is that God Himself tells the best "happily-ever-after" story. It is more than a vain concluding flourish to a fictional story or a lame way of saying, "Hope things work out well." God's story is far more incredible than any romantic novel or fantasy fiction or human daydream.

God promises Himself. And that's the guarantee. For this is absolute reality, ultimate truth. The opposite of fiction is the strange truth that the greatest happy ending of all comes as the free gift of God, the God of promise who does not lie.

From "In the beginning, God" to God of the end, the person of God is the proof positive of being happy ever after—only in God's eternal presence can we truly be.

CHAPTER 13

Hope Blazes Bright!

ENDINGS

As I drive mile upon mile at day's end, the glory of sunset forces me to a stop.

I stare out across the vast flatness to the wide overspreading sky. In flaming fire the sun goes down, casting shadowed glows of intense gold and orange over red and purple. The winter fields, plowed and empty, remind me of similar fields in a place I called home for many years, now long gone.

With exaggerated slowness the light fades and the sky turns deeper purple, until the final rays of golden light vanish and the intense darkness of night overcomes the world. Like an inconsolable sadness, the end comes, and I fight it. With Dylan Thomas, I want to "rage against the dying of the light."

Why does everything always have to end? Days end. Lives end. Worlds end. Everything ends.

Suddenly I realize that I have stopped right beside a cemetery almost hidden in the vastness of the fields all around. A few grave markers break the skyline, shadowed monuments of death. The last resting place of those who farmed these empty fields, now dark and barren.

What of their hopes and dreams now? All their toil and labor under the sun? Vanity, vanity, all is vanity. Our little lives end with the deepest of all sleeps.

End. The finality of termination, the ceasing of life. The last breath, the inescapable close, the falling of the curtain. Like a heavy weight, the inevitability of where life leads burdens my every thought. How foolish we all are to live as if we are here forever. One day every last one of us breathes our last.

Endings are all we see, the eventual close of everything and everyone—of every thought and feeling and ambition. The recognition of that fact is as hard and empty as the fields around me.

Lifting up my eyes from the headstones and empty fields to the dark sky, I search for answers. Even the stars that shine so serenely, seemingly so permanent, will eventually burn themselves out. Nothing lasts forever. And all dissolves in the mistiness of my eyes.

In a world so full of endings and loss, of partings and death, the most valuable thing of all is the eternal. But here none exists. The day vanishes away, the light dies, life ebbs to a close. The cemetery disappears into the night, lost among the fields that stretch to the horizon, the grave markers the last to fade.

Nothing is left. Even the memories fade, the place once called home grows dim.

Then I notice a flash of brilliant light. For a brief moment a shooting star burns a bright trail in the sky overhead before it too vaporizes into dust. Dust to dust, ashes to ashes . . .

But I understand. In the sky a message written in a blaze of light declares: "Soon!"

Soon, and very soon, this world of endings, of life-wearying impermanence, will itself cease to be. But in its ending comes God's re-creation, His glorious new beginning of eternity. We will have a home, permanent and never-ending.

But most of all, we will have an everlasting life in the presence of the One without beginning and without end: God Himself.

Now I turn away, to drive on, hoping for the end. For in the end comes God's eternal beginning.

HOPE SPRINGS ETERNAL

"Hope springs eternal"—but as we have seen, sometimes hope dies away, or is mistaken or disappointed. In trying to make their hope a solid reality, some have taken wrong roads, such as setting dates for the Lord's return or making false prophecies or misunderstanding the signs.

Praise God that our hope does not depend on us! It is God's hope that we trust, not ourselves with all our faults and failings. He alone is trustworthy, and He will deliver on His promise.

The early Christian believers spread the hope because it was their dearest joy. How is it with us? While none of us would put our hands up and say "I'm ready for heaven" and trust in our own works, we surely must be looking for our returning Savior, keenly awaiting His appearing.

The inmates interned in a World War II prison camp anxiously followed news reports. As it became clear that the war was coming to an end, they wondered what would happen to them. Would their guards kill them before they left? Would they be in the middle of a battle, caught in the cross fire? Would they be left to starve? What would happen?

They prayed and looked forward to freedom, despite their dangerous situation. Each of them lived by hope.

Suddenly, one day they looked up and saw paratroopers descending from the skies. Rescue! Liberation! Salvation from above!

HAPPY TO SEE HIM

Though none of us should arrogantly claim that we are ready to go to heaven, we should all be looking forward to being with Jesus. In the same way as we want to be together with the people we love here on this earth, we will eagerly await being together with the Lord of love.

What would it say about our relationship with those we claimed to love, if we tried to avoid meeting or at least delayed our appointment with them? Clearly we would be demonstrating that the loving relationship we claimed was not all we said it was.

That is why we need to be clear, here and now, about our relationship with our Savior. If we will not be happy to see Him whenever He chooses to return, then we have not made Him number one in our lives. But our response should be that we "rejoice in the hope of the glory of God" (Rom. 5:2), "rejoicing in hope" (Rom. 12:12, NKJV).

If somehow we feel uncomfortable with the idea of soon seeing Jesus, we must examine how we relate to Him. For example, if we regard Jesus as hostile, as being against us, then it is hard to love Him. Or if we cling to actions we know are wrong, then we feel guilty. But if we claim His promises, while still admitting our imperfections, we can truly look forward to His coming with hope and happiness.

"Even so, come, Lord Jesus" (Rev. 22:20).

HOPING TO THE END!

"Hope to the end for the grace that is to be brought unto you at the revelation of Jesus Christ" (1 Peter 1:13).

Hope to the end. That's what our lives need to be filled with. We must never give up hope, never let its blaze go out. As life continues, it can be easy to lose that first love and that burning hope. Some have faltered, perhaps because they identified their hope too much with a specific time. But though time may have continued longer than you once thought, that fact does not kill God's hope. In fact, the opposite should happen: the longer time runs, the closer we come to the return of Jesus. Besides, the time is not the most important aspect—it is the certainty of Jesus' second advent, and He emphatically declares that He will return. While we do not know the day or hour, He does expect us to watch and to be ready whenever it happens (see Matt. 24:42).

"Hoping is disciplined waiting," E. Hoffmann observed. We need to remain true to the Hope. After all, what else is there? Is there any other perspective on the future for the Christian who sees hope like a bright silver thread running through the whole tapestry of the Bible?

VITAL AND PERSONAL HOPE

Scripture intimately links hope and resurrection (Acts 23:6). Instead of a "miserable hope" we now have eternal hope. First Corinthians 15:19-28 contrasts the present life (where we do our hoping) with the resurrection to everlasting life (where hope will be realized). As Paul says, if this life were all, what would happen to hope? That is why the resurrection is vital—it is the way in which hope is fulfilled. Death is destroyed—the ultimate enemy—so that our hope and future with God may be realized. Truly there is no other hope. That is why the blessed hope is so vital—so essential for Christian life.

This hope is also incredibly personal. Paul speaks of "the faith and love that spring from the hope that is stored up for you in heaven" (Col. 1:5, NIV). It awaits us where there will be no rust or moths (Matt. 6:19, 20). Who we are and what we will be—all this is defined by this hope. That's why it's so personal. Hope affects us right where it counts, and is truly meaningful for us all individually.

The biblical promise is "Christ in you, the hope of glory" (Col. 1:27). Hope is not something separate from our Christian life now, but an essential part of it—it is who Christians are. If we have Christ "in us"—in other words, if we are so totally in harmony with Him and His will that we are identified with Christ—then we have that wonderful hope of glory! Not that this is the reason or purpose of hope, as if we look only for the reward, but it is its consequence.

Like a seed growing inside us, this hope that we plant in the soil of God's word and allow the Holy Spirit to water will blossom into a mighty tree of assurance. We cannot simply say "I believe" and let such hope be just one of the doctrines we have signed our names to. This hope must become a personal reality for all of us, because in the words of Thomas Carlyle, "Man is . . . based on hope. He has no other possession than hope."

Some hopes may be helpful and genuine, while others may actually oppose the blessed hope. We need to make sure what we hope for is in harmony with the hope of God. Why? Because Jesus comes for each one of us!

A PRAYER OF HOPE IN THE GOD OF HOPE

Assured of the power and presence of the God of hope, Paul declared: "May the God of hope fill you with all joy and peace as you trust in him, so that you may overflow with hope by the power of the Holy Spirit" (Rom. 15:13, NIV).

Our hope is to so fill us that we overflow with it. Only then can we share it with others by the power of the Holy Spirit! We are not just to be hopeful people, but people crammed full of hope! What attracts others to God's gift of hope?—Christians who are so full of hope that they cannot keep the good news to themselves, but just have to share it.

If you feel that your own experience with Jesus lacks something, then go and taste again the excitement and fulfillment of hope in your life. For in the words of the author of *Pilgrim's Progress,* John Bunyan, "Hope is never ill when faith is well."

God wants your faith and hope to be well, to be spiritually healthy. He came at incredible sacrifice to bring us the good news that offers so much hope to us who once had no hope at all. With God, hope lives eternally now, and will be fulfilled soon as Jesus comes to complete His promise of hope.

Hope cannot be forced. It will blaze as bright as the promises of God as it becomes through the Holy Spirit an essential part of the way we live. Recognizing how Jesus comes for each one of us, we look forward with joy for that wonderful meeting. Our aim—our hope—is for all to be part of that glorious Advent hope!

And when the day comes, as surely it will, we can say in the words of Isaiah: "He is our God! We have put our trust in him, and he has rescued us. He is the Lord! We have put our trust in him, and now we are happy and joyful because he has saved us" (Isa. 25:9, TEV).

Let's all be there, exalting just that! As Paul tells the church in Thessalonica: "So then, encourage one another with these words" (1 Thess. 4:18, TEV).

THE FORBIDDING OF HOPE?

I step out of the light into the darkness. Here in the basilica of Spain's Valle de los Caidos each footstep echoes back off walls, ceiling, and floor. For a moment I pause to let my eyes adjust to the dimness.

In the cavernous emptiness the dark stillness is oppressive. I look up and see cracked and broken stone overhead—the mountain into which men have carved this mausoleum. Around me on the walls are huge, magnificent tapestries portraying every violent scene from the book of Revelation: dragons, flaming fire, and the apocalyptic horsemen riding on their mission of death and destruction. I can already hear the shrieking finale of *Carmina Burana* and the incessant drumbeat of doom.

As I approach the inner sanctum, eight horrific figures hooded in gray stone cowls stare down at me, reminiscent of Tolkien's ring wraiths. Carved images of warfare crowd the dark wooden paneling. Around me on the walls every giant angel wields a mighty sword.

This is the celebration of death.

Slowly I walk to the right into the memorial of the dead of Spain's civil war. Dark. Gloomy. Sepulchral. Dim orange lighting glints harshly from metal and polished stone. A figure lies on the tomb, its body contorted in the agonies of dying.

Enough!

Overwhelmed with despair in this Hall of Valhalla, I expect the arrival of the Valkyries at any moment.

I know, I know. What did I expect? A mausoleum, the last resting place of Spain's dictator General Francisco Franco, it's not supposed to be a pleasant, uplifting experience.

But my heart is heavy and my thoughts depressive. For what is there here but the end of life, the sense of loss, the forbidding of hope?

Yet it only reflects a world that has chosen darkness over light, death over life, despair over hope.

I long to escape. As I turn on my heels and walk quickly back down the echoing chamber, I glance at the tapestries, still bearing their testimony of annihilation. Then I fix my eyes on the light shining in through the open door, symbol of hope in a dark, dark place.

At the end I'm almost running for the exit. But when the warm white light of the southern sun shines down on me, I feel reborn. As I turn and glance back, I see nothing, for the sunlight has overcome the darkness as the sunrise chases away the nightmare shadows.

Up above, a massive stone cross surmounts the hillside. Drawn upward to its arms, I look from its base across a green valley of delight. For in this instrument of death, there is hope, the Christian paradox. This is the answer to the tomb below—death, where is your sting? Grave, where is your victory?

Out in the brightness of the daylight, under a clear blue sky, I see eternity. An eternity that has no mausoleums, no throbbing drumbeats of death, no pain, no loss, no anguish, no despair.

In answer to the gloomy cavern below that forbids hope, the cross of Christ transforms His death and ours into a glorious resurrection.

For with our God of hope, hope can never be forbidden as long as we stay at the foot of his cross, looking up and waiting for the return of our crucified, now glorified, Lord.

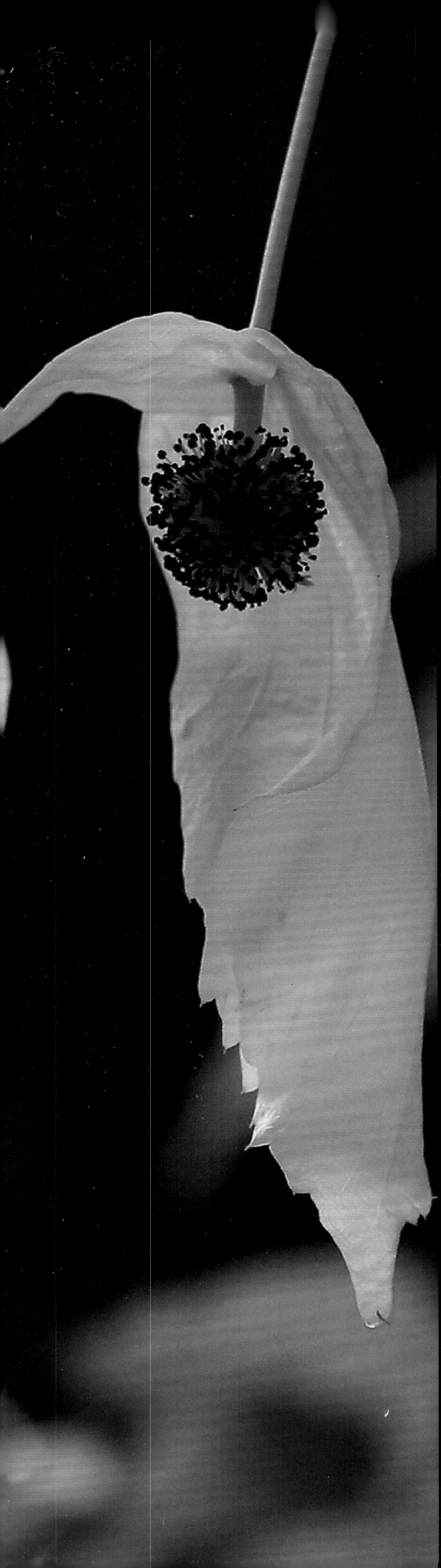

Time for trees

A guide to species selection for the UK

"Planting a tree is a large investment of time and resource for everyone's benefit and the best time to plant that tree is now. Before planting, selecting the right species of tree for the right place is one the most important factors to consider; choosing a species with the right attributes for the right site and space.

If we get that wrong the investment will be wasted. There is no excuse today for getting this process wrong, especially with books like "Time for Trees" to help the planter with the selection process.

This wonderful book is packed full of very useful information on the dimensions of trees at maturity, soil preferences and their attributes in terms of leaf, flower and fruit supported by quality images making it an extremely useful guide to species selection for the UK. Now there is no excuse for planting the wrong tree in the wrong place."

Tony Kirkham
Head of the Arboretum,
Royal Botanic Gardens, Kew

Telephone 01353 720 748 | www.barcham.co.uk

Contents

About the author

Mike Glover

Mike Glover graduated from Writtle Agricultural College in 1990 with a Higher National Diploma in Commercial Horticulture.

The following year he was awarded the Wilfred Cave Scholarship by the Royal Bath & West Society to study 'Instant Garden Techniques' in California.

Returning to the UK, Mike took up a position with Barcham Trees, where he is now Managing Director. In 2003 he patented the Light Pot in both Europe and the UK with the aim of producing trees with sustainable root systems geared for long term transplanting success. Barcham Trees is now the largest nursery of its type in Europe.

Acknowledgements

Many thanks to our magnificent staff here at Barcham who grow, sell and distribute our trees throughout the length and breadth of the UK.

Look out for further information online...
www.barcham.co.uk
www.barchampro.co.uk

You're in safe hands with a Barcham Tree...

View our online video: www.barcham.co.uk

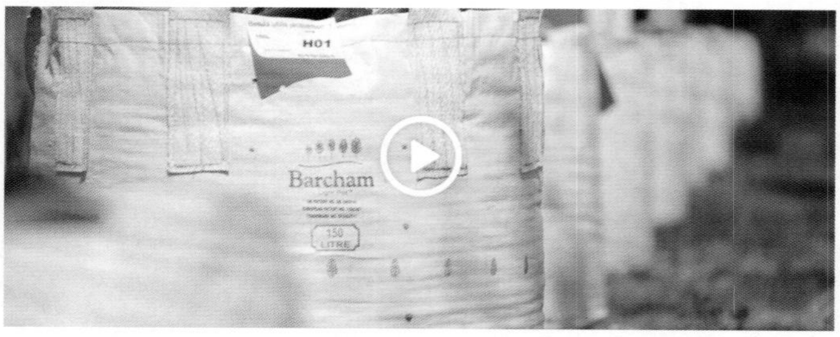

The importance of biosecurity

Trees have had a lot of media coverage in recent years and mostly for the wrong reasons. New pests and diseases carried on imported trees from Europe have put many native UK trees in jeopardy and this could have been so easily avoided if greater importance was put onto biosecurity...

The importance of biosecurity

There are very few tree growers in the UK but plenty of tree brokers who trade stock from all over Europe and import trees direct to site without any checks for pest and diseases that they may carry. This is how Ash Die Back arrived into the country which forced the government to implement a movement ban on this genus a few years later. As a result, no Fraxinus varieties have been planted in the UK since October 2012 and our indigenous trees are under severe threat of disease.

Oak Processionary Moth is another nasty new entrant and this was introduced into London in 2006 and again from trees imported from the continent for planting within the Olympic Park. The bristles on the caterpillars backs contain a toxin that is both a skin irritant or, if inhaled, can cause respiratory difficulties including asthma and in severe cases anaphylatic shock.

The incidence of importing problems goes away if you grow your own! We harvest our trees for containerisation from our field stock that we have grown from scratch and tended for years. We collect acorns from veteran Oaks to grow through to semi mature specimens and line out young plants in our fenland fields to harvest between four and nine years later. From there we containerise them into our patented white Light Pots which allow a small amount of light penetration into the root zone. This triggers a phototropic and geotropic reaction where the roots grow away from the light and obey the pull of gravity. When these trees are planted out the roots are not impeded by each other's growth and are able to explore the soil effectively, allowing rapid and sustained establishment.

A non-spiralled and viable root system produced using Barcham Light Pots. *Betula utilis Jacquemontii*

Our fen fields are a hostile environment for tree growing and we grow on wide spacings to encourage strong tapered trunks. Once the crop has been containerised they are health checked by a third party using supportive data from leaf fluorescence, electrolyte leakage and leaf chlorophyll content.

We took the decision many years ago that if the crop hasn't been through our containerisation unit it doesn't leave the nursery for sale. This gives us a year to assess any imported trees and effectively places them in quarantine over this period. During this time they are checked by ourselves and government agency and passed clear of pest and disease so they can then be planted out into the wider environment without risk.

The importance of biosecurity

The incidence of importing problems goes away if you grow your own!

Barcham
The Tree Specialists

Tree Diversity

Coupled with a need for a greater awareness of biosecurity, tree diversity is now increasingly important. Arborists in the USA thought they would learn from the huge outbreak of Dutch Elm Disease in the 1970's when hundreds of thousands of urban Elms had to be felled due to this catastrophic infection. Unfortunately for them they replanted their cities predominately with the Acer genus which is today proving very susceptible to insect borers imported from the Far East.

With this in mind it makes more sense to apply a wide range of genus into your planting plan so if a single genus runs into problems later on down the line only a little is lost and this can be quickly rectified. Instead of a traditional single genus avenue it is best to plant with more of a diverse range of trees with a similar ultimate growing size such as Lime, Hornbeam and Oak rather than concentrate on the complete uniformity of one specific type. For woodland mixes there should be no one genus accounting for more than 10% of the total scheme. Similarly, in urban settings, a diverse range of genus used in streets and parks will protect our cities from an over reliance on just a few types, such as Horse Chestnut and Plane in London.

This new thinking makes the planting of trees a little more complicated. Differing genus can require different conditions in which to thrive, but with nearly 100 genus and over 400 varieties listed in the following pages, there is still plenty of choice to create a future proofed treescape for our gardens, towns and cities here in the UK.

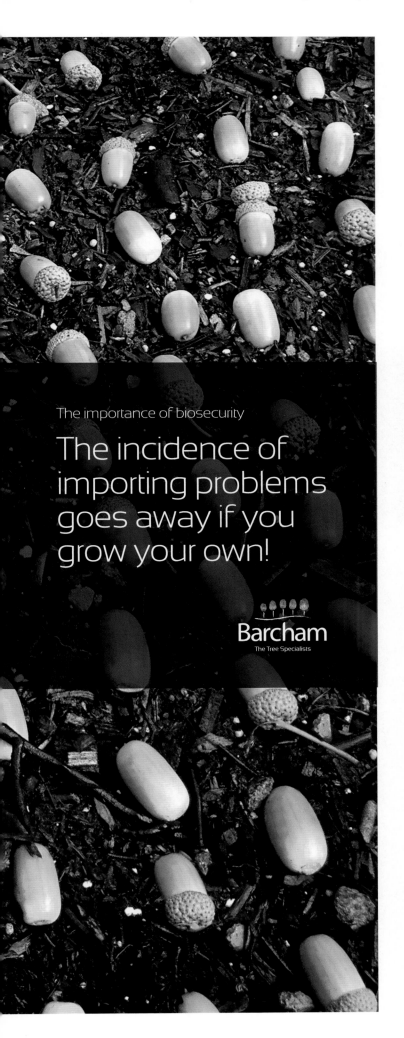

Honey Bees Need Trees...

It's easy to take trees for granted, as they stand majestically throughout the seasons. However, they do not just provide us with ornament bearing flowers and fruit for our pleasure but provide a much needed food source for Honey bees.

Planting a collection of trees that flower for each month of the bees foraging year, provides continuous forage for the bees throughout the year. Start off with Alder, which has masses of pollen that is much needed early in the year when the bees are feeding their brood.

Amelanchier, which is pretty, provides lots of nectar which is collected to make honey stores for winter, and then Whitebeam, Lime, Sweet Chestnut and Pride of India for the summer months. It is believed that 5 or 6 trees provide more forage for bees than an acre of wildflower meadow. It's so much easier to plant a tree than to try and grow an abundance of flowers.

Honey bees also use the sticky resin from buds and trees to produce propolis, which varies in composition and colour from colony to colony, season to season depending on the sources available.

This sticky resin is metabolised and then used to seal and protect the hive. Propolis has sterile qualities and therefore helps to keep disease and draughts at bay.

Detailed below are trees which are beneficial to bees by season.

Early Spring: Alnus, Cornus mas, Corylus.

Late Spring/Early Summer: Amelanchier, Crataegus, Cydonia, Malus, Mespilus, Prunus, Pyrus, Sorbus.

Mid-Summer: Castanea, Koelreuteria, Liriodendron, Tilia cordata, Tilia platyphyllos.

Autumn: Prunus subhirtella Autumnalis

Trees in action
Barcham
The Tree Specialists

TESCO

ABIES Fraserii
Fraser Fir

Introduced by John Fraser in 1811 from the USA, this stately evergreen can reach up to 15 metres in the UK with a spread of about 8 metres. The biggest recorded in its native environment has reached 30 metres tall by 17 metres wide. Its pyramidal habit and dark shiny leaves, which have two silver bands on their underside, make it the Christmas Tree of choice in many south eastern states of America.

It grows well on most free draining soils and produces small purple tinged cones that mature to dark brown. The leaves are only about 1.5cm long and in our experience of growing them in East Anglia they can extend growth of up to 40cm per year.

12|17		
Mature height: 12-17m	Shape of mature tree	Evergreen trees

ABIES koreana
Korean Fir

Introduced in 1905 from Korea, this slow growing fir forms a stout compact tree at maturity and is characterised by its violet /purple cylindrical cones that can get to 7cm in length.

It is tolerant of more heat than most firs but still thrives best in colder climates. The 1-2cm leaves are dark green above and white beneath divided by a thin green midrib. Remarkably, the glorious cone display is prominent even on young trees that are only 1-2 metres in height.

7|12		
Mature height: 7-12m	Shape of mature tree	Evergreen trees

ABIES nordmanniana
Nordmann/Caucasian Fir

Introduced from Northern Turkey in 1840, this striking conifer has risen steeply in popularity over recent years for being able to hold onto its leaf as a Christmas tree. Arguably the most attractive of the firs it can grow immensely tall with some specimens in Europe attaining 85m in height.

Its tiered branches support dark green leaves 2-3cm in length with cones that can grow up to 20cm. It is very robust and disease resistant but our advice is to plant after the 25th December for municipal plantings! Like most firs it tends to scorch up in very hot climates.

17|22		
Mature height: 17-22m	Shape of mature tree	Evergreen trees

ACACIA dealbata
Silver Wattle

This fast growing pioneer species is a native of Southern Australia and Tasmania and was introduced to the UK in 1820 but is only hardy down to about -5 Celsius.

The evergreen greenish blue leaves are bipinnate and the trees are overtaken by profuse racemes of fragrant bright yellow flowers in spring. We recommend this tree to be planted in protected south facing aspects in Southern England as until they girth up they can be susceptible to getting nipped back by frost. Until the bark matures the trunk is a smooth blue which adds to its exotic appeal.

3|8 Mature height: 3-8m | Shape of mature tree | Flowering trees

ACER buergerianum
Trident Maple

Native to Eastern China and Korea, this very pretty maple was introduced in 1890. It forms an oval to rounded crown at maturity and is well suited to streets or gardens.

New spring foliage emerges a rich bronze colour before hardening to a glossy dark green by summer. Greenish yellow flowers are borne in March and maturing trunks flake to brown / orange colours to provide a patchwork of winter interest. Autumn colours can be variable but seldom disappointing with leaves turning yellow through to red before falling. It is considered a slow to medium grower and is fully hardy down to -25 Celsius.

Recent arborist opinion coming out of the USA place this as a highly prized urban tree. Its increased popularity is not only due to its seasonal interest but also its durability. For the UK it represents an alternative to Acer campestre types.

7|12 Mature height: 7-12m | Shape of mature tree | Urban trees

ACER campestre
Field Maple

Native to England and Wales, but not in Scotland or Ireland, this small to medium tree of rounded form was widely used in the Middle Ages for making musical instruments. In autumn its leaves turn not just clear yellow, but also red and golden brown.

It does best in rich, well drained soils, but is equally at home in virtually any soil type, and will readily tolerate drought, soil compaction and air pollution. A versatile, resilient and attractive species with a wide range of uses. Available both as multi-stem and single stem.

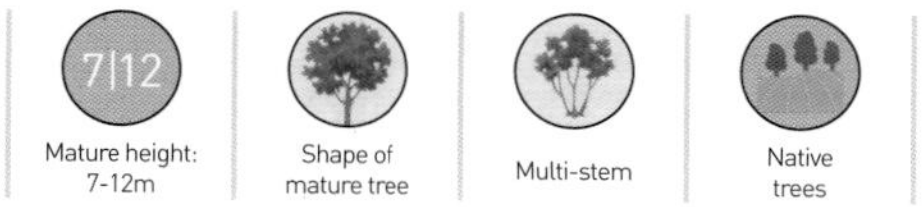

Field Maple also makes an excellent hedgerow plant. Being native, it is very 'wildlife friendly' and it can cope well to rough pruning during the dormant season to keep the hedge to shape. Many of its clones listed next are far more suitable for urban and street planting as they form crowns of more regular shape than that of their parent.

ACER campestre Arends

This cultivar of Field Maple has a much more regular and oval habit than the species. We were first introduced to it in the mid 1990s and placed it into our range soon after as its habit ticked all the boxes for urban planting.

It does best in rich, well drained soils, but does well in virtually any soil type, and will readily tolerate drought, soil compaction and air pollution. Compared to Norway Maple types, Acer campestre clones have much smaller leaves so are a better prospect in the urban environment at leaf fall.

ACER campestre Elegant

This cultivar of Field Maple is, in our opinion, the pick of the Acer campestre clones for street planting. It retains a compact ascending habit, is vigorous in growth, and gives uniformity if planted in an avenue. Many clones are tricky to tell apart at maturity but Elegant's stubby thick growth makes it easier to distinguish. I have seen Elegant over 25 years old and they were about a third as wide as they were tall.

It does best in rich, well drained soils, but does well in virtually any soil type, and will readily tolerate drought, soil compaction and air pollution. Typical of its type, it can go a glorious yellow in autumn and is a great host to a range of native wildlife. There are some great specimens performing admirably in UK cities which is comforting for urban planners when selecting this clone for planting.

7|12		
Mature height: 10-15m	Shape of mature tree	Urban trees

ACER campestre Elsrijk

This cultivar of the Field Maple is named after the park in Amstelveen, Holland, where it was discovered in the 1950s. It differs from the species in that it has a more regular, oval habit. At maturity one could mistake it for straight forward Acer campestre but one with a lovely compact shape.

It does best in rich, well drained soils, but does well in virtually any soil type, and will readily tolerate drought, soil compaction and air pollution. A medium sized tree which we particularly recommend for urban and street plantings, its foliage turns a magnificent clear yellow in autumn.

7|12		
Mature height: 7-12m	Shape of mature tree	Urban trees

ACER
campestre Lineco

New to Barcham in 2011, this superb tight headed clone is ideal for a tidy street tree in an urban environment. Many clonal selections are produced by growers but most are too similar to existing varieties to be worthy of special interest. This selection stands out as one to watch as it ticks many boxes for city planting.

Selections of our native Acer campestre are a marvellous compromise to planting indigenous trees within our urban settings as they are tough and relatively low maintenance. Good for wildlife, the leaves turn a glorious yellow in the autumn and it thrives on most soils.

7|12 Mature height: 7-12m | Shape of mature tree | Urban trees

ACER campestre Louisa Red Shine

A most attractive small to medium tree with a rounded habit. The new leaves are flushed with crimson before turning mauve/ green as the season progresses. There are very few trees with native origin that have this degree of leaf colour and as it has smaller leaves than the red clones of the Norway Maple it provides a softer contrast on the landscape.

It does best in rich, well drained soils, but does well in virtually any soil type, and will readily tolerate drought, soil compaction and air pollution. An ideal subject for streets, parks and verges, it has been used with great effect in London in recent years. Each growth flush is rewarded with red to crimson leaves so there is plenty of interest throughout the summer.

The foliage display turns to yellow with hints of orange by the autumn to round off eight months of succession leaf interest. Being of native origin it is also a good host to insects and birds. We planted one of these outside our offices at Barcham in 2006 and it has developed beautifully.

7|12 Mature height: 7-12m | Shape of mature tree | Urban trees

ACER campestre Nanum

A top worked variety with a very dwarfing, rounded habit. Its leaves are smaller than those of the species and they form a very dense crown.

It does best in rich, well drained soils, but does well in virtually any soil type, and will readily tolerate drought, soil compaction and air pollution. Very good for streets and residential plantings, or any site where space is at a premium. This clone has long been in cultivation and was introduced in the 1830s.

3|7 Mature height: 3-7m | Shape of mature tree | Urban trees

ACER campestre Queen Elizabeth

This American cultivar is also known as Evelyn and was introduced in the mid 1980s. It is fast growing, has a relatively narrow habit and is larger and darker leaved than the species. The ascending branches are produced at angle of 45° to the dominant central leader.

It does best in rich, well drained soils, but does well in virtually any soil type, and will readily tolerate drought, soil compaction and air pollution. An excellent choice as a street tree, it has a tighter habit than Elsrijk and was first brought into general cultivation by the well known Frank Schmidt nursery in Oregon.

7|12 Mature height: 7-12m | Shape of mature tree | Urban trees

Acer campestre William Caldwell

Cloned from a seedling raised on the William Caldwell nursery in Knutsford, Cheshire in the super hot summer of 1976. This nursery is sadly no longer in business but its name lives on with this upright form that is proving popular as a self maintaining urban tree where space is restricted.

Thriving in most free draining aspects, it can colour up nicely in the autumn on acid soils with leaves turning orange and sometimes red. On alkaline soils the leaves are more likely to turn buttercup yellow in line with its Field Maple parents.

ACER cappadocicum

This broad spreading maple has five to seven-lobed green glossy leaves that turn a glorious yellow in autumn. The bark is veined with a hint of yellow when young and it is a native of Western Asia to Himalaya.

Tip die back is commonly seen on these genera during establishment, sometimes causing a complete collapse of the plant, and this is generally caused by verticillium. This fungus accounts for many in the maple family and is carried on water so is difficult to avoid. Like Acer rubrum, the susceptibility is probably caused by inadequate availability of trace elements such as manganese.

ACER cappadocicum Aureum

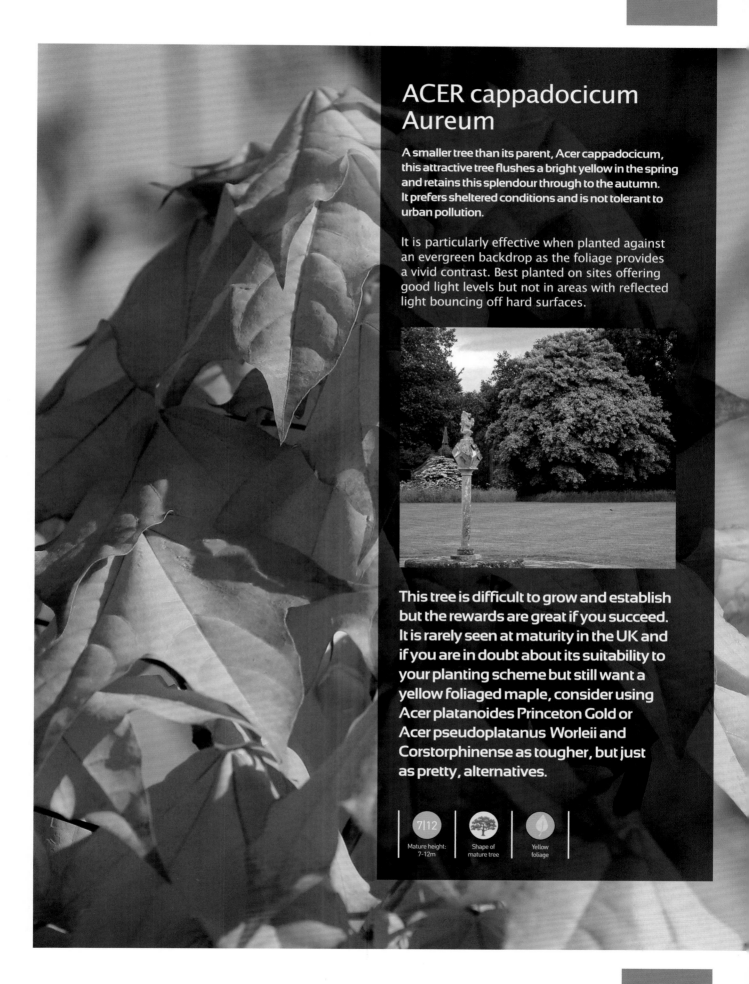

A smaller tree than its parent, Acer cappadocicum, this attractive tree flushes a bright yellow in the spring and retains this splendour through to the autumn. It prefers sheltered conditions and is not tolerant to urban pollution.

It is particularly effective when planted against an evergreen backdrop as the foliage provides a vivid contrast. Best planted on sites offering good light levels but not in areas with reflected light bouncing off hard surfaces.

This tree is difficult to grow and establish but the rewards are great if you succeed. It is rarely seen at maturity in the UK and if you are in doubt about its suitability to your planting scheme but still want a yellow foliaged maple, consider using Acer platanoides Princeton Gold or Acer pseudoplatanus Worleii and Corstorphinense as tougher, but just as pretty, alternatives.

7|12		
Mature height: 7-12m	Shape of mature tree	Yellow foliage

ACER cappadocicum Rubrum

Also known as the Caucasian Maple, this cultivar dates back to at least 1838 but remains rather uncommon. It is a medium to large tree with a rounded habit. The young, dark red leaves turn green and then back to red, gold and yellow in autumn. This superb autumn colour lasts for many weeks.

Although best on moist, well drained soil, it is adaptable and flourishes in either full sun or light shade. It is best grown with a little shelter from strong winds. A good tree for avenues and verges, but not good where soil becomes compacted.

12|17 Mature height: 12-17m	Shape of mature tree	Autumn colour

ACER x freemanii Armstrong

Selected by Newton Armstrong in the States in 1947, this small to medium tree has a tightly columnar habit, making it very useful as a street and car park tree. It is half Acer rubrum and half Acer saccharinum but the latter dominates with autumn colour of orange and yellows rather than glorious scarlet.

The toughness of its Silver Maple parentage makes it a better bet than Acer rubrum and its cultivars when manganese is not present in the soil. It tolerates urban conditions but as a warning note is very susceptible to glyphosate (Roundup) so beware.

7|12 Mature height: 7-12m	Shape of mature tree	Autumn Colour

ACER x freemanii Autumn Blaze

This is a cultivar of a naturally occurring hybrid of Acer rubrum and Acer saccharinum, named after Oliver Freeman, who made the crossing at the US National Arboretum in the 1930s.

This vigorous, oval headed, large tree has dark green, deeply indented leaves, which turn rich flame red in autumn. Acer rubrum is often specified for this effect but very rarely does well on UK soils as it is dependent on the trace element manganese which it can only access at low ph. Autumn Blaze possesses the prettiness of rubrum but the toughness of saccharinum so it is the much safer bet.

12|17 Mature height: 12-17m | Shape of mature tree | Multi-stem | Autumn colour

This variety is very highly thought of in the United States where there are nurseries, principally in Oregon, that grow little else to satisfy their domestic market. It is a highly dramatic tree, rivalling even Liquidambar for autumn colour. As a word of caution, it is slightly brittle, so planting sites exposed to strong and persistent winds should be avoided.

ACER x freemanii Autumn Fantasy

This charming clone resembles Acer saccharinum more than Acer rubrum with its silvery summer leaves and upright oval habit giving a pleasing effect. Introduced from the USA by Bill Wandell of Illinois and new to our range in 2010.

Its real delight comes in the autumn when the leaves turn a gorgeous red to crimson making this a highly prized ornamental tree. Suitable for both parks and large gardens, it thrives on most soils, though it finds it tougher on arid ground.

12|17 Mature height: 12-17m | Shape of mature tree | Autumn colour

ACER ginnala
Amur Maple

Its common name derives from the Amur River, which divides China and Russia. One of the very best trees for autumn colour, when its foliage turns a stunning red, it is also very early into leaf in spring and produces yellow-white fragrant flowers in May. This is a small to medium tree with a rounded habit, and is good for parks and public gardens.

It flourishes in full sun or light shade and in most soil types, and has the added advantages of being wind and drought resistant. I have had experience of planting this in the north of Scotland and they performed poorly so if planned for north of Glasgow beware!

7|12 Mature height: 7-12m	Shape of mature tree	Autumn colour

ACER griseum
Paperbark Maple

A small tree, but a magnificent one! Originally from China, from an early age the bark peels to reveal cinnamon coloured under-bark and the trifoliate leaves have attractive reddish tints in autumn. Introduced by Ernest Wilson in 1901.

This maple does well in sun or partial shade and appreciates a sheltered position. Growing tips generally frost out over winter giving the tree a very rounded habit. It does best in moist, well drained soil, and is not drought tolerant. Nutrient rich, wet soil can inhibit autumn colour.

3|8 Mature height: 3-8m	Shape of mature tree	Bark interest

It is always tempting to plant a tree as pleasing as this in a hard area subjected to reflected heat and light but in view for all to see. It is so important to match the tree's physiology with complementing planting locations for the plant to thrive. This tree will fare poorly when surrounded by hard surfaces. I have one in my garden, planted in 2002, and it is performing admirably under the dappled shade of larger trees.

ACER lobelii
Lobels Maple

Thought to be a naturally occurring hybrid between Acer platanoides and Acer cappadocicum, this native of Southern Italy was introduced in 1683 and is one of the few maples to be naturally fastigiate.

Great for restricted spaces, this vigorous narrow growing maple tolerates most soils and turns a glorious yellow in the autumn. Dark green leaves in summer gives the tree a very neat and tidy appearance and its juvenile smooth grey bark graduates to a browner and shallowly furrowed trunk at maturity.

7|12		
Mature height: 7-12m	Shape of mature tree	Narrow trees

ACER negundo
Box Elder

A medium to large tree, which is particularly fast growing in its first few years. A row of these makes a good screen or windbreak, and it is well worth considering where there is an incidence of honey fungus as it shows good resistance. Its compound leaves, more like those of an ash, make this species unique among maples.

A good choice for heavy clay soils and for waterside plantings, it performs just as well in lighter, drier ones. It also tolerates air pollution and soil compaction as well as withstanding periodic flooding. Native of the USA, this tree is a real tough performer.

12|17		
Mature height: 12-17m	Shape of mature tree	Clay soils

ACER negundo Flamingo

This male clone, raised in Holland in the 1970s, has young leaves that have a wide, soft pink margin which turns to white. Best displays of foliage appear when plants are hard pruned in winter. We supply bottom worked standard trees as it tends to break out when top worked onto a negundo stem.

A good choice for heavy clay soils and for waterside plantings, it performs just as well in lighter, drier ones. It also tolerates air pollution and soil compaction. Very adaptable and recommended as a garden or verge tree.

7|12		
Mature height: 7-12m	Shape of mature tree	Variegated trees

ACER negundo Variegata
Variegated Box Elder

Introduced from a branch sport off a nursery in southern France in 1845, this striking garden tree has to be well maintained to continually reward with its stunning display of silver lined variegated leaves. As with 'Flamingo' we grow this tree as a bottom grafted specimen as it gets too congested and heavy if grafted at the top of an Acer negundo stem and is then prone to collapse. The trick to keeping this tree in order is to prune heavily each winter to encourage vigorous and vibrant regrowth. If left alone, the tree has a tendency to slowly revert to green.

Suitable for most soils, this tough tree is best for gardens where they can be kept an eye on. Don't let me put you off; the foliage display is stunning if you butcher it once a year!

7|12 Mature height: 7-12m	Shape of mature tree	Variegated trees

ACER palmatum
Japanese Maple

The Japanese maple was introduced from its native land to Britain in the 1820s. Also a native of both China and Korea, this magnificent tree can outstrip size expectation if left alone in an area large enough to accommodate.

A delightful, small tree for a sheltered position such as a courtyard or an urban garden. It has a rounded habit and its deeply lobed leaves turn shades of yellow, red and orange in autumn. They do best in rich, moist, but free draining, loamy soils. It is remarkably self reliant post establishment for seemingly such a dainty tree.

3|8 Mature height: 3-8m	Multi-stem	Garden trees

ACER palmatum Bloodgood

A superb Japanese maple with long lasting and unfading reddish purple leaves that turn a glorious red before they drop in autumn. This clone won the Award of Garden Merit in 2002.

Recognised as one of the best clones of its type, it also produces beautiful red fruits and is particularly hardy even in the coldest of winters. We grow this as a full standard tree with a rounded crown so it is best suited for gardens and parks. It thrives on most soils.

3|8 Mature height: 3-8m	Shape of mature tree	Multi-stem	Red/purple foliage

ACER palmatum Dissectum Garnet

A lovely cut leaf deep purple Japanese maple that was raised in Holland around 1950 and won the Award of Garden Merit in 2002.

It is a strong growing form with good autumn colour. We grow this as a full standard tree with a rounded crown so it is best suited for gardens and parks. It thrives on most soils. When grown under the shade of other trees the leaves are more dark green than purple so make sure it has plenty of light to trigger the true colour of the summer foliage display.

3|8 Mature height: 3-8m | Shape of mature tree | Red/purple foliage

ACER palmatum Fireglow

Developed around 1977, this is thought to be an improved clone of the superb 'Bloodgood'. In truth there is little to choose between them so try not to agonise over the choice!

We grow this as a full standard tree with a rounded crown so it is best suited for gardens and parks. It thrives on most soils. The glorious display of summer leaves provide great contrast in any garden so time should be taken to carefully select its planting position to achieve greatest effect. As a rule the eye picks up on deep reds and purples first, if you place it further back in your landscape it draws the focus through your garden rather than blocking off the view behind it.

3|8 Mature height: 3-8m | Multi-stem | Red/purple foliage

ACER palmatum Osakazuki

The best of all Japanese Maples for red autumn colour, this clone won the Award of Garden Merit in 2002 and was introduced in the 1880s.

An attractive, small tree for a sheltered position such as a courtyard or an urban garden. It has a rounded habit and its deeply lobed leaves turn shades of yellow, red and orange in autumn. They do best in rich, moist, but free draining, loamy soils. A stunning tree that never fails to impress.

3|8 Mature height: 3-8m | Multi-stem | Autumn colour

ACER palmatum Purpurea

A superb tree for those who like purple foliage, this clone was introduced in the 1850s but has since been unfairly superseded by improved selections such as Bloodgood.

It makes a small tree for a sheltered position such as a courtyard or an urban garden and has a rounded habit with its deeply lobed purple leaves turning shades of luminescent red in autumn.

They do best in rich, moist, but free draining, loamy soils.

3|8 Mature height: 3-8m | Multi-stem | Red/purple foliage

ACER palmatum Polymorphum

Chaos reigns in the naming of this tree that most classify as straight Acer palmatum. Certainly its attributes are very similar but there are so many slightly different types of the same thing that they all tend to blur into one. However, we are listing this differently as we recognize it to be both vigorous and less prone to disease. Its small dainty leaves are numerous and turn a mix of yellow, orange and red in the autumn.

Best suited to free draining and well fertilized loamy soils, this shrubby tree can form a very pleasing architectural shape at maturity. Young leaves can bruise in strong winds so sheltered aspects give better results.

3|8 Mature height: 3-8m | Multi-stem | Garden trees

ACER platanoides
Norway Maple

An imposing and fast growing tree of great size and the parent of the many cultivars listed on the following pages. The yellow flowers appear in spring, ahead of the leaves which turn yellow and sometimes red in autumn. A native tree of Norway and Europe, but not of Britain, and used widely in parks and streets.

Many of its clones are more suitable for urban and street planting as they form crowns of more regular shape than that of their parent. If planting north of the M62, we would recommend using the selection 'Farlakes Green' as it is the toughest on the market and looks just the same.

It does well on most soil types, tolerates air pollution and resists drought.

17|22 Mature height: 17-22m | Shape of mature tree | Urban trees

ACER platanoides Cleveland

In cultivation since 1948, this selection has an upright habit and an oval head of branches with big, dark green foliage. It has never really caught on in the UK, with varieties like Emerald Queen and Columnare preferred, but in our opinion this clone should not be overlooked!

Considered as one of the best clones for street planting by arborists in America, it does well on most soil types, tolerates air pollution and resists drought. It has an excellent autumn colour of golden yellow and retains its oval to rounded habit through to maturity.

12|17		
Mature height: 12-17m	Shape of mature tree	Urban trees

ACER platanoides Columnare

Raised in France by the Simon Louis nursery in the 1850s, this slow growing cultivar has an oval / compact habit and is superb as a street tree because its columnar form needs virtually no maintenance. The crown stays closed even when the tree is mature.

It does well on most soil types, tolerates air pollution and resists drought. The Dutch have confused matters by calling several similar types 'Columnare' but we reckon they are all distinctly different so beware!! From Barcham you will get the original and what we think is the best clone.

12|17		
Mature height: 12-17m	Shape of mature tree	Urban trees

ACER platanoides Crimson King

A large and most impressive tree with a well rounded form, it looks good from spring through to autumn as its red foliage turns gradually to maroon. A seedling of Schwedleri, it was raised in Belgium in the 1930s.

It does well on most soil types, tolerates air pollution and resists drought. The yellow flowers contrast impressively against the dark emerging spring foliage. We so often see this tree planted in avenues too close together but there is no need as it is quick to grow. Ten metres should be the minimum planting distance but planting in bulk can give too much of a good thing in that the dark leaves tends to gobble up all the light and create a sombre environment below.

A tougher and quicker prospect than Purple Beech, this can be planted on the boundary of a site to draw the eye through the landscape. Dark leaved trees can be superb for defining the overall effect of the landscape but only if used sparingly. Too often I see this tree planted in areas where it will have to be felled before maturity as the planting position is too small to accommodate it.

12|17 Mature height: 12-17m | Shape of mature tree | Red/purple foliage

ACER platanoides Crimson Sentry

Derived from 'Crimson King' in Oregon in the mid 1970s , this far smaller tree is far more appropriate as a garden tree with its stubby ascending branches supporting purple / red leaves that can give great contrast without taking over valued space in restricted areas. It is a tough tree, thriving on most free draining soils light or heavy.

Visually very striking, emerging leaves are more red than crimson and autumn turns them to a mix of orange and reds before leaf fall. We quite often grow this tree as a low crowned half standard as its columnar shape is best shown off with the lower branches retained.

3|8 Mature height: 3-8m	Shape of mature tree	Urban trees	Red/purple foliage

ACER platanoides Deborah

Another seedling from Schwedleri, fast growing Deborah comes from Canada and makes a large tree with a rounded form. Introduced in the 1970s, the spring leaves are bright red, gradually turning to dark green. When the second flush appears there is a superb contrast between the red and the green foliage together.

It does well on most soil types, tolerates air pollution and resists drought. The leaves have a distinctive wavy margin and colour to a rich orange / yellow in the autumn. Most suited for parks, verges and large gardens.

Its newly emerging flush of spring red leaves are particularly effective against the profuse yellow flowers that are borne in April. For those of you who feel 'Royal Red' or 'Crimson King' are too much, 'Deborah' offers a superb compromise

12|17 Mature height: 12-17m	Shape of mature tree	Urban trees

ACER platanoides Drummondii

In cultivation since 1903, this form produces magnificently variegated foliage which has a wide, creamy white margin. It is widely known in North America as the Harlequin Maple. Any shoots which show signs of reversion are best removed. A medium to large tree with a rounded form.

It does well on most soil types, tolerates air pollution and resists drought. It is most impressive in the spring when the variegation is at its most vivid but summer winds can bruise the leaf margins of young trees which then scorch brown. This however is only superficial and does not affect its performance the following year.

This clone can provide vivid contrast within a garden, particularly against a dark evergreen backdrop so take care to place this tree as the results can be very rewarding. It won the Award of Merit in 1956.

7|12			
Mature height: 7-12m	Shape of mature tree	Urban trees	Variegated trees

ACER platanoides Emerald Queen

Selected in the USA in the late 1950s, this has a brighter green leaf colour and more regular habit than the species. It tends to keep a dominant central leader and a more regular habit. A superb cultivar and strongly recommended for street and urban plantings. Where uniformity is required, this is a far better choice than its parent, Acer platanoides.

It does well on most soil types, tolerates air pollution and resists drought. Although ascending when young, it usually gets as wide as it gets broad after about 25 years so it is only ideal for wide verges and areas large enough to accommodate it. It is by far the most popular of the Norway Maple clones and a much safer bet than planting the seedling parent.

17|22 Mature height: 17-22m | Shape of mature tree | Urban trees

ACER platanoides Fairview

This tough newcomer to our range is derived from a seedling of 'Crimson King'. It thrives on poor urban soils and maintains an upright oval habit and at maturity its dimensions are approximately 15 metres tall with a diameter of 12 metres, making it a very useful urban tree.

Reddish purple foliage in the spring hardens to a deep bronze by late summer. It bears green / yellow flowers from April onwards that are a lovely contrast with the dark leaves as they first emerge. Like "Deborah" every growth flush gives a reward of vibrant red foliage throughout the growing season.

12|17 Mature height: 12-17m | Shape of mature tree | Urban trees | Red/purple foliage

ACER platanoides Farlakes Green

This Swedish clone has similar characteristics to those of Emerald Queen, but does not grow quite as high. This clone is preferred in Scandinavia as it is deemed hardier, resisting very low temperatures.

It does well on most soil types, tolerates air pollution and resists drought. Yellow spring flowers are replaced by crisp green foliage that turns yellow in autumn. A better clone for exposed conditions, we would recommend it more the further north you get.

12|17		
Mature height: 12-17m	Shape of mature tree	Urban trees

ACER platanoides Globosum

Introduced in the early 1870s, this 'lollipop' tree is top grafted onto platanoides stem to form a dense mop headed tree. A very good choice as a street tree and for urban plantings and particularly popular in Germany.

It does well on most soil types, tolerates air pollution and resists drought. The dense rounded formality of the crown makes this a delight for architects seeking contrast. Wonderful when in full foliage, it can be rather a let down in a garden after leaf fall as the crown network is small and stubby. Best for urban environments where small is beautiful.

3|8		
Mature height: 3-8m	Shape of mature tree	Urban trees

ACER platanoides Olmstead

Selected in Rochester, New York, in the mid 1950s, this cultivar is similar to Acer platanoides Columnare in having a columnar habit. A good choice as a street tree and where space is restricted.

It does well on most soil types, tolerates air pollution and resists drought. Generally at maturity its height is twice its breadth making this a popular urban tree requiring little maintenance.

12|17		
Mature height: 12-17m	Shape of mature tree	Urban trees

ACER platanoides Pacific Sunset

A cross between Acer truncatum and Acer platanoides Warrenred, this Oregon clone was selected for its autumn colour of orange and red. Its ascending but broad crown emerges with green leaves in the spring making it best suited for large gardens and urban verges. It thrives on most free draining soils and is a tougher bet than some of the Acer rubrum cultivars that have specific soil requirements and Acer freemanii types which can be prone to damage in heavy winds.

Not as long lasting for autumn colour as Liquidambar, the October / November display is nevertheless very striking and its urban toughness makes this clone a great addition to our range of Norway maple types.

12|17			
Mature height: 12-17m	Shape of mature tree	Urban trees	Autumn colour

ACER platanoides Princeton Gold

Also known as Prigo, this sparkling new cultivar has golden yellow spring foliage which hardens to yellow / green in summer. We recommend it for both park and street planting.

Developed in the States, the foliage can tend to scorch up in really hot conditions so it is not widely used. However, our wonderfully temperate climate in the UK suits it down to the ground and the leaf colour makes it one of the best 'yellows' on the market. It does well on most soil types, tolerates air pollution and resists drought.

There are very few reliable yellow foliaged trees that thrive in the UK but in our opinion this clone rates as one that shouldn't be overlooked. Lighter coloured leaves can provide stunning contrast to a garden with a sombre evergreen backdrop.

12|17		
Mature height: 12-17m	Shape of mature tree	Yellow foliage

ACER platanoides Royal Red

A large tree with a crown which is originally conical before becoming broadly round. It has dark purple leaves which turn golden yellow and orange in autumn. Attractive, bright red "keys" are an added feature. Yellow flowers in spring contrast beautifully with emerging purple foliage.

Supposedly smaller and hardier than 'Crimson King' there is an underlying suspicion that it is in fact the same tree but with a different name. I can't make my mind up either way but I certainly wouldn't agonise over the choice for planting.
It does well on most soil types, tolerates air pollution and resists drought.

12|17 Mature height: 12-17m | Shape of mature tree | Red/purple foliage

ACER pseudoplatanus
Sycamore / Celtic Maple

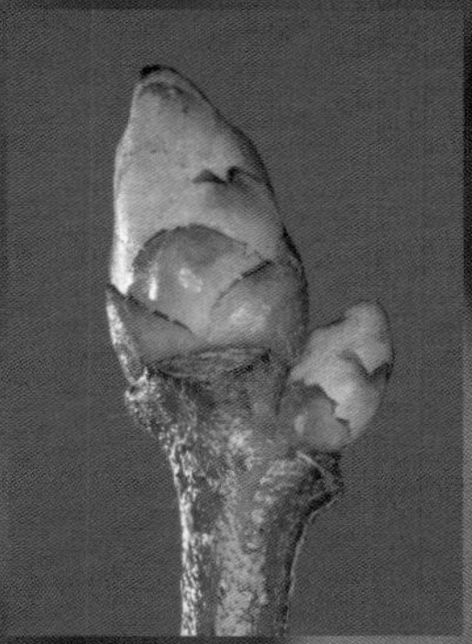

A native of central and southern Europe, the Sycamore has long been naturalised in Britain. Its wood has been used for making innumerable small items from violins to wooden spoons. It is a very large tree, and very fast growing for the first 20 years. It is also one of the very toughest. Many of its cultivars are smaller, but equally as durable.

It tolerates air pollution and thrives in most soils, and is particularly useful for coastal sites where it can make an effective defence against strong winds and salt-laden air. Interestingly, recent work is now suggesting Sycamore is actually a native tree of the UK with both pollen and wood samples predating historical measures.

The success of this tree gives it an unfair tag of being rather a 'weed'. It is however an incredibly versatile plant that thrives in the most difficult of circumstances so it shouldn't be overlooked. Improved clones such as 'Negenia' are widely used on the continent as a street / verge tree as it forms a more regular crown shape at maturity.

17|22 Mature height: 17-22m | Shape of mature tree | Urban trees

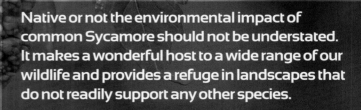

Native or not the environmental impact of common Sycamore should not be understated. It makes a wonderful host to a wide range of our wildlife and provides a refuge in landscapes that do not readily support any other species.

ACER pseudoplatanus Brilliantissimum

Smaller than the species and much slower growing, this top worked cultivar forms a round and dense crown. The young leaves in spring are a wonderful shell pink, hardening to light green by June. An excellent street tree and for where space is limited.

It tolerates air pollution and thrives in most soils, and is particularly useful for coastal sites where it can make an effective defence against strong winds and salt-laden air. Introduced in the early 1900s, this eye catching cultivar won the Award of Garden Merit in 2002.

3|8 Mature height: 3-8m | Shape of mature tree | Garden trees

ACER pseudoplatanus Leopoldii

A really eye-catching cultivar first grown in the 1860s, it is a medium tree with a rounded habit. The leaves begin yellowish pink turning green later and are splashed with yellow and pink. Particularly attractive from leaf emergence in the spring to early summer.

It tolerates air pollution and thrives in most soils, and is particularly useful for coastal sites where it can make an effective defence against strong winds and salt-laden air. A great tree for providing contrast, it is not prone to the problem of reverting back to green like Acer platanoides Drummondii.

12|17		
Mature height: 12-17m	Shape of mature tree	Variegated trees

ACER pseudoplatanus Negenia

A vigorous, large and conical cultivar, it was selected in the late 1940s in the Netherlands, where it is widely used as a street tree. Negenia has dark green, red stalked leaves.

It tolerates air pollution and thrives in most soils, and is particularly useful for coastal sites where it can make an effective defence against strong winds and salt-laden air. Like many clones, as it matures it represents a model shape and form of its seedling parent.

17|22		
Mature height: 17-22m	Shape of mature tree	Coastal sites

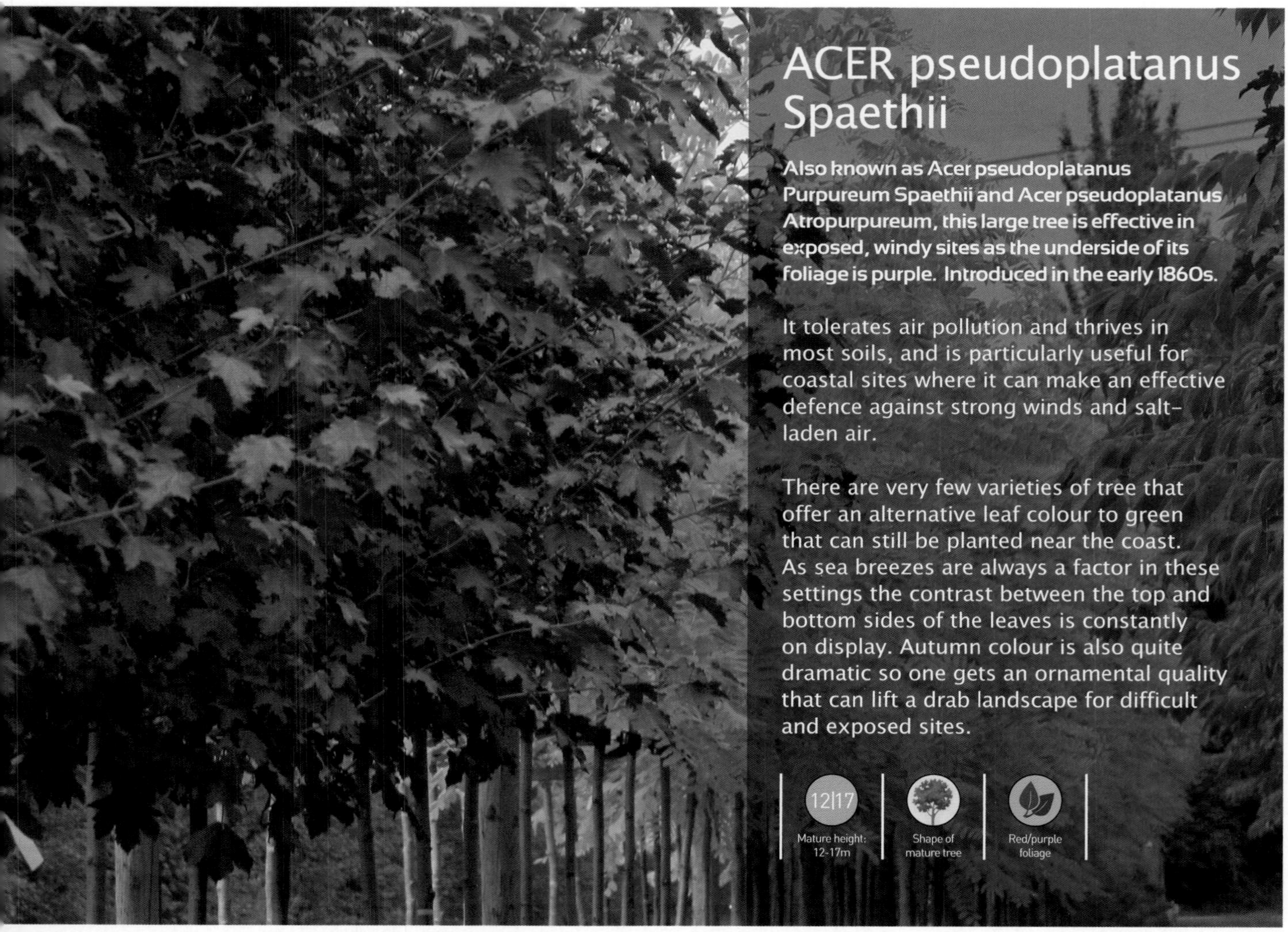

ACER pseudoplatanus Spaethii

Also known as Acer pseudoplatanus Purpureum Spaethii and Acer pseudoplatanus Atropurpureum, this large tree is effective in exposed, windy sites as the underside of its foliage is purple. Introduced in the early 1860s.

It tolerates air pollution and thrives in most soils, and is particularly useful for coastal sites where it can make an effective defence against strong winds and salt-laden air.

There are very few varieties of tree that offer an alternative leaf colour to green that can still be planted near the coast. As sea breezes are always a factor in these settings the contrast between the top and bottom sides of the leaves is constantly on display. Autumn colour is also quite dramatic so one gets an ornamental quality that can lift a drab landscape for difficult and exposed sites.

12|17		
Mature height: 12-17m	Shape of mature tree	Red/purple foliage

ACER pseudoplatanus Worleii
Golden Sycamore

Bred in Germany in the 1890s, this is a beautiful cultivar similar to Corstorphinense. The leaves are primrose yellow as they open, darkening to gold before turning green in summer. A most elegant, medium tree.

It tolerates air pollution and thrives in most soils, and is particularly useful for coastal sites where it can make an effective defence against strong winds and salt-laden air. Michael Dirr, the famous American arborist, reckons that he has come across eight different spellings of Worleii. This represents a trait of tree growers, never satisfied until they have completely baffled their customers!

12|17		
Mature height: 12-17m	Shape of mature tree	Yellow foliage

ACER rubrum
Canadian Maple

Cultivated in Europe for its fabulous autumn colour and in America for the manufacture of furniture, this large tree has a rounded habit. The dark green leaves, slightly purple underneath, turn a brilliant scarlet in autumn.

It tolerates air pollution and wet soil. However, as a warning note, for all the attributes of this tree it is very rarely seen thriving in the UK as it is dependent on accessing the trace element manganese which it can only derive from acid soils. Please refer back to Acer freemanii types if you haven't the soil to support your choice.

17|22		
Mature height: 17-22m	Shape of mature tree	Autumn colour

ACER rubrum Bowhall

I first saw this tree in Portland, Oregon, growing in narrow pavements and thriving. Although its autumn colour is not as vivid as other Acer rubrum varieties we list, it still produces a fair show of yellow and orange leaves in October. Introduced in the States in 1948, this superb urban clone has never caught on in the UK and I am at a loss to understand why!

Its symmetrical ascending habit makes it an ideal subject for city planting where space is at a premium and we introduced it into our range in 2010. Its shape resembles a Lombardy Poplar as it can reach 10 metres in height with a width only of 3 metres. A low maintenance Acer that is more controlled than Acer platanoides Columnare.

12|17 Mature height: 12-17m | Shape of mature tree | Narrow trees

ACER rubrum October Glory

This superb female clone produces a good oval crown at maturity with an autumn display that is hard to beat. An aptly named variety, it was patented in the States in 1961 and introduced by the now closed Princeton Nursery. Widely planted, along with 'Red Sunset' and regarded as one of the best selections.

Its stunning display of vivid red and burgundy leaves in October/November is all the more memorable by the length of time they are held on the tree. This clone rivals Liquidambar for its brilliant autumn display and is a great tree for parks and gardens.

12|17 Mature height: 12-17m | Shape of mature tree | Autumn colour

ACER rubrum Red Sunset

An American form of Red Maple, bred in the 1960s, is also known by the name "Franksred". Rated very highly by arborists for its good branch angle formation and landscape architects for its outstanding and long lived autumn display of leaf colour.

Surely one of the most beautiful cultivars of Acer rubrum, this medium, broadly oval tree is regularly branched, and is an excellent choice for sheltered avenues. Its thick, dark, shiny foliage puts on a great display of red autumn colour. As a cautionary note, the presence of manganese in the soil is vital for Acer rubrum types to perform. Please refer back to Acer freemanii types if you haven't the soil to support your choice.

12|17 Mature height: 12-17m | Shape of mature tree | Autumn colour

ACER saccharinum

Silver Maple

A stately tree which grows along river banks in its native eastern North America, its common name is on account of the silvery underneath of its leaves, which turn golden yellow in autumn. Large and fast growing, its branches are often brittle and prone to breaking. Suitable for large and open spaces but never be tempted to shoehorn in restricted areas or you will inherit a maintenance nightmare.

It tolerates air pollution and wet soils. There are several examples that have reached over 30 metres in height in as little as 100 years so be sure to give it plenty of room at planting.

17|22 Mature height: 17-22m | Shape of mature tree | Wet soils

ACER saccharinum Laciniata Wierii

Discovered in 1873 by DB Wier, this large spreading tree has pendulous lower branches and deeply divided sharply toothed leaves. Its large, wide limbs make it a splendid subject for parks and other open spaces.

Like its parent plant it thrives on most soils and extreme conditions and grows with great vigour. Given enough space it can be truly dramatic but if planted for the moment rather than for the next generation you can pass on a legacy of high maintenance. Best to avoid excessively windy sites.

17|22 Mature height: 17-22m	Shape of mature tree	Wet soils

ACER saccharinum Pyramidale

Introduced in the mid 1880s, this large, broadly pyramidal tree is best suited for parkland, open spaces and wide verges. It has heavy, ascending branches with smaller leaves than those of the species and is a good choice for verges and avenues.

Tolerating most soils and conditions it grows about half as wide as it is tall whilst often retaining its apically dominant central leader. Like other clones of Silver Maple it is best not to manipulate by pruning as this will lead to a corrective cycle that is hard to break. Even though this could be perceived as a street form, don't be tempted as it is too vigorous and will quickly upset the pavement levels.

17|22 Mature height: 17-22m | Shape of mature tree | Wet soils

ACER saccharum Green Mountain

Sugar Maple

Introduced into our range in 2010, this American Clone is actually thought to be a hybrid of Acer saccharum and Acer nigrum. Once established it responds well to arid and restricted planting sites as well as also coping well with reflected heat and light.

Autumn colour can be quite dramatic with the dark green summer foliage turning to yellow / orange and sometimes red / scarlet. It forms a broadly oval crown at maturity. Although widely planted in the USA, Sugar Maple rarely makes an appearance in the UK so this introduction will be of interest to the tree enthusiast.

17|22 Mature height: 17-22m | Shape of mature tree | Autumn colour

AESCULUS x carnea Briotii

Red Horse Chestnut

This large tree is wonderful in parks and planted in avenues. Of rounded habit, it produces dark pink, almost red, flowers in May and dates back to the late 1850s. Given the Award of Garden Merit in 2002, this stately tree is a great favourite in the UK.

The fruits are smaller and less spiny, if at all, than those of the Horse Chestnut. Although they thrive in all soils and tolerate air pollution they are most impressive in early spring when the stocky strong growth bursts into life seemingly on the first warm day in April. Having said this, trees that emerge early in the spring are often on the wane by September so don't expect a glorious autumn display.

17|22		
Mature height: 17-22m	Shape of mature tree	Avenue trees

AESCULUS x carnea Plantierensis

Raised in France in the mid 1890s this splendid, large tree produces pale pink flowers with yellow throats in late spring. Probably the best of the carnea types it is resistant to many of the leaf afflictions that affect horse chestnuts from late summer onwards.

Raised in the famous Simon-Louis Frere nursery near Metz, it is a backcross between carnea and hippocastanum and being a triploid it does not produce fruit. It does best in large open areas and makes a stately show when planted in avenues. It thrives in all soils and tolerates air pollution but like all the species of this type it is best in the spring and early summer.

17|22		
Mature height: 17-22m	Shape of mature tree	Avenue trees

AESCULUS flava
Yellow Buckeye

Also known as Sweet Buckeye, this medium to large tree has creamy yellow flowers marked with red, the nearest to yellow in a horse chestnut. In its native south eastern United States it grows on river banks and mountain sides, and it was once widely used to produce paper pulp. In Britain, it is a good choice for parks and open spaces.

It thrives in all soils, tolerates air pollution and, unusually for horse chestnut, has a good show of yellow autumn colour. Introduced from America in 1764, it won the Award of Garden Merit in 2002. The national champion in America is over 45 metres tall by 17 metres wide.

17|22 Mature height: 17-22m | Shape of mature tree | Flowering trees

AESCULUS hippocastanum
Horse Chestnut

One of the most well-known and loved of all trees! Very attractive in late spring with its white, tinged yellow then pink, candle-like flowers, followed by burnished "conkers" in their spiky casings. It originates from the borders of Greece and Albania and was introduced to Britain in the early 1600s. Wonderful in parks and open spaces.

Over recent years it has been subjected to a number of debilitating pests ranging from bleeding canker to leaf blotch and leaf miner so beware!

17|22 Mature height: 17-22m | Shape of mature tree | Avenue trees

AESCULUS hippocastanum Baumannii

This cultivar was discovered by A.N. Baumann near Geneva in 1820 and was propagated as a branch sport from the mother hippocastanum tree. It is notable for its double white flowers and the fact that it does not produce "conkers", which may be seen as an advantage if required for large streets and avenues. The main branches are rather horizontal, so high pruning is required when used as a street tree.

It can commonly grow in excess of 30 metres and it is always amusing to see kids chucking objects at one in full foliage in anticipation of a shower of conkers as a reward, not knowing it is sterile. Particularly grand in the spring with its strong growth and flower display, it thrives in most soils and tolerates air pollution. Like all hippocastanum types however they are the first to wane in September prior to dormancy.

Like the rest of this genus, recent years have seen a wide range of debilitating pests and diseases that are making people think twice about planting this once much favoured tree. Leaf blotch, scale insect, leaf miner and bleeding canker may prove too much for this tremendous tree to withstand.

17|22 Mature height: 17-22m | Shape of mature tree | Avenue trees

The further north you get in the UK the less the associated problems seem to be but our advise is to stop the avenue planting and stick to specimen individuals just in case. Baumannii's flowers herald the spring and its stout growth gives it a solid appearance.

AESCULUS indica
Indian Horse Chestnut

The Indian Horse Chestnut originates in the Himalayas, having been introduced to Britain in the 1850s and we are indebted to Henry Girling who very kindly gives us seed from the clonal selection Sydney Pearce from his garden to grow on. He has trained his Labrador to collect them!

A majestic tall tree, well suited to parkland and large estates, it has a rounded habit. It bears pyramidal panicles of pink flushed flowers in summer, while its foliage is bronze when young, turning glossy and dark green before changing to orange and yellow in autumn. It tolerates chalky soils well.

There has been increased incidence of what was thought to be Phytophthora bleeding canker on Horse Chestnuts, especially in the South East and Midlands of England. Research is ongoing but it is now believed the cause is a bacterium rather than a fungus, but feedback from arborists suggests Aesculus indica has immunity from the infection. However, it is not a common tree so the jury is out on this one.

Its deeply cut leaves make it the prettiest of the Chestnut family but annoyingly it sometimes sets flower on the terminal growing bud, making it difficult to grow straight. However this is our problem to resolve, not yours!

17|22		
Mature height: 17-22m	Shape of mature tree	Urban trees

AILANTHUS altissima
Tree of Heaven

Introduced in 1751, this fast growing native of Northern China was said to reach for the sky. In hot summers it is quick to naturalise and it can make fun of growing in truly inhospitable urban or rural environments.

Living up to its common name, it is certainly large and broadly columnar in habit. Although not botanically related, it produces long, ash-like foliage. Tolerant of air pollution and ideal for street plantings where space permits, it is best suited on wide verges or central reservations. It thrives in most soils.

Old Chinese medicine texts puts great faith in this tree for cures against mental illness or its ability to combat baldness. The roots, bark and leaves are still used today in the Far East to manage all sorts of ills but over here we enjoy it for its fine architectural shape.

17|22 Mature height: 17-22m | Shape of mature tree | Urban trees

ALNUS cordata
Italian Alder

Originating in southern Italy and introduced in 1820, this fast growing, medium tree has a conical habit. It's shiny, green, pear-like leaves last well into winter, particularly under street lighting. It produces notably larger fruits than other alders. Good for parks and verges, we also recommend for coastal plantings.

It thrives on all ground including dry, high ph soils but is most at home nearest water. Being highly tolerant of urban pollution it is a particularly adaptable urban tree but must be given enough room or it can outstay its welcome. Italian trials indicate that it can even tolerate acid rain. The bark is a glistening brown when young but matures to be rougher.

Once heralded by many as the perfect candidate for an urban tree, its vigour can cause the lifting of hard areas over time so I would advise planting on verges rather than paved streets where it can outstay its welcome.

12|17 Mature height: 12-17m	Shape of mature tree	Clay soils	Bee friendly trees

ALNUS glutinosa
Common Alder

Once used for the production of clogs in northern England, this medium sized native tree has a conical growth habit and produces yellow catkins in March. Its natural habitat is boggy land and river banks. However it is also very good for urban plantings as it thrives in all soils and tolerates air pollution. Available as both multi-stemmed and as a single stem.

Being a native tree, it is a wonderful host to a wide range of wildlife. It is a very useful variety to plant where the ground is liable to flood and survives many weeks with its roots underwater. There was a scare about Alder being susceptible to Phytophthora along water courses up and down the country but this was highly overstated and Alnus glutinosa remains a vital inclusion to any native planting mix.

In its early years Common Alder can grow very quickly, sometimes putting on over two metres of growth in a single growing season when the availability of water coupled with high temperatures predominate. A great tree for use as a screen, it is often seen flanking orchards for this reason.

12|17 Mature height: 12-17m

Shape of mature tree

Native trees

Multi-stem

Wet soils

Bee friendly trees

ALNUS glutinosa Laciniata

Introduced from France in the 1820's, this cultivar has finely cut deep green leaves that are a joy to behold when looking up through the canopy against a rich blue sky. A tree of medium size, it has a graceful, conical habit, and is very good for broad verges and for parks.

It thrives in all soils, though prefers damp ground, and tolerates air pollution. Being a variation of a native tree, the cut leaves make this truly striking. It is particularly effective when planted as a triangle at 7 metre centres as the foliage eventually merges to magnify the effect.

12|17			
Mature height: 12-17m	Shape of mature tree	Wet soils	Bee friendly trees

ALNUS glutinosa Imperialis

Introduced in the early 1860s this finely cut leaf tree won the Award of Garden Merit in 2002 to back up its Award of Merit in 1973. I have seen it used both in Leicester and Liverpool as a very effective street tree but it is usually best seen planted on damp soils in parkland or gardens.

The leaves are more densely cut than Alnus glutinosa Laciniata to create a uniquely fluffy and soft foliage effect that is unrivalled by other trees in the UK. It is wonderful when planted in groups to accentuate the effect but strangely it is little used. However, once seen never forgotten and I am convinced that its popularity will grow over the coming years.

12|17			
Mature height: 12-17m	Shape of mature tree	Wet soils	Bee friendly trees

ALNUS incana
Grey Alder

A really hardy and tough medium tree, capable of coping with cold, wet soils and exposed situations. Grey alder is a fast grower, well suited to industrial areas and street plantings. Its pointed grey leaves readily distinguish it from Alnus glutinosa.

Introduced from Europe in the 1780s it does best on calcareous soils and tolerates air pollution. In the recent past the North American tree bearing the same generic name has been changed to Alnus rugosa to avoid confusion amongst well travelled tree enthusiasts. Profuse pink/yellow catkins are produced just prior to spring.

12|17			
Mature height: 12-17m	Shape of mature tree	Wet soils	Bee friendly trees

ALNUS incana Aurea

Winning the Award of Merit in 1995 and introduced in the early 1860s, this magnificent small tree is a must for any garden in need of winter interest. Unlike the species, this is a slow grower. It does best in moist soil and semi-shaded areas.

The young shoots and leaves emerge a golden yellow in spring which contrast beautifully with vivid red catkins that open to a pink/yellow. The catkins form as early as August and get better and better in colour and size throughout the winter. The bark and twiggy branches also turn orange during the winter. Good as a street tree and for parks and gardens.

As the catkins show so early this is one of the few trees we have that can legitimately offer all year round interest. It has always been underplayed by growers but we have been bulking up our numbers over recent years to market it effectively. Quick to grow when juvenile, it is far more sedate in growth at maturity that its parent, Alnus incana, so is an ideal subject for a garden.

7|12			
Mature height: 7-12m	Shape of mature tree	Urban trees	Bee friendly trees

This lovely clone can provide wonderful contrast within a garden so care should be taken on where to site it. On frosty or even snowy winter days its vivid red catkin display can be simply stunning. Similarly its light coloured foliage can brighten a dour evergreen backdrop.

ALNUS incana Laciniata

Introduced in the early 1860s this superb cut leaf form won the First Class Certificate in 1873. A medium tree with dissected leaves, it has a conical habit when mature and is most attractive. Equally at home in a street, park, verge or garden.

It does best in moist soil but can tolerate the vagaries of urban conditions. There is not much to choose between this variety and the cut leaf forms of Alnus glutinosa as all are remarkably striking and probably the pick of all the cut-leaved trees we offer.

12|17 Mature height: 12-17m	Shape of mature tree	Wet soils	Bee friendly trees

I have seen this tree used most effectively in several towns and cities in the UK. The selections in Liverpool have outstripped expectation and must be between 12 and 15 metres tall. Their pyramidal crowns are lovely in season as the cut leaves give it a very soft and graceful appearance. Best specimens are usually found in the west as annual rainfall is higher.

ALNUS spaethii

Of garden origin and dating from 1908, this fast growing tree of medium size has a rounded habit and is good as a park and street tree. It will also tolerate coastal conditions. The large leaves are purple tinged when young and it is at its best in spring when displaying its beautiful and numerous catkins.

It does best in moist soil, though can cope with dry soils once established, and tolerates air pollution. This variety catches many of our customers out in that it looks like a cherry when in full leaf in the summer. The leaves are vivid green and large as well as being long. The bark gives the game away but this is always a good tree to throw into a plant identification competition for the over confident!

A cross between Alnus japonica and Alnus subcordata, it is little surprise that this is a rarely seen tree but in our opinion it could and should be used more often to bring greater diversity to Alnus plantings in the UK. Its catkin display is second to none amongst the large growing Alders more regularly planted.

12|17 Mature height: 12-17m	Shape of mature tree	Wet soils	Bee friendly trees

There are very few trees that offer wonderful floral displays in the spring and glorious autumn leaf colour but this is one of them. It does best in moist, well drained, lime free soils.

AMELANCHIER arborea Robin Hill

Serviceberry

A wonderful small tree that we consider to be by far the best tree form of Serviceberry on the market. It forms a dense, oval habit and produces its masses of spring flowers that open pink and turn white. A North American selection and as highly rated there as it is here. I have planted one outside of my office window at Barcham so I am rarely far away from this tree!

The young leaves emerge coppery red and then harden to green by late spring before they turn vivid red in autumn.

A very good choice for street plantings and residential areas as it provides plenty of interest with virtually no maintenance. Being such a small tree of ultimate size, it can be placed much closer to buildings than most trees which make it a fantastic choice for urban planting. There are very few trees that offer wonderful floral displays in the spring and glorious autumn leaf colour but this is one of them. It does best in moist, well drained, lime free soils.

5|7 Mature height: 5-7m | Shape of mature tree | Flowering trees | Bee friendly trees

We latched onto this clone in the late 1990s and there are now some fine examples of how they progress at maturity. It makes a fantastic small urban tree suitable for both streets and gardens and its seasonal interest makes it one of the glamour trees of our range.

AMELANCHIER Ballerina

Serviceberry

This small tree, with its finely toothed leaves, was selected by the Experimental Station at Boskoop in the Netherlands in the 1970s and named in 1980. It forms a broader crown than Robin Hill and is less tall making it a better choice for verges and gardens than it is for streets.

It has abundant white flowers in spring and excellent red autumn colour. It does best in moist, well drained, lime free soils and is remarkably resistant to fire blight. It won the Award of Garden Merit in 2002 and remains a great choice for any garden. Sometimes grown as a bushy shrub, we train ours to tree form with a 1.5-1.8m clear stem with a well defined central stem and rounded crown.

A hybrid of Amelanchier laevis, its flowers are larger than 'Robin Hill' or lamarckii making it a very showy performer in the spring. Its fruits are edible and are a particular favourite of blackbirds in my garden. Its spreading crown gives it a more rustic feel than 'Robin Hill' making it more suited to rural gardens.

5|7 Mature height: 5-7m	Shape of mature tree	Flowering trees	Bee friendly trees

AMELANCHIER
lamarckii
Serviceberry

Naturalised over much of Western Europe, it is a simply stunning sight when in full bloom with its white flowers produced in plentiful racemes. It is a small, shrubby tree with emerging copper coloured leaves turning green by late spring before they mature to a rich red as autumn progresses. The rounded fruits, red in summer before turning black in autumn, are edible.

Although we grow this both as a multi-stem and single stemmed tree please be aware that if you buy the latter form it is prone to sucker and broaden with age so requiring far more maintenance than Robin Hill if planted as a street tree. In our opinion it makes a far better subject if planted as a coppiced multi tem tree for verge or garden plantings as you maximise its flowering potential and are going with its natural habit. It does best in moist, well drained, lime free soils. Fine near buildings, I have one growing happily two metres from my front door!

5|7 Mature height: 5-7m | Shape of mature tree | Multi-stem | Flowering trees | Bee friendly trees

ARALIA elata
Japanese Angelica Tree

Introduced to Britain in the 1830s from its native Japan, it won the Award of Merit in 1959 and the Award of Garden Merit in 2002. A remarkably odd looking tree, wonderfully exotic in foliage which falls away in autumn to leave only a few spiky branches.

It makes a small rounded tree and is remarkable for its very large, doubly pinnate leaves, produced mainly in a "ruff" towards the tips of its stems. The foliage often gives vivid and luminous autumn colour, coinciding with its extraordinary stunning display of white panicle flowers.

3|5 Mature height: 3-5m | Multi-stem | Flowering trees

ARAUCARIA araucana
Monkey Puzzle

Sometimes referred to as the Chile Pine it is also a native of Argentina. This ancient slow growing evergreen tree is well known for its distinctive long slender branches that are densely covered with overlapping spiked leaves. Introduced into the UK in 1795 by Archibald Menzies, the famous Navy surgeon who later turned plant collector, it won the Award of Merit in 1980. Amazingly enough, it was once a native of Britain. The fossilized wood from this tree was highly coveted by Queen Victoria. Otherwise known as Jet, it was used in the making of mourning jewellery.

Hardy in the UK, they are often planted far too close to houses so have to be removed before they get to maturity. This unusual conifer prefers a moist loamy soil and has great apical dominance drawing the tree up strongly vertical so it is very suited to crown lifting. Try not to handle the foliage unless you are well protected as the leaves are very sharp! The cones are globular, up to 20cm in length and take up to three years to mature.

17|22 Mature height: 17-22m | Shape of mature tree | Evergreen trees

ARBUTUS unedo
Killarney Strawberry Tree

This native of South West Ireland and the Mediterranean is, unusually for an ericaceous plant, tolerant of lime. It is a small evergreen with brown, shedding bark, and its flowers and fruits are produced together in the autumn. A good choice for exposed and coastal sites, it is also good for urban plantings.

A winner of the Award of Garden Merit in 2002 and of a First Class Certificate in 1933, it does well in most soil types, but prefers it moist. Don't be afraid to hard prune if getting untidy as if this is done in late March/April it grows back beautifully. We grow it as both a bushy shrub and a full standard tree. Young shoots are tinged red which contrasts well against the dark green leaves.

3|8			
Mature height: 3-8m	Shape of mature tree	Multi-stem	Garden trees

BETULA albosinensis Fascination

Chinese Birch

The species from which Fascination was developed was brought back from China in 1901 by Ernest Wilson. He was very taken with it, describing it as follows: "The bark is singularly lovely, being a rich orange-red or orange-brown and peels off in sheets, each no thicker than fine tissue paper, and each successive layer is clothed with a white glaucous bloom."

Further to this the catkins in the spring are amazing, up to 10cm in length, opening to a rich yellow-brown and so numerous my kids call it the 'caterpillar tree'.

Fascination is a refined clone with dark green leaves, which are large for a birch, appearing in April, along with the showy display of yellow catkins. It has outstanding stem colour, orange peeling to pink and cream and then purest white once the tree gets beyond 20cm girth. It is a medium sized tree, becoming oval as it matures, has stiffly ascending branches and the one outside my kitchen window, now over 63cm girth, is a constant joy and often commented on. A great choice for parks and verges growing well on most soils. It is listed by a few as Betula utilis Fascination but we put it firmly classified in the albosinensis group.

12|17		
Mature height: 12-17m	Shape of mature tree	Bark interest

BETULA ermanii
Ermans Birch

This birch was originally from North East Asia and Japan and was first cultivated in the 1880s. Always the first tree to emerge with new leaf in the spring at Barcham, and one of the first to fall in autumn. Importantly it tolerates reflected heat and light very adequately so is a great urban tree that requires little maintenance.

An elegant and vigorous medium to large tree, the bright green, often heart shaped and prominently veined leaves which appear very early in spring become clear yellow in autumn. It grows well on most soils. There is a variety named Betula ermanii Holland but in my view this is synonymous with what I have described.

12|17		
Mature height: 12-17m	Shape of mature tree	Bark interest

BETULA nigra
River Birch

Also known as the Red Birch, this is one of the very best trees for wet soils and we favour the clonal selection from the States called Heritage, selected in 1968, for its vigour and uniformity.

Originally found along the river banks of the South Eastern United States, this medium sized tree makes a great show with its shaggy, flaking, cinnamon/ orange bark. Mature trees are truly statuesque and broadly pyramidal in form. Foliage is soft green and diamond shaped.

Its common name of River Birch is misleading as we have seen this tree thriving in arid London tree pits. Once established, it can tolerate extreme heat in the summer, thriving in Florida as well as Kentucky in the States. This could become a good choice for the South East of the UK as temperatures continue to break records during the summer months. Available as both a standard tree and as a multi-stem.

12|17 Mature height: 12-17m	Shape of mature tree	Urban trees	Multi-stem

BETULA maximowicziana
Monarch Birch

An oddity within our Birch range, hardly looking like a member of the same family. It is a native of Japan where it can reach up to 35 metres in height but it is rare to see in the UK and reaches a more modest height of between 15-20cm. Introduced into the UK in 1893, this is one to catch someone out on a tree identification competition.

It is fast growing and has a dark brown trunk when young, maturing into greyish tinges. The large heart shaped leaves turn clear yellow in the autumn. It retains a pyramidal shape when young but this broadens at maturity. The leaves are the biggest of all the Birch family, sometimes attaining over 12cm in length.

12|17		
Mature height: 12-17m	Shape of mature tree	Avenue trees

BETULA papyrifera
Paper Birch

The Paper Birch is also known as the Canoe Birch in its native North America and was introduced into the UK in 1750. Until it clears 20-25cm girth the bark is a brown/red and very distinguishable from other juvenile birch but after this point the bark starts to whiten markedly. A pioneer species, particularly quick to colonise areas devastated by fire.

The waterproof qualities of its bark made it an important tree for the Native Americans who used it for making canoes and wigwam covers, as well as eating utensils. It makes a medium to large tree with a conical habit. It has white, papery bark, the colour being carried high into the canopy, and attractive yellow autumn foliage. One of the most elegant of trees for parks. It does best on moist, well drained sandy soil, but is tolerant of most conditions.

12|17		
Mature height: 12-17m	Shape of mature tree	Bark interest

BETULA pendula
Silver Birch

The Silver Birch is also known as the "Lady of the Woods" - so called because of its slender and graceful appearance. It is a pioneer species and particularly admired in the UK. Even though it seemingly grows anywhere it is remarkably difficult to successfully transplant bare rooted but our containerised trees solve this problem. A group of three silver birches that we supplied were planted in Stamford, Lincolnshire and grew from 12-14cm girth to 30-35cm girth in 6 years!

A medium tree with a conical, but semi weeping habit, the bark is white with horizontal lines and large, diamond shaped cracks as the tree matures. Very good for parks and woodland, but not suitable for areas where soil becomes compacted. It grows well on most soils and we grow it as both a single stemmed tree and a multi-stemmed tree.

Multi-stemmed trees are particularly useful when planted on elevated or exposed ground as they have a low centre of gravity and need no staking. Our multi-stemmed birch is grown as true single plant coppices, not three or four plants bundled together in a pot that can lead to issues further down the line.

The clonal selection 'Zwisters Glory' is reliably white stemmed and more upright in habit. It is vigorous in its younger years and may represent a better choice for the urban environment.

12|17			
Mature height: 12-17m	Shape of mature tree	Multi-stem	Native trees

BETULA pendula Dalecarlica
Swedish Birch

A most elegant tree and perfect for specimen planting. For those of you that went to Writtle Agricultural College you will remember the splendid short avenue of them leading to the refectory block. Some call this clone 'Laciniata' or 'Crispa' but don't worry about it as the differences are too slight to cause a dilemma.

Found in Sweden in the 1760s, it is a medium to large tree of slender form and with a broadly columnar habit. The leaves are deeply cut and branches weep gracefully. Bark is white and peeling. Very good for parks and woodland, but not suitable for areas where soil becomes compacted or where there is too much reflected heat and light. It grows well on most soils.

It is always good to bear in mind a tree's origin to assess its physiology. Sweden has shorter day lengths than southern England so to place this clone in a paved area in London would represent extreme conditions for this tree. It is much happier planted in greener areas and further north.

12|17 Mature height: 12-17m	Shape of mature tree	Bark interest

BETULA pendula Fastigiata
Upright Birch

An upright form of the Silver Birch, resembling the shape of a Lombardy Poplar. It tends to spiral its way upwards giving a corkscrew effect of twiggy birch branches that hold their leaves slightly longer than most other varieties. The bark, although similar to Betula pendula is not as spectacular as the white barked clones.

This medium to large tree has stiffly ascending branches which give it a columnar habit. In cultivation since the 1870s, it makes a good street and car park tree as it requires little space. It grows well on most soils and the highest recorded specimen comes in at over 30 metres although I have never seen any at half that size.

7|12 Mature height: 7-12m	Shape of mature tree	Narrow trees

BETULA pendula Obelisk

Originating from Northern France in the mid 1950s, this densely branched tree has typical silver birch foliage and silver white trunk but grows in a very ascending fashion so doesn't exceed 3 metres diameter, making it a very useful birch for restricted areas and small gardens. I have seen this clone used to great effect on a roundabout in Oakham, Rutland where width was at a premium.

Thriving on most free draining soils, this tough little tree is quite often growth feathered, with branches all the way down its stem. Its green leaves turn to a clear yellow for the autumn and its twiggy brown branches gives great contrast to its thicker white trunk as it matures.

7|12 Mature height: 7-12m	Shape of mature tree	Bark interest

BETULA pendula Purpurea
Purple Birch

Introduced in the early 1870s, this slow growing and rare variety won the First Class Certificate in 1874. One of the largest specimens I have seen happens to be in my next door neighbour's garden in Rutland and has reached over 10 metres whilst retaining a slender habit.

Dark purple leaves emerge in spring soften to a dark green/purple by summer. The bark is similar to that of Betula pendula and the habit is similarly repeated. It will grow on most soils and is best suited for gardens and arboretums.

12|17 Mature height: 12-17m	Shape of mature tree	Red/purple foliage

BETULA pendula Tristis
Weeping Birch

Introduced in 1867 this outstanding cultivar won the Award of Garden Merit in 2002. It is a sight to behold in winter when its twiggy growth, supported on pendulous limbs, is shrouded in frost on a bright morning. If space is restricted, or for small gardens, Betula pendula Youngii should be chosen instead.

A most graceful and particularly beautiful tall tree, with slender, pendent branches. Although a weeping birch, it maintains a central leader, and is excellent planted as a specimen. Also good for wide verges and avenues, it grows well on most soils. The bark matures to a decent white making this, in our opinion, one of the best tall weeping trees on the market.

I think this tree is at its best when it stands still and dormant in winter with a severe frost covering its fine cascading twiggy branches.

12|17		
Mature height: 12-17m	Shape of mature tree	Bark interest

BETULA pendula Youngii
Young's Weeping Birch

Originating in the early 1870s, this small to medium weeping birch has no defined central leader and therefore eventually forms an attractive dome shape. Sometimes produced top worked to get the initial height, we prefer to grow a structurally stronger plant from the base and draw up a leader until we have formed a 1.8-2 metre clear stem that can support the crown thereafter.

The thin branches eventually reach the ground and the serrated, triangular leaves show good autumn colour. It develops a smooth white bark and is an attractive specimen tree for lawns. It grows well on most soils and has been a great favourite in the UK for many years.

3|8		
Mature height: 3-8m	Shape of mature tree	Bark interest

BETULA pendula Zwisters Glory

This new selection originated from J van Roessel in Switzerland and was introduced into the European market in 1994. In effect it is a very uniform version of seed grown Betula pendula with a gleaming white bark so it makes an ideal choice for avenue planting. The branches grow at a 45 degree angle from the stem and remain subordinate to the main trunk to retain a graceful pyramidal crown.

This tree has great apical dominance so lends itself to crown lifting over time if needed. It is a splendid choice for the urban environment and quick to grow on most soils. The bark is nearly as good as Betula utilis Jacquemontii so we can expect to see a lot more of this clone in future years.

17|22		
Mature height: 17-22m	Shape of mature tree	Bark interest

BETULA pubescens
Common White Birch

The Common White Birch is also known as Downy Birch and Hairy Birch. Oil from its stem is used in the production of leather, while the bark was once used for roofing in Scandinavia. A native of both the UK and Europe, it ideally prefers damper soils than Betula pendula so is more commonly seen in the west. In our opinion it is an undervalued tree for planting in the general landscape and should be used more frequently ahead of the more popular Silver Birch.

Linnaeus classed this with Betula pendula, but it differs in not having pendulous branches and in having darker bark and downy young shoots. The white bark peels into papery layers, but does not have the characteristic diamond shaped cracks of Silver Birch. Very good for parks and verges. It grows well on most soils.

17|22 Mature height: 17-22m | Shape of mature tree | Bark interest | Native trees

To vouch for its hardiness, Betula pubescens can be seen growing further north than any other broadleaf tree. It generally forms a scrubby low lying tree at this latitude and is native of both Greenland and Iceland. Its ascending branches give it a more solid appearance than Betula pendula and this makes it a tougher prospect to grow on exposed sites.

BETULA utilis Jacquemontii/Doorenbos
Himalayan Birch

There are now so many differing clones put under this banner that the trade is tying itself in knots of confusion, but suffice it to say if you are after the gleaming white barked birch under the above cultivar name from Barcham you will not be disappointed! The unsurpassed whiteness of the trunk and branches peels routinely each year and is accentuated by lenticel lines.

A native of the western Himalayas, it makes a medium tree with ascending branches, and is also spectacular when grown as a multi-stem. However, beware those growers who palm off a multi-stem as three separate trees grown together as this will only lead to structural problems later on. Its oval, dark green leaves turn golden yellow in autumn. Excellent for urban plantings, it grows well on most soils.

This tree can be very effectively placed against a dark background in a garden as the white stems bounce back to you in contrast. I normally advocate a planting distance of a minimum of seven metres for any of our trees but have conceded in recent years that this clone is sensational when planted en mas at three to five metre centres. Anglesey Abbey in Cambridgeshire proves this point and a trip to this lovely National Trust garden is a must in winter.

12|17 Mature height: 12-17m	Shape of mature tree	Multi-stem	Bark interest

Some nurseries have tried growing this clone through micro propagation but the results at maturity are more than disappointing, with a loose and poor crown formation. We strongly recommend a budded/ grafted plant as the result is proven and the mature crown structure assured.

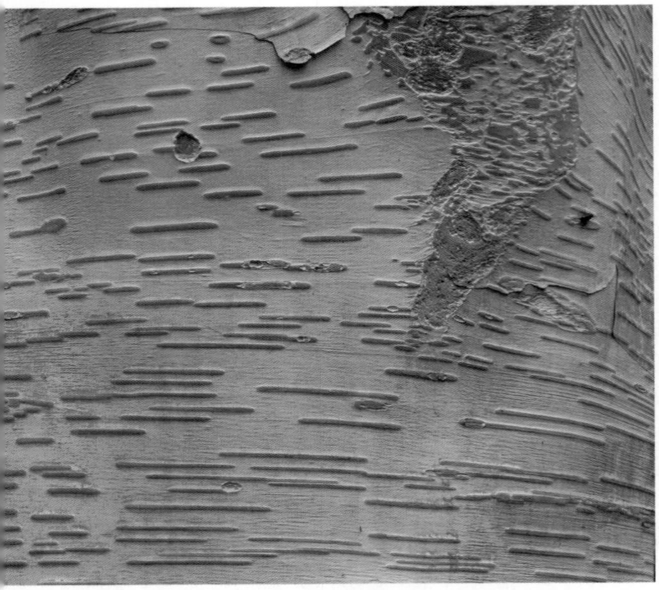

BETULA utilis Long Trunk

This botanical oddity is a tricky one to describe as it possesses so many traits of unrelated cultivars. I suppose a habit of Betula pendula Youngii with the same measure of Betula pendula Tristis on a tree with Betula utilis Jacquemontii trunk and leaves sums it up. The combination makes it an ideal candidate for gardens or parks.

This small to medium sized tree has glistening white bark, which routinely peels each year to make it look even more attractive. Its oval, dark green leaves turn golden yellow in autumn. It has a weeping habit but possesses enough apical dominance to keep growing upwards so retaining a relatively slender and not mushroomed habit. It is tolerant of most soils.

3|8		
Mature height: 3-8m	Shape of mature tree	Bark interest

BROUSSONETIA papyrifera
Paper Mulberry

Introduced in the early 18th century and now naturalised in America, fibre from the Paper Mulberry was once woven into a fine cloth in Polynesia and its bark is still processed to make paper in its native Japan.

In Europe it is regarded as a highly ornamental specimen tree suitable for gardens, parks and arboretums.

7|12		
Mature height: 7-12m	Shape of mature tree	Bark interest

A small to medium tree, it has lobed, hairy leaves, no two of which are the same shape. Male plants have pendent catkins, while the females bear orange-red fruits. The young stems are green and brown blotched giving it a somewhat unusual camouflaged effect. Tied to the same family as Morus, this is one for the plant collector. It does best on fertile, calcareous soil.

BUXUS sempervirens Arborescens

Box

This large shrub can occasionally be classified as a small tree and is a clonal selection of common box that won the Award of Garden Merit in 2002.

The small but numerous evergreen leaves make this plant an ideal subject for screening/hedging. If left unclipped it will eventually reach approximately 7 metres after about 40 years. For those of you that enjoy topiary, this is an ideal candidate. It thrives on most soils and doesn't mind both sun and shade.

3|8 Mature height: 3-8m | Shape of mature tree | Garden trees

CALOCEDRUS decurrens

Incense Cedar

Native to California and Oregon, this large, evergreen conifer has a columnar habit making it unmistakable. Introduced in 1853, it won the Award of Garden Merit in 2002. Resembling Thuja when young, this superb truly fastigiate conifer is often overlooked but it makes a fabulous impact in garden, verge or park with no ongoing maintenance issues.

Perfect as a specimen tree or grown in avenues, it has dark green leaves crowded into fan-like sprays with oval, hanging cones. It grows well on most soils and is well suited to growing in the UK.

I first saw some maturing Calocedrus in the UK at the Royal Horticultural Society's garden at Harlow Carr near Harrogate and was struck by their architectural elegance. When young, they are fairly unremarkable but given time their wonderful shape makes them a fantastic asset to any landscape. As the tree matures its bark lightly cracks to produce a pleasing patchwork effect.

CAMELLIA sasanqua Rosea

Introduced in the early 1800s and a native of China and Japan, this acid loving small evergreen tree is grown at Barcham as a full standard.

It is better planted in the south facing gardens of southern England where it thrives to make a small tree about 5 metres in height. Glossy evergreen leaves are beautifully contrasted with luscious pink fragrant flowers in both autumn and spring. Generally, the hotter the preceding summer, the better the performance.
It is also best to position the plant in a sheltered spot, protecting it against cold winter winds.

3|8 Mature height: 3-8m	Shape of mature tree	Flowering trees	Multi-stem

CARPINUS betulus
Hornbeam

The timber of the Hornbeam has traditionally been used to produce mallets, skittles and even the moving parts of pianos. Winning the Award of Garden Merit in 2002, this wonderful native tree is closely related to the hop hornbeam, Ostrya carpinifolia.

Wonderful in a parkland setting, growing in groups and ideal for pleaching, the Hornbeam is a large tree with a characteristic grey fluted trunk and ovate, ribbed and serrated leaves which turn a lovely clear yellow in autumn. This British native produces hard, finely grained timber with many uses. It grows well on most soils, including clay and chalk. A most useful tree for poor planting conditions.

Hornbeam is a super tree to fashion into different shapes. We once had a project that required hornbeam in 8 foot letters spelling 'Welcome to Doncaster' and this can still be seen thriving on the Doncaster / Rotherham roundabout off the A1. More normally it is trained into pleach panels to give architectural effect or to provide privacy above fence height.

17|22			
Mature height: 17-22m	Shape of mature tree	Native trees	Clay soils

CARPINUS betulus Fastigiata

This Hornbeam received an Award of Garden Merit from the Royal Horticultural Society in 2002. A tree of medium size and pyramidal habit. Slender in its youth, it can often be seen growing in restricted areas despite the fact that it develops "middle age spread", reaching up to 10m wide. It is better growing in an open, parkland setting and is very effective if left feathered to the base, producing gold and orange autumn colours. It grows well on most soils, including clay and chalk. A most useful tree for poor planting conditions.

In our opinion this clone should be renamed Carpinus betulus Globosum and if care isn't taken when selecting, some are very difficult to prune and manage when older. Always look out for a straight central trunk tapering to a well defined leader because if the main stem is supplied co-dominant at a low level the tree can never be satisfactorily crown lifted at maturity and the tree gently becomes wider and wider.

For those impatient amongst you, the denser ascending branches can be used to form an instant hedge. Simply plant a four year old tree at two metre centres and hedge trim the tops to achieve immediate privacy.

12|17 Mature height: 12-17m	Shape of mature tree	Clay soils

CARPINUS betulus Fastigiata Frans Fontaine

This Hornbeam cultivar was selected from a street in the Netherlands in the early 1980s. A far better proposition for planting in restricted areas than Carpinus betulus Fastigiata, it retains its columnar habit, being only 3m wide after 25 years. It tolerates pollution and soil compaction, so makes an excellent street tree. It grows well on most soils, including clay and chalk. A most useful tree for poor planting conditions.

Frans Fontaine is very similar to Carpinus betulus Fastigiata when small and we often get called to describe the differences. The former sometimes has a rough fissured bark at the base of the main stem and its leaves are more crinkly than the latter.

12|17		
Mature height: 12-17m	Shape of mature tree	Urban trees

CARPINUS japonica Japanese Hornbeam

Introduced from Japan in 1895, this small tree won the Award of Garden Merit in 2002. It is particularly effective when used for pleaching as the spreading horizontal branches can be easily trained and the flowering hop display along their length is a fantastic bonus compared to using native hornbeam for the same purpose.

A most beautiful and widely spreading, rounded small tree, it has heavily corrugated foliage, which is darker than the European Hornbeam, and attractive fruiting catkins which resemble hops. An excellent park tree, it has smooth, pink / grey bark. It grows well on most soils, including clay and chalk. A most useful and pretty tree for poor planting conditions.

I saw a fine specimen of this tree in Calderstones Park in Liverpool several years ago and this convinced me on its merits. Carpinus japonica needs little maintenance and combines an ornamental twist while passing for our native tree which can prove very useful in a rural garden.

7|12		
Mature height: 7-12m	Shape of mature tree	Garden trees

CARYA Illinoinensis Pecan

The USA champion is 35 metres tall by 48 metres wide but don't let this put you off as it will never attain this in the UK! This majestic tree has a symmetric broadly oval crown and long compound dark green leaves, regularly composed of over a dozen leaflets. It grows best on deep well drained soils that retains a good moisture content throughout the summer. Introduced in the early 1760's it never delivers the quantity of fruit that it bears in its native north America but where soil conditions allow it is a great addition for parkland and arboretum planting here in the UK.

Like Quercus petraea, it is best suited for the wetter south western half of Britain, but should be given enough room around it for it, about 20 metres, to thrive without competition.

17|22		
Mature height: 17-22m	Shape of mature tree	Parkland trees

CASTANEA sativa
Sweet Chestnut

Chestnuts roasting on an open fire or bought piping hot from a street vendor so evocative of Christmas long ago! Believed to have been introduced by the Romans, this tree is native of Southern Europe and North Africa but has long been naturalised in the UK. It won the Award of Garden Merit in 2002. Its spiralling rough bark at maturity is lovely.

A versatile and beautiful, fast growing, large tree, which is particularly attractive in early summer when laden with its male and female catkins. Its long, glossy leaves turn gold and bronze before falling. The timber is highly prized around the Mediterranean and in Provence much furniture is made from chestnut wood. A splendid tree for grouping and quite outstanding planted as an avenue. It does best on reasonably dry, light soils, and is moderately lime tolerant.

There are many glorious specimens of this tree in the UK including within the fabulous parkland landscape at Burghley House, near Stamford, in Lincolnshire.

17|22			
Mature height: 17-22m	Shape of mature tree	Avenue trees	Bee friendly trees

CATALPA bignonioides
Indian Bean Tree

12|17 Mature height: 12-17m | Shape of mature tree | Flowering trees

From the south eastern United States comes this magnificent, medium to large tree, which is very good as an urban subject, but not in paved areas. Introduced in 1726, this eye catching tree won the Award of Garden Merit in 2002 and there are fine specimens in Palace Yard, Westminster.

It is late into leaf and produces exotic, orchid-like flowers in midsummer. These are followed by the "beans", which look like dark vanilla pods, in autumn. Outstanding as a specimen tree and tolerant of air pollution. It does well on most soils but avoid windy exposed sites as the large fleshy leaves can bruise.

The top worked clone, 'Bungeii' forms a rounded and dense canopy but is too similar in leaf and flower to merit its own listing.

CATALPA bignonioides Bungeii

CATALPA bignonioides Aurea

This golden-leaved form of the superb Indian Bean Tree was introduced in the late 1870s and won the Award of Merit in 1974.

Its large fleshy golden yellow leaves turn to a yellow green by the time the flowers open in summer. Often top worked it forms a broadly rounded crown at maturity. It is suitable for urban plantings, does best in a sheltered position and does well on most soils.

7|12 Mature height: 7-12m | Shape of mature tree | Yellow foliage

Like most yellow-leaved trees, it is best placed in a south facing aspect as shade tends to dull the leaf colour to a light green.

CEDRUS atlantica
Atlas Cedar

Introduced in the 1840s, Atlas Cedars make most imposing and stately subjects perfect for large estates. To the untrained eye it is too similar to Cedrus libani to call and the Dutch try and clear the trade of confusion by listing it as Cedrus libani Atlantica as a catchall. We list it separately for the sake of purity!

This large, evergreen tree from the Atlas Mountains of Algeria and Morocco forms an impressive structure of wide, horizontal branches when mature. It grows rapidly in its early years and is regarded by many as a classical parkland tree. It thrives on most soils but is better equipped to withstand urban pollution compared to Cedrus libani or deodara. Cones, 5-7 cm in length, are produced along its numerous branches.

Very difficult to transplant as bare rooted or root balled, our containers solve this problem and facilitate good establishment.

17|22		
Mature height: 17-22m	Shape of mature tree	Evergreen trees

We always think of this superb tree as an individual specimen but in their native habitat they can form imposing forests on mountainsides at an altitude of 1000 metres to 2200 metres. These forests still sustain the endangered Barbary Macaque.

CEDRUS atlantica Glauca
Blue Cedar

The Blue Cedar is probably the most dramatic and striking of all blue conifers. A winner of both the First Class Certificate in 1972 and the Award of Garden Merit in 2002, it is both quick growing and sparsely furnished when young but thickens out with time.

This is another superb subject for specimen and parkland planting, where its form can be best appreciated. Its silvery blue foliage is very attractive but if it suffers stress during the establishment phase after planting, it can lose its leaves. This is alarming for an evergreen plant but it is fairly tough and usually reflushes the following spring. It thrives on most soils but doesn't appreciate waterlogged ground.

It is often seen planted too close to buildings and I think this is because it is bought my many as a tiny plant from a garden centre. Be sure not to let its initial size mislead you, it needs to be situated at least twenty metres away from a building for best long term effect! As with most trees with foliage different to the normal green, it immediately draws the eye to provide marvellous contrast within a landscape.

Mature height: 17-22m | Shape of mature tree | Urban trees

CEDRUS deodara
Deodar Cedar

The Deodar Cedar is grown for its timber in parts of southern Europe, but is grown as an ornamental in Britain. Its root system is more fibrous and compact than that of Cedrus atlantica and libani so is often used as the rootstock for these species to avoid transplantation issues. This was pioneered by Belgium growers but they didn't account for the fact that deodara is not as long lived so we favour plants grown from seedlings.

Different from all other cedars due to its trailing leader, this large, evergreen conifer has a gently pendulous habit and soft, blue/green foliage. It thrives on most soils but does not do as well in wet ground with poor drainage.

17|22		
Mature height: 17-22m	Shape of mature tree	Evergreen trees

Brought from the Himalayas in the reign of George IV in 1831, this soon became a favourite planted on the lawns of large country houses and Georgian rectories.

CEDRUS libani
Cedar of Lebanon

Few trees, deciduous or evergreen, can compare with the beauty and elegance of a mature Cedar of Lebanon. Some think it is its own species or that it is a geographical sub species of Cedrus atlantica but either way there is little to choose between them. It won the Award of Garden Merit in 2002.

One of the most majestic of all trees and extensively planted as part of the enduring landscape of some of our grandest stately homes and estates. It is slower growing than the Atlas Cedar, conical when young before assuming the flat topped and tiered habit of maturity. Introduced to England around the time of the Civil War in the mid 1640s, it has large, barrel shaped cones and green or grey/green foliage. It thrives on most soils though does not appreciate wet ground.

So impressive are the trees at the Cedars Conservancy Parks in Lebanon it was put forward as a candidate for the new listing of the Seven Wonders of the World.
The variety 'Brevifolia' is sometimes listed and is a native of Cyprus.

Cedar of Lebanon has been very important to many civilizations including the ancient Egyptians who used its resin for mummification. Sawdust from the tree has also been present in many of the Pharaohs tombs. However its range has been sadly depleted over time as its timber has been too highly prized by humankind and much of the original forests are no more.

17|22		
Mature height: 17-22m	Shape of mature tree	Evergreen trees

CELTIS australis
Nettle Tree

The wood of the Nettle Tree was once used to produce charcoal. A native of Southern Europe and North Africa, it has been grown in the UK since the 16th century and is used commonly as a verge or street tree in the Mediterranean as it is tolerant of both reflected heat and salt laden air.

Related to the elms, this small to medium tree has broad, lanceolate, rough leaves. It has a broad crown and smooth trunk. It is widely planted for roadside shade in southern Europe, and the bark has been used to produce a yellow dye. Good for avenue and park plantings, where it will withstand much pollution, and is also very good close to coasts. It thrives on most soils, including very dry ones.

12|17 Mature height: 12-17m	Shape of mature tree	Coastal sites	Urban trees

CELTIS occidentalis
Hackberry

Although part of the Elm family, this tree is immune to Dutch elm disease. A native of North America, it makes a medium sized tree in the UK.

It is a vigorous tree with arching stems that support large heart shaped soft green leaves. At maturity the bark becomes corky and rough and the tree produces small black fruits in profusion. A great tree for parkland and estates, it thrives on most soils. In the States on deep fertile soils they have been known to reach 35 metres in height and live for over 200 years.

12|17 Mature height: 12-17m	Shape of mature tree	Parkland trees

CERCIDIPHYLLUM japonicum
Katsura Tree/Candyfloss Tree

The Katsura Tree was introduced from the Far East in the early 1880s and won the Award of Garden Merit in 2002. Often thought of as a small ornamental tree I stumbled across one in Rutland a few years ago that must have been over 20 metres tall. It is best grown away from frost pockets or exposed windy sites as new foliage can scorch before they harden.

Sometimes mistaken for Cercis siliquastrum, this has smaller leaves. It is sensational both in spring with emerging coppery green leaves and autumn when the foliage turns yellow or pink whilst exuding a fragrant scent reminiscent of burnt sugar. A great choice for gardens and parks, doing best on deep, fertile soils.

12|17 Mature height: 12-17m	Multi-stem	Shape of mature tree	Garden trees

CERCIS canadensis Forest Pansy

North American Redbud

A native of South Eastern Canada and Eastern USA, it is not as free flowering as Cercis siliquastrum but this clone makes up for it by its stunning deep red/purple leaf colour. Grown and supplied as either a standard tree or multi-stemmed specimen, we rate this as one of the best purple foliaged trees on the market. It won the Award of Garden Merit in 2002.

It makes a small tree of rounded habit and is ideal for sunny urban gardens and courtyards. It does best in free draining soils and like Cercis siliquastrum is slow to root so we recommend stakes to be retained for the first three years after planting. Flowers are a light pink and the autumn brings a luminescent red quality to the senescing leaves. A wonderful small garden tree.

5|10 Mature height: 5-10m | Shape of mature tree | Red/purple foliage

Like many trees with distinctly coloured leaves, full sun is needed to keep the leaf tone vivid. Too much shade dulls the leaf to a dark green. This tree is also keen on hot summer temperatures to encourage growth so south facing locations are a must for this clone.

CERCIS siliquastrum
Judas Tree

A most beautiful tree despite its association with Judas Iscariot. Introduced in the 16th century, it won the Award of Garden Merit in 2002. It is very slow to root so is one of the few trees we recommend to stake for up to three years after planting. A native of the Eastern Mediterranean, it is a must for any garden large enough to give it justice!

A stunning sight in May when clusters of rosy-lilac, pea-like flowers wreathe the wood, sometimes springing direct from mature branches and even from the trunk. These are followed by purple tinted seed pods from July onwards.

3|8		
Mature height: 3-8m	Shape of mature tree	Flowering trees

It slowly forms a well rounded tree, and is perfect for sunny urban gardens and courtyards, tolerating dry conditions well. It thrives on most soils, including very dry ones.

CERCIS siliquastrum Alba

Similar in every way to the traditional Judas Tree, but producing lovely ivory white flowers in May instead of the well-known rosy-lilac. It was awarded the Royal Horticulture Society's Award of Merit from a plant grown by the Wellcome Foundation at Langley Court in Kent.

Slow to root and establish but well worth the wait, it is always wise to stake for several years after planting to give time for the roots to anchor the tree in place.

3|8 Mature height: 3-8m | Shape of mature tree | Flowering trees

CHAMAECYPARIS lawsoniana Columnaris Glauca

Raised in Boskoop, Holland, in the 1940s, this small and narrow conical tree has enormous garden or parkland appeal.

Densely arranged ascending branches carry flattened foliage sprays which are greenish blue and pure blue on the growing tips. Many conifer clones of this type have come and gone over the years but this one has passed the test of time and remains one of the best blue conifers around for restricted areas. It thrives best on most soils, though it is not happy on wet ground.

5|7 Mature height: 5-7m | Shape of mature tree | Evergreen trees

CHAMAECYPARIS lawsoniana Stardust

Introduced from Holland in the 1960s, this outstanding yellow variety won the Award of Garden Merit in 2002.

Densely arranged branches carry flattened foliage sprays which are golden yellow and bronze on the growing tips. It is columnar in habit so suitable for most gardens and parks. It tolerates most soils although, like most Chamaecyparis, soils prone to water logging should be avoided.

5|7 Mature height: 5-7m | Shape of mature tree | Evergreen trees

CHAMAECYPARIS lawsoniana Yvonne

I liken this to the golden equivalent of 'columnaris Glauca'. Surely one of the most stunning golden uprights on the market, this clone is ideal for gardens and parks.

Ascending branches support green/gold sprays of foliage that are luminescent gold on the growing tips. Like others of its group, it dislikes water logged ground and thrives on well drained sunny sites. The overall habit is columnar so it is a great plant for restricted places.

5|7		
Mature height: 5-7m	Shape of mature tree	Evergreen trees

CHITALPA tashkentensis Summer Bells

A recent hybrid between Chilopsis and Catalpa. Original work on these pairings was undertaken at the Uzbek Academy of Science in Tashkent, Uzbekistan, in the 1960s before being introduced internationally in the mid 1970s.

This small hybrid with a rounded form initiates flower bud in June/July which open to produce an abundant display of frilly pink flowers with yellow throats for the rest of the summer. Best planted on well drained soils in full sun with protection from strong winds. Ideal for sheltered gardens and streets.

5|7		
Mature height: 5-7m	Shape of mature tree	Flowering trees

CLADRASTIS kentukia
Yellow Wood

Introduced from its native South Eastern USA in 1812, this lovely tree was given the Award of Merit in 1926 by the Royal Horticultural Society. Fragrant white flowers are produced in June, hanging in drooping panicles like a Wisteria. Compound alternate leaflets can accumulate to 25cm in length on the one stalk. Flowering can be hit and miss rather than consistent every year and is usually seen only on maturing specimens.

It grows on most well drained soils, including acid and alkaline, but is better to prune, if needed, in the summer as the wounds tend to weep if pruned in the winter or spring.

7|12		
Mature height: 7-12m	Shape of mature tree	Flowering trees

CLERODENDRUM trichotomum

It is a small tree, but a strong grower. White, strongly fragrant flowers, enclosed in maroon calyces, appear in August and September.

They are followed by bright blue berries and a glorious display of autumn foliage of luminescent reds to yellows. It thrives on most soils but is best to avoid wet and exposed sites. Although very hardy in England, it would be put to the test if subjected to colder and more northerly aspects of the UK.

3|8		
Mature height: 3-8m	Shape of mature tree	Flowering trees

Brought from China and Japan and in cultivation since the 1880s this highly interesting tree won the Royal Horticultural Society's First Class Certificate in 1893.

CORNUS alba Sibirica
Westonbirt Dogwood

This spectacular red stemmed dog wood rose to fame in the 1960s. Winter stem colour is one of the few ways to retain vivid interest in a garden for those dreary overcast months and the best way to promote this is to routinely coppice down to 5cm above ground level every March. If left to its own devices the red stem colour is restricted to the outer edges of the plant and the thicker older stems lose their lustre.

This great garden plant thrives on most soils and is particularly effective when planted in groups next to contrasting white birch varieties. Strictly more of a shrub than a tree, we have included this as it compliments so many others!

1|3		
Mature height: 1-3m	Multi-stem	Bark interest

CORNUS controversa
Wedding Cake Tree

This wonderful introduction from China and Japan has been grown in the UK since the 1880s and won the Award of Merit in 1984. One of the best specimens to look out for is at the Bath Botanic Garden. Wonderfully architectural, its striking form draws the eye through any garden.

A small to medium tree with a conical habit, its common name relates to the layered effect of its branches. Broad clusters of creamy flowers cover the branches in May. Small, black fruits develop in autumn as the foliage turns to a rich purple-red. Excellent for parks and gardens, it thrives on most soils.

5|7 Mature height: 5-7m | Shape of mature tree | Garden trees

CORNUS controversa Variegata

Introduced in the 1890s this variegated version of the Wedding Cake Tree is a sight to behold when seen at its full potential. It is far from easy, hence the fact you hardly ever see one, but planted in a sheltered spot with plenty of care and time it is uniquely beautiful.

Layered branches take shape from an early age that are characterised by the striking white to yellow margin of the otherwise green leaves. A winner of the Award of Garden Merit in 2002 it is far more sedate than its parent listed previously but well worth the wait.

3|5 Mature height: 3-5m | Shape of mature tree | Variegated trees

CORNUS Eddie's White Wonder

This is a cross between Cornus florida and Cornus nuttallii which has won a host of awards including the First Class Certificate, the Cory Cup, and the Award of Garden Merit. It has fallen out of favour in America, where it was raised, for not being as hardy as first thought but it is absolutely fine in the more temperate UK.

We supply this superb garden plant as a maturing bush which produces large white flower heads in the spring. It thrives on most soils but we do not recommend planting on alkaline or waterlogged ground. It forms a compact small garden tree at maturity.

3|5 Mature height: 3-5m | Multi-stem | Garden trees

CORNUS kousa China Girl

Introduced in the late 1970s and selected in Holland, this variety has large bracts, great autumn colour and good sized fruits. Plants as small as 40-60cm are capable of setting flower buds making this an ideal garden tree that exhibits lots of interest.

Flowers are borne in abundance in early spring and the foliage turns vivid colours by autumn. Supplied as a maturing bushy shrub, it will eventually make a small tree. Cornus kousa types do not thrive in alkaline soils, they just linger. Best only to plant on ground with a ph less than 7 and to avoid waterlogged or compacted soils.

3|5 Mature height: 3-5m | Multi-stem | Garden trees

CORNUS kousa Chinensis

Perhaps the most reliable of all flowering dogwoods. Bean reckoned the fruits were both sweet and edible but I think he was getting carried away by the glamour of the plant as believe me there are better things to eat.

This small, open tree flowers in June, the white bracts turning from soft green to white to pink and lining the upper sides of almost horizontal, slender branches. It goes on to give pink, arbutus-like berries and rich bronze and crimson autumn leaves. It prefers acid and well drained soils.

5|7			
Mature height: 5-7m	Shape of mature tree	Multi-stem	Garden trees

CORNUS kousa Milky Way

Selected from a seedbed in Ohio USA in the 1960s, this highly floriferous clone is considered to be one of the very best of its type.

We grow this as a multi-stem bush rather than as a standard tree as the flowers are so plentiful it is nice to view them from ground level upwards. Like all kousa types it does not thrive on alkaline soils. Ideal for small gardens or for centre pieces on estates.

3|5		
Mature height: 3-5m	Multi-stem	Garden trees

CORNUS kousa Stella Pink

It is not easy to grow a kousa type as a standard form but this delightful small garden tree lends itself to be grown with a single trunk and a dominant central leader. Raised by Dr Elwin Orton at Rutgers University, New Jersey in the late 1980s for its vigour and disease resistance.

The glossy leaves of this rounded tree turn a rich crimson-bronze in autumn. Remarkable for its pink, star-shaped bracts, this stunning clone is a marvel when it is in full flower. Very good for parks and gardens, but will not thrive on alkaline soils and waterlogged or compacted ground.

5|7		
Mature height: 5-7m	Shape of mature tree	Garden trees

CORNUS mas
Cornelian Cherry

Introduced in the late 1890s, the Cornelian Cherry gives a very long period of interest. A native of central and southern Europe, it won the Award of Merit in 1929.

From February onwards when the small, yellow flowers appear on the bare twigs this Cornus puts on a great display. The bright red, cherry-like fruits are edible, and the leaves turn a delightful reddish purple in autumn. Often grown as a multi-stem bush, we have managed to raise ours on a single stem to 1.8m with a well balanced and compact crown. A very good choice for parks and gardens, it thrives on most free draining soils.

3|8 Mature height: 3-8m | Shape of mature tree | Multi-stem | Flowering trees | Bee friendly trees

CORYLUS avellana
Hazel

The squirrel's favourite, also known as the cobnut or Filbert, this is our native Hazel. We supplied our neighbour with 34 plants in 2007 and this has now made a fantastic instant hedge that you can view when you visit Barcham.

A small tree with a rounded habit, it looks particularly striking in the early spring when it is adorned with its long yellow "lambs tail" catkins. The nuts in autumn aren't bad either! A very good choice for gardens, parks and woodlands. We supply this tree as a multi-stemmed coppiced specimen that makes a great under plant for a woodland or instant infill within a hedgerow.

Quick to grow, we recommend a five year cycle of coppicing down to only a few inches above ground level. This can be done in February March after the catkins finish and although you will sacrifice any fruiting potential for that year, you will end up with a more bushy and vibrant plant as a result.

3|8 Mature height: 3-8m	Multi-stem	Native trees	Hedging trees	Bee friendly trees

CORYLUS avellana Contorta
Corkskrew Hazel

This Hazel is also known as Harry Lauder's Walking Stick, after the Scottish music hall performer who had a trademark "twisted" walking stick. At maturity it looks like a quirky bonsai and the best example of this I have seen is in my mother's garden in Surrey.

A very small and slow growing tree that has strangely twisted and contorted branches which create a dense and rounded habit. It is believed to have been discovered in a Gloucestershire hedgerow in the 1860s. A real curiosity for parks and gardens. Small twiggy branches can be sympathetically removed and used to add interest to seasonal floral displays.

3|5 Mature height: 3-5m | Multi-stem | Garden trees | Bee friendly trees

CORYLUS avellana Zellernus

Also known as Red Filbert, this is a great improvement on Corylus maxima Purpurea. I have one in my garden that I coppice on a four yearly rotation to encourage the young red foliage to shine out in the spring.

This rounded and rather rare tree looks spectacular in spring when it is festooned with pink catkins set against its rich purple foliage that turns dark green by early summer. Delicious red Filbert nuts are an added bonus in the autumn. It is most attractive in gardens or parks and particularly effective when randomly scattered into a hedgerow.

As with Common Hazel, coppicing every five years invigorates the plant and keeps it bushy from ground level upwards.

3|5 Mature height: 3-5m | Multi-stem | Edible nuts | Bee friendly trees

CORYLUS colurna
Turkish Hazel

A splendid and truly beautiful tree from South East Europe and West Asia that was introduced in 1582 and won the Award of Garden Merit in 2002. It is large, imposing and rather columnar when young before broadening to a symmetrical pyramid on maturity. Notable for its roughly textured, corky bark, it produces long, yellow catkins in early spring and clusters of fringed nuts in autumn.

Turkish Hazel is a superb choice for parkland and avenue planting, and it will tolerate paved areas. It thrives in all soils, including chalky and clay soils and is now used in cities as a substitute for Lime to combat the problem of aphid drop on cars and pavements.

CORYLUS colurna
Te-Terra Red

This unusual sport of Turkish Hazel is smaller growing than its parent but far more striking. Fresh red coloured leaves emerge in the spring that harden to a purple green by mid summer. Pink catkins are produced in February / March and the young thickening trunk has a hint of purple about it before it matures to a rough textured brown.

This relatively slow growing clone makes a fine garden tree that gives lots of year-round interest. It will grow on most well drained soils. Red husks hold the promise of pink cobnuts but this tree is rarely fertile so they are for ornamental purposes only.

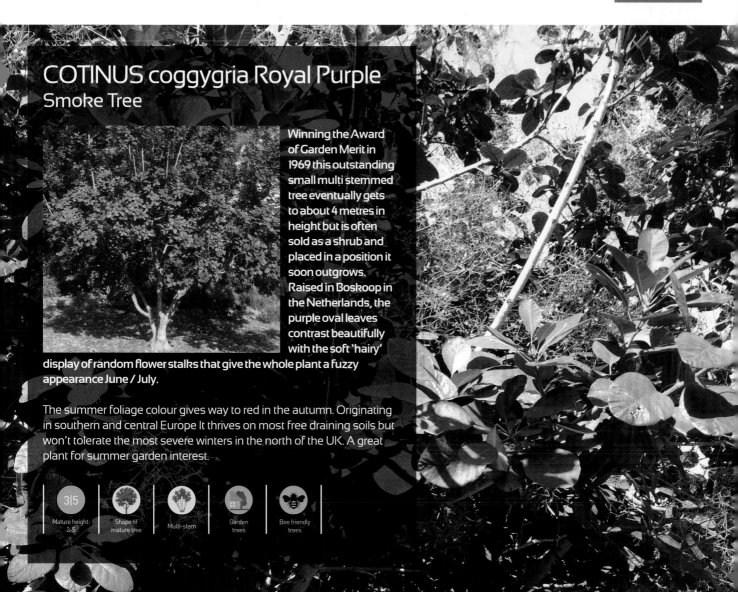

COTINUS coggygria Royal Purple
Smoke Tree

Winning the Award of Garden Merit in 1969 this outstanding small multi stemmed tree eventually gets to about 4 metres in height but is often sold as a shrub and placed in a position it soon outgrows. Raised in Boskoop in the Netherlands, the purple oval leaves contrast beautifully with the soft 'hairy' display of random flower stalks that give the whole plant a fuzzy appearance June / July.

The summer foliage colour gives way to red in the autumn. Originating in southern and central Europe It thrives on most free draining soils but won't tolerate the most severe winters in the north of the UK. A great plant for summer garden interest.

3|5 Mature height: 3-5	Shape of mature tree	Multi-stem	Garden trees	Bee friendly trees

COTONEASTER Cornubia

Raised at the famous Exbury Gardens in the early 1930s this versatile small tree won the Award of Garden Merit in 2002 and 1933 as well as the First Class Certificate in 1936. It is a particularly useful tree for stilted semi evergreen screening in small gardens where privacy is needed.

3|8 Mature height: 3-8m	Shape of mature tree	Urban trees

CRATAEGUS x grignonensis

This is a hybrid of Crataegus mexicana and has been in cultivation since the mid 1870s. In southern parts of Britain it can be considered as a semi evergreen making it a useful small tree for dappled screening.

This small tree of rounded habit is late both in flowering and in the ripening of its big, scarlet fruits. A good choice for urban and coastal planting it is also tolerant of air pollution. It does well in most soils, both wet and dry. The leaves are sometimes retained throughout winter if the weather is mild enough.

5|7 Mature height: 5-7m	Shape of mature tree	Garden trees	Bee friendly trees

CRATAEGUS laevigata Paul's Scarlet

This small hawthorn tree was a sport of Crataegus Rosea Flore Plena found in a Herefordshire garden in the 1850s. Probably the most popular of thorns on the market, it won both the First Class Certificate in 1858 and the Award of Garden Merit in 2002.

It becomes smothered in double, red flowers in May which are all the more stunning as the spring flowering cherries have finished their display by then. As root development can be rather slow, we recommend moderate pruning in the first few years after planting so that good anchorage is achieved. A good choice for urban and coastal planting, it is tolerant of air pollution. It does well in most soils, including very dry and wet soils.

5|7 Mature height: 5-7m	Shape of mature tree	Garden trees	Bee friendly trees

CRATAEGUS x lavalleei
Hybrid Cockspur Thorn

A small hawthorn tree which produces a dense crown of thorn clad branches that give rise to its trademark rounded habit at maturity. Originating back to the 1870s this fine tree won the Award of Garden Merit in 2002 and 1924.

The large white flowers are followed by orange haws, which are retained for most of the winter. The oval, glossy, leathery leaves persist until December, colouring from red through to yellow. As it is only slightly thorny, it makes a better street tree than most other hawthorns. A good choice for urban and coastal planting, it is tolerant of air pollution. It does well in most soils, including very dry and wet soils.

5|7 Mature height: 5-7m | Shape of mature tree | Urban trees | Bee friendly trees

CRATAEGUS x lavalleei Carrièrei

A hawthorn of garden origin, dating from around 1870, that won the Award of Garden Merit in both 1924 and 2002. This clone is particularly resistant against rust.

It makes a small, densely headed tree with glossy, deep green foliage which lasts through to December. The orange-red haws are also long lasting, often right through winter, and they contrast well with the dark foliage. A good choice for urban and coastal planting, it is also tolerant of air pollution. It does well in most soils, including very dry and wet soils. Like many clonal variations it is difficult to tell apart from its parent variety.

5|7 Mature height: 5-7m | Shape of mature tree | Urban trees | Bee friendly trees

CRATAEGUS monogyna
Common Hawthorn

Also known as Quickthorn or May, this small native hawthorn has many ancient associations and is most seen as hedgerow plants along the span of the UK. However we run it up to make a standard tree for specimen planting and it is without doubt one of our prettiest native trees.

The small white, fragrant flowers which appear in May and June are followed by small red fruits in abundance during autumn, providing much needed food for wild birds. A good choice for urban and coastal planting it is also tolerant of air pollution. It does well in most soils, including very dry and wet soils.

5|7 Mature height: 5-7m	Shape of mature tree	Native trees	Bee friendly trees

CRATAEGUS monogyna Alboplena

This small tree is very similar in most respects to Crataegus monogyna, but has double white flowers. It is worth remembering that while hawthorns are often seen as hedgerow trees, they also make fine garden trees and this is one of the best.

A good choice for urban and coastal planting it is also tolerant of air pollution. It does well in most soils, including very dry and wet soils. Originating back to the 1770s, many classify this as Crataegus laevigata Alba Plena but the differences are too close to call and as both are derivatives of native trees we choose to place it here.

5|7 Mature height: 5-7m	Shape of mature tree	Garden trees	Bee friendly trees

CRATAEGUS monogyna Stricta

A tough and durable hawthorn, ideal for exposed situations. Its dark green leaves and very regular habit make this a favourite for urban planners where space is at a premium. It thinks nothing of reflected heat and light bouncing off windows and pavements making it a very versatile native variation of the traditional hedgerow parent.

Very different from other hawthorns in that it has a columnar habit with tightly ascending branches, making it a very good prospect for both streets and small gardens. It is also a good choice for coastal planting and tolerant of salt laden winds. It does well on most ground, including very dry and wet soils.

5|7 Mature height: 5-7m	Shape of mature tree	Narrow trees	Bee friendly trees

CRATAEGUS x prunifolia
Broad-Leaved Cockspur Thorn

This small hawthorn is thornier than most others and won the Award of Garden Merit in 2002. It has wonderful autumn colour and is a winter provider for birds feasting on its profuse red fruits.

Sometimes referred to as Crataegus x persimilis, it is a hybrid between Crataegus crus galli and Crataegus macracantha and originates from Eastern America.

This small, compact, round-headed tree produces long sharp thorns along the span of its branches. The burnished, oval leaves, which turn a glorious red in autumn, are accompanied by plentiful small, red fruits. A good choice for urban and coastal planting, it is also tolerant of air pollution. It does well on most ground, including very dry and wet soils.

5|7			
Mature height: 5-7m	Shape of mature tree	Urban trees	Bee friendly trees

CRATAEGUS x prunifolia Splendens

A clonal selection of Crataegus prunifolia that is very similar to its parent in every way apart from its uniformity. Originating from Holland, it is ideal for both street verges and gardens and has all the inbuilt durability of its genera. It is a great tree for wildlife with birds especially benefitting from the abundant autumn crop of shiny red berries.

Wonderful red and golden autumn foliage is a striking feature of this small tree with a regular and rounded habit at maturity. It also has characteristic white flowers and shiny, leathery, oval leaves. A good choice for park and coastal planting it is also tolerant of air pollution. It does well in most soils, including very dry and wet soils. Be sure to crown lift the stem to 2 metres over time to keep the thorns out of reach.

This much underused tree requires little maintenance after establishment and is seldom seen in Garden Centres where 'Paul Scarlet' seems to dominate. It is a small tree of ultimate size that makes a wonderful garden tree offering spring flower, lovely berry colour and great autumnal colour.

CRYPTOMERIA japonica Elegans
Japanese Cedar

Introduced by Thomas Lobb from Japan in 1854, this beautiful bushy conifer eventually makes a small tree at maturity. Its wonderful texture and feathery appearance makes you want to touch it!

Evergreen feathery foliage turns bronze in winter and at this point many despair and make a phone call to us but this is all part of the annual show it performs. It tends to grow as wide as it does high but reacts well to pruning if necessary. It thrives in most soils though does not like water logged ground.

Japanese Cedar can be prone to dry out in the first year after planting before it has time to establish. Its dense foliage can end up deflecting rainfall away from the roots so be sure to water well at planting and once per month during the dormant season before stepping this up to once a week in its first full growing season.

It is such an unusual foliage plant that it provides wonderful contrast within a garden and many gardeners struggle to indentify it quite simply as it looks like nothing else!

3|8 Mature height: 3-8m | Shape of mature tree | Evergreen trees

CUPRESSUS arizonica Glauca

A selection of the Smooth Arizona Cypress, this striking conifer is a native of South Eastern America. I have seen this grown as a hedging conifer in Southern France and it positively glitters when it is filmed by a morning dew.

This medium to large evergreen conifer forms a dense, pyramidal habit at maturity with very distinctive rich brown bark that peels in flakes. Its deeply fragrant blue foliage is particularly attractive and its rounded cones swell in spring. Tolerant of air pollution, it is good for urban plantings and large gardens. It thrives on most soils.

12|17 Mature height: 12-17m | Shape of mature tree | Evergreen trees

CUPRESSUS macrocarpa Goldcrest

A British-bred form of the Monterey Cypress, raised by Treseder of Truro in the late 1940s, this spectacular conifer won the Award of Garden Merit in 2002. Its yellow colour is so vivid that it provides wonderful contrast to a dark landscape.

A medium size tree, and therefore much smaller than the species, Goldcrest has a narrow, columnar habit and rich yellow, feathery foliage. Certainly one of the best of its colour, it remains dense and compact. Very good for avenues, gardens and parks. It thrives on most soils.

12|17 Mature height: 12-17m | Shape of mature tree | Evergreen trees

CUPRESSUS sempervirens Italian Cypress

The Italian Cypress is surely one of the most beautiful and evocative trees in the world! If you ever get out to Tuscany or Umbria you will be well and truly hooked on this wonderful conifer.

The cypress of Mediterranean antiquity, and widely used in the Middle Ages to make chests because its pleasant smelling timber helped to keep clothes sweet. In Britain it is best to avoid cold, exposed sites for this architecturally columnar beauty, but it is a splendid choice for urban plantings and courtyard gardens. It does best in rich, fertile soils.

12|17 — Mature height: 12-17m | Shape of mature tree | Narrow trees

CUPRESSOCYPARIS leylandii
Leyland Cypress

Love it or loathe it, the Leyland Cypress is Europe's fastest growing conifer. It is a cross between Chamaecyparis nootkatensis and Cupressus macrocarpa and is probably Britain's most well known tree.

Unbeatable for screening, but rather too tall for most small gardens, this is a large, handsome tree with a dense, columnar habit. Single specimens and plantings in avenues show off this rather unfairly maligned conifer to best advantage. Very good for coastal plantings, where it tolerates salt laden winds. It does well in most soils, including chalk.

17|22			
Mature height: 20m+	Shape of mature tree	Hedging trees	Evergreen trees

The trick to taming Leylandii is to prune once per year without fail in the spring but if you miss even one year it can get away from you, so fast is its growth. Once a hedge has grown too big for its surrounds there is no going back as pruning into old wood will leave it bare and patchy. The height of your hedge is usually set by how far you want to stand on a step ladder and if done correctly a Leylandii hedge is hard to beat for year round privacy.

CUPRESSOCYPARIS leylandii Castlewellan

Golden Leyland Cypress

The Golden Leyland Cypress is often considered more amenable than the green leaved form though in Ireland it has been so overplanted there is a lobby for making future plantings illegal! However, this is not the trees fault and it remains an excellent choice for evergreen hedging.

Slower growing and rather more useful for hedging than its green parent, it is also rather smaller and the pale golden foliage adds to the interest of this attractive seedling, which was raised in County Down in the early 1960s. Very good for coastal plantings, where it tolerates salt laden winds. It does well in most soils, including chalk.

12|17			
Mature height: 12-17m	Shape of mature tree	Hedging trees	Evergreen trees

CYDONIA oblonga

Quince

This recent introduction to our range has proved very popular, especially as fruit trees are exempt from the dreaded VAT! This small genus of trees is related to the better known Chaenomeles and produces golden yellow fragrant fruit that hold on the tree for several weeks if left unpicked.

Native of south west Asia, it is fine to be grown in the UK and forms into a small rounded tree sometimes tipping 20 feet in height. Autumn leaf colour is a good and reliable yellow. It does best in south facing sheltered gardens and benefits from a free draining nutritious soil.

5|7			
Mature height: 5-7m	Shape of mature tree	Edible fruits	Bee friendly trees

DAVIDIA involucrata
Handkerchief Tree, Dove Tree

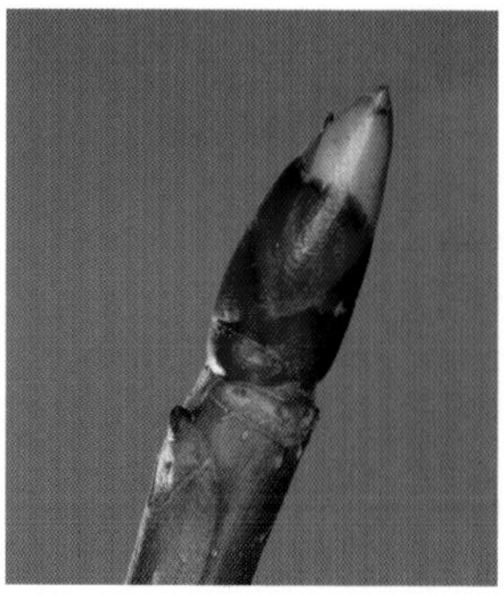

Whether known as the Handkerchief Tree or Dove Tree, it is well-named and much-loved. Discovered in China by Père David in 1869 and introduced in 1904, this is one of the great beauties of the plant world. The variety 'Vilmoriniana' is often specified but there is little or nothing to choose between this and its parent.

Its common names derive from the large white bracts which appear in May. These are followed by large, oval fruits in autumn. Foliage and habit are similar to those of the lime. A medium to large tree, it is very good for parks and does best in a fairly sheltered position. On a historical note, it first flowered in England in 1911 on Vieitch's Coombe Wood Nursery. It thrives best on deep fertile soil.

I first saw this tree at Kew's sister garden Wakehurst Place in Sussex. It was in full flower and even though the tree was still relatively young it was mighty impressive.

Difficult and slow to grow from a young age, it seems to thrive when beyond 8-10 feet tall. For every hundred we grow only 20 or so come through as saleable which explains its price tag!

12|17
Mature height: 12-17m

Shape of mature tree

Parkland trees

From our experience of growing this tree in the Fens it is clear that it thrives best on less exposed sites and is best pruned lightly in the summer rather than when it is dormant in the winter. Growing tips can frost off if subjected to icy winds and invariably the best specimens are seen nestled away in a comfy sheltered spot.

EUCALYPTUS debeuzevillei

Jounama Snow Gum

One of the hardiest of all Eucalyptus, being a native of the high mountains of south east Australia, it is also one of the most dramatic. As a point of interest, grab hold of its leaves on a hot summer's day and you will immediately notice how cold they are. This is true of all Eucalyptus; they are nature's air conditioning units!

A medium sized tree of broadly pyramidal form, it has a beautiful white patchwork trunk and thick lanceolate evergreen leaves. A superb specimen for both parks and gardens, it produces stunning and unexpected dandelion clock like flowers from mid summer straight from its branches. It thrives on most soils.

Mature height: 12-17m | Shape of mature tree | Bark interest

This wonderfully dramatic tree has so much year round interest that it should be considered more often for large gardens and municipal parks and verges. Its foliage provides great contrast within the landscape and always seems to draw the eye. Interestingly, Eucalyptus does not have a dormancy period and carries on growing, very slowly, even in the winter months.

EUCALYPTUS gunnii
Cider Gum

This Gum is a native of the highlands of Tasmania and Australia and was introduced to the UK in the mid 1850s. A winner of the Award of Garden Merit in both 2002 and 1950, this striking tree is also well suited to being grown as a multi-stemmed coppiced specimen.

A very well known Eucalyptus - and a very hardy one - this large, broadly pyramidal tree has smooth grey-pink to red-brown bark. The young leaves are grey-green and glaucous providing a wonderful contrast to gardens and municipal landscapes. For those florists amongst you, the foliage is particularly good to compliment cut flower arrangements. It thrives on most soils.

When faced with selecting Eucalyptus never be tempted to go for the biggest and probably most pot bound. A strange physiology comes into play in that when Eucalyptus roots spiral they tend to carry on that way and are prone to falling over through lack of anchorage over time. This is a particular problem exasperated by trees grown in black pots.

12|17		
Mature height: 12-17m	Shape of mature tree	Garden trees

EUCALYPTUS niphophila
Snow Gum

A well known and lovely Eucalyptus with attractive grey, green and cream patchwork bark. A winner of the Award of Garden Merit in 2002.

Its leaves are narrow and grey-green when matured and it is well suited as a specimen tree to provide lovely soft contrast in parks and large gardens. It is slower growing than the more common Eucalyptus gunnii but it forms such a pleasing architectural shape of superb patchwork stems it is hard to beat. If the decision was forced upon me I would choose this as a multi-stem and Eucalyptus debeuzevillei as a single stem as they are both superb trees!

12|17		
Mature height: 12-17 m	Shape of mature tree	Garden trees

EUCOMMIA ulmoides
Rubber Tree

Introduced at the very end of the 1800s, this Chinese tree is actually capable of producing rubber through very fine latex produced within their green glossy leaves. It forms a broadly pyramidal shape at maturity and will thrive on most free draining and fertile soils. This tree is quite unusual for the UK so is quite an interesting selection to throw into the mix for an arboretum as not many can identify it!

It prefers full sun but is fully hardy down to about -20 degrees Celsius once mature. Its flower and seed is hardly worthy of notice but its lustrous leathery leaves are lovely in the summer.

12|17 Mature height: 12-17m | Shape of mature tree | Parkland trees

EUODIA hupehensis

A small genus and a must for any collector with an arboretum. Others list this as Tetradium daniellii but it is the same tree, caught up in a botanical debate to confuse everyone. Native of China and Korea, it was introduced into the UK in 1905 and won the First Class Certificate in 1976.

Its compound leaves and panicles of small white flowers make this an attractive specimen tree that is excellent for shallow chalk soils. Bright red fruits are borne on female trees in the autumn. The flowers are characterised by lovely yellow anthers and are pleasingly fragrant. Autumn colour is a pale yellow.

12|17 Mature height: 12-17m | Shape of mature tree | Parkland trees

EUONYMOUS europaeus Red Cascade

A good choice even on chalky soils. This wonderful garden tree won the Award of Garden Merit in both 1949 and 2002. It has so much interest from September onwards that it is one of my favourite trees for a small garden. Named 'Red Caps' in America, this clone was selected by the University of Nebraska for the richness in colour of its fruits.

This small, arching tree produces an abundance of rosy red fruits which open up to reveal vivid orange seed cases. The foliage display in the autumn is fantastic with green leaves turning into rich red foliage by November. It is one of the very best forms for gardens, parks and restricted areas. It thrives on most soils though avoid waterlogged ground.

3|8		
Mature height: 3-8m	Shape of mature tree	Garden trees

FAGUS orientalis Iskander

Oriental Beech was first introduced into the UK in 1904 but 86 years later saw this fantastic new selection coming through. The leaves of Iskander are crisper, shinier and slightly larger than those of Fagus sylvatica but the defining difference is that it is far more resistant to woolly aphid, the bane of our native Beech which sucks and distorts new leaves throughout the spring and summer.

It has a great upright habit akin to Fagus sylvatica Dawyck but somehow Iskander just looks more vigorous and healthier! On its own you may not recognize that it is not the native clone which is a good thing as it slips into our landscape seamlessly. The lush green leaves turn to yellow in the autumn and its dead leaves can hold for sometime in the tree until the wind eventually blows them away. Great for either city verges or gardens, this new introduction is a lovely addition to our range. I estimate its mature width to be only 5 metres or so.

12|17		
Mature height: 12-17m	Shape of mature tree	Garden trees

FAGUS sylvatica
Common Beech

One of the most majestic of our native trees, the Common Beech can become very large with its low branched habit. My favourite specimen is in a private garden in North Luffenham, Rutland and what a beauty it is!

It has a wide range of uses in woodland, parkland and in broad verge plantings and few trees can surpass its rich, copper autumn foliage. Beech thrives just about anywhere other than exposed and coastal locations. As it is shallow rooted, under planting is not recommended. It does well in most reasonably fertile, well drained soils, except heavy clay or light sand.

Beech tends to favour more temperate climates and is difficult to establish when faced with extreme heat and drought. With this in mind avoid planting in paved or tarmac areas where reflected heat and light makes Beech suffer.

17|22				
Mature height: 17-22m	Shape of mature tree	Parkland trees	Hedging trees	Native trees

Sometimes referred to as Fagus sylvatica Heterophylla, it is in fact the same thing. There are few cut leaf trees that last the test of time but this is surely one of the best. The key for planting is to give it the space it merits at maturity, a minimum ten metre radius.

FAGUS sylvatica Asplenifolia
Cut-Leaved Beech

The common name of Cut-leaved Beech comes from the deeply serrated and long leaves of this beautiful tree of medium height. Introduced in the early 1800s, this wonderful specimen tree won the Award of Garden Merit in 2002.

It is pyramidal in its early years, but is eventually capable of becoming as wide as it is tall. A lovely choice for parkland where its cut leaves gives magnificent contrast. Beech thrives just about anywhere other than exposed and coastal locations. As it is shallow rooted, under planting is not recommended. It does well in most reasonably fertile, well drained soils, except heavy clay or light sand.

12|17 Mature height: 12-17m | Shape of mature tree | Parkland trees

FAGUS sylvatica Black Swan

There are several Dutch clones of purple foliaged weepers but this one is the pick of them for habit and leaf colour. The leaf size is slightly larger than a rival clone, Purple Fountain, and they emerge deep red before hardening to a rich purple by mid summer. Even though this is a true weeper, this tree remains fairly narrow so is great for gardens as well as parks.

It thrives on most free draining soils and its dark foliage and weeping branches gives excellent contrast within the landscape. Unlike other clones, there is nothing wishy washy about its foliage display which can harden to a black side of purple by late summer.

Mature height: 12-17m

Shape of mature tree

Garden trees

FAGUS sylvatica Dawyck

Fastigiate Beech

The Fastigiate Beech   a rather ugly name for a rather beautiful tree! Originating in Dawyck, Scotland, in the mid 1800s, this architectural beauty won the Award of Garden Merit in 2002. There are some wonderful specimens planted by some of the university colleges in Cambridge.

This medium to large tree has a columnar habit and is a very good choice for both wide verges and specimen plantings in parks. Even when mature, it is seldom more than 3m wide. Beech thrives just about anywhere other than exposed and coastal locations. As it is shallow rooted, under planting is not recommended.

Mature height: 12-17m

Shape of mature tree

Narrow trees

FAGUS sylvatica Dawyck Gold

A golden-leaved form of the Fastigiate Beech. It is thought to be a seedling cross between Fagus sylvatica Dawyck and Fagus sylvatica Zlatia and was raised by JRP van Hoey-Smith in 1969. A real architectural beauty and winner of the Award of Garden Merit in 2002.

A fairly large, columnar tree, which looks good from spring right through to autumn. In spring the leaves are golden yellow, turning pale green in summer before reverting to a golden yellow in autumn. It looks especially attractive planted against a dark background and is good as a specimen in parks and as a verge tree.

12|17 Mature height: 12-17m | Shape of mature tree | Narrow trees

Beech thrives just about anywhere other than exposed and coastal locations. As it is shallow rooted, under planting is not recommended. It does well in most reasonably fertile, well drained soils, except heavy clay or light sand.

FAGUS sylvatica Dawyck Purple

A Fastigiate Beech with stunning dark foliage. Raised from the same seed source as Dawyck Gold in 1969 from a Dawyck at Trompenburg Arboretum near Rotterdam in Holland, it won the Award of Garden Merit in both 1973 and 2002. It remains a rare but stunning architectural specimen tree.

A little narrower than Dawyck Gold but not quite as dense. It makes a splendid tree for parks and verges and has striking, deep purple foliage. Beech thrives just about anywhere other than exposed and coastal locations. As it is shallow rooted, under planting is not recommended. It does well in most reasonably fertile, well drained soils, except heavy clay or light sand.

12|17 Mature height: 12-17m | Shape of mature tree | Narrow trees

FAGUS sylvatica Pendula
Weeping Beech

The Weeping Beech is a wonderful choice as a specimen in parks and large estates. Introduced in the mid 1830s, this stately tree won the Award of Garden Merit in 2002. Mature specimens have been known to weep to the ground and then layer up from the soil to weep again when a new trunk is formed. With this in mind they can get pretty big over the long term!

This medium to large tree has a majestic crown with large, horizontal and pendulous branches which gives the tree a unique architectural beauty. Beech thrives just about anywhere other than exposed and coastal locations.

12|17 Mature height: 12-17m | Shape of mature tree | Parkland trees

FAGUS sylvatica Purpurea
Purple Beech

The Purple Beech is one of our most beautiful trees. A superb tree for creating contrast in a parkland or large garden as the darkness of the foliage draws the eye through the landscape. With this in mind it is useful to plant this on the perimeter of your area. If it is too close in view you never notice beyond it.

This large, rather conical tree with its dark purple leaves is sometimes wrongly referred to as "Copper Beech", which is seed grown and variable in leaf colour.

17|22			
Mature height: 17-22m	Shape of mature tree	Hedging trees	Red/purple foliage

This cultivar has a much deeper purple leaf, and is a tree of great beauty and majesty. It makes a magnificent subject planted as a specimen in parks and large estates. Beech thrives just about anywhere other than exposed and coastal locations. As it is shallow rooted, under planting is not recommended. It does well in most reasonably fertile, well drained soils, except heavy clay or light sand.

FAGUS sylvatica Rohanii

Thought to be a cross between Fagus sylvatica Quercifolia and Purpurea, this extremely pretty tree is relatively rare but highly prized. Introduced in the mid 1890s, we only ever have a few to sell every year so if you wanted one for your collection it would be best to reserve in good time!

Perhaps best described as a purple leaved form of Fagus sylvatica Asplenifolia, this slow growing, small, pyramidal tree is perfect for parks and large open spaces. Beech thrives just about anywhere other than exposed and coastal locations. As it is shallow rooted, under planting is not recommended. It does well in most reasonably fertile, well drained soils, except heavy clay or light sand.

12|17		
Mature height: 12-17m	Shape of mature tree	Parkland trees

FAGUS sylvatica Zlatia

First discovered in Serbia in 1890, this selection is rarely seen in the UK. Its claim to fame is a wonderful spring flush of yellow foliage that hardens to a yellow green by late summer before turning to yellow once again in the autumn. It forms a rounded habit at maturity and is smaller growing than Fagus sylvatica.

Thriving on most free draining soils, it gives great contrast, especially against a dark backdrop. There aren't many yellows on the market so this is a nice addition to this range. We generally leave this clone fully branches to show off its golden leaves to the full and it is a good choice for large gardens and parkland.

12|17		
Mature height: 12-17m	Shape of mature tree	Parkland trees

FICUS carica
Common Fig

A native of Western Asia, this well known fruiting tree was introduced into the UK in the early 16th century. It is remarkably resistant to pest and disease and can be grown for either its foliage or fruit as both add ornamental interest to a south facing garden. We grow the variety Ficus carica 'Nero' for its lovely shape and vigour as well as its rich fruits as a half standard and Ficus carica Verdino as a full standard.

It makes a small and elegant tree with a rounded habit that does best in a warm, sheltered position, producing its green fruits by early August. Perfect for gardens or where space is restricted and often grown up against south facing walls to maximize fruiting potential.

3|8		
Mature height: 3-8m	Shape of mature tree	Edible fruits

F

FRAXINUS

Sadly this much loved genus has fallen foul of disease imported from Europe. The Government served an importation ban on all Fraxinus in October 2012 which also restricts any movement of the genus within the UK. We culled the last of our Fraxinus in November 2014 having once grown and sold over 6,000 per year.

Ash Die Back (Chalara fraxinea) may cause a huge shift in our treescape over the coming years as this very common tree diminishes. The important thing is that lessons are learnt to prevent this from happening again. Diversity is the key to a healthy tree population as a reliance on one genus places a massive risk once a pest takes a hold. Importing trees direct from the continent without quarantine is also asking for trouble.
Rather than stripping out their listing completely I have included the clones of this genus as footnotes:

FRAXINUS americana Autumn Purple
Great autumn colour, selected in America in 1956.
Mature height: 12-17m

FRAXINUS angustifolia Raywood
Introduced from Australia in the mid 1920s. Superb autumn colour but prone to limb collapse when older.
Mature height: 12-17m

FRAXINUS excelsior Common Ash
Tough native tree, very free seeding which may prove its savour. Huge genetic diversity may give rise to resistance against Ash Die Back in the years to come.
Mature height: 12-17m

FRAXINUS excelsior Altena
Forestry Commission introduction in the 1940s, selected for its uniform pyramidal habit.
Mature height: 12-17m

FRAXINUS excelsior Diversifolia One-leaved Ash
Introduced in the 1780s. Tough with single rather than compound leaves.
Mature height: 12-17m

FRAXINUS excelsior Jaspidea Golden Ash
Introduced in the late and particularly susceptible to Chalara. Golden stems.
Mature height: 12-17m

FRAXINUS excelsior Pendula Weeping Ash
Introduced in the 1700s, a fine weeping tree at maturity.
Mature height: 12-17m

FRAXINUS excelsior Westhofs Glorie
Introduced in the mid 1950s and widely planted since then. As this is a clonal selection there is a high risk that Ash Die Back will take all.
Mature height: 12-17m

FRAXINUS ornus Manna Ash, Flowering Ash
Introduced before 1700. Lovely flowers in late spring.
Mature height: 12-17m

FRAXINUS ornus Arie Peters
Dutch clone, selected for its enhanced flower.
Mature height: 12-17m

FRAXINUS ornus Louisa Lady
Selected for its enhanced flower and autumn colour.
Mature height: 12-17m

FRAXINUS ornus Meczek
Introduced from Hungary in the early 1980s.
Top grafted dwarfing type.
Mature height: 3-8m

FRAXINUS ornus Obelisk
Selected for its columnar habit.
Mature height: 12-17m

FRAXINUS pennsylvanica Summit
Introduced from trials in Minnesota in 1957.
Fast growing and a tough urban tree.
Mature height: 12-17m

GINKGO biloba
Maidenhair Tree

Very common about 200 million years ago, this marvellous gymnosperm is making a comeback as an urban tree due to its no nonsense toughness.

As it survived the radiation and devastation that wiped out 90% of all life when the comet fell to end the reign of the dinosaurs, it can cope well with traffic exhaust as well as reflected heat and light in our urban environments! Reintroduced into the UK from prehistoric times in 1754.

This large, conical tree remains relatively narrow if the central dominant leader is retained. Female plants fruit after 35 years or so and it is not possible to determine the gender until this event. Male clones such as Mayfield, Saratoga and Tremonia are disappointing in their lack of vigour. Lakeview and Princeton Sentry are the pick of the male types but remain difficult to grow, rarely come to market and command a tidy premium.

17|22 Mature height: 17-22m | Shape of mature tree | Urban trees

It is a good choice for parks and avenues, tolerating paved areas well. It has a deep root system, and curious, fan shaped leaves.

GINKGO biloba Nanum

Top worked on Ginkgo biloba stem at 2m this spherical dwarfing shrub form makes as ideal little tree on sites that are too restricted to accommodate a more conventional choice.

Particularly useful for narrow city streets, this clone is well suited to deal with the reflected heat and light that bounces off pavements and buildings. It also copes with urban pollution making this clone a useful addition to the Ginkgo range.

3|8 Mature height: 3-8m | Shape of mature tree | Urban trees

GLEDITSIA triacanthos
Honey Locust

A wonderful choice for heavily polluted environments prone to vandalism. Introduced from America in 1700, its seed pods hold a sticky sweet resin from which it derives its common name.

This large, oval and rather elegant tree has leaves which resemble fronds. When mature, it looks most striking with its shiny, long seed pods. A good choice for parks and industrial areas, it does well in most soils. Be careful on handling this tree as it is very thorny!

12|17 Mature height: 12-17m | Shape of mature tree | Parkland trees

GLEDITSIA triacanthos Draves Street Keeper

This urban clone has been bred in the USA for its form: it grows half as wide as it does tall. Gleditzia can be a rather messy looking tree but this clone is far more suitable for the urban street scene and large garden. Mostly thornless, the leaves are darker green than Skyline and turn the same vivid yellow in the autumn.

Thriving on most soils, this tough tree was discovered just outside New York by Tom Draves who monitored it for twenty years before releasing the clone into commercial production.

12|17 Mature height: 12-17m	Shape of mature tree	Urban trees

GLEDITSIA triacanthos Inermis
Thornless Common Honey Locust

For those tree surgeons among you this is a far better bet than seedling Gleditsia triacanthos for climbing and pruning as you haven't got to contend with the numerous vicious 3-5cm thorns.

Otherwise, it has the same attributes as the preceding listing and makes a useful choice for hard built up areas or a graceful inclusion for parkland.

12|17 Mature height: 12-17m	Shape of mature tree	Urban trees

GLEDITSIA triacanthos Skyline

One of the toughest and most reliable Honey Locust on the market, this American clone is both thornless and near fruitless as well as being very cold tolerant. Its lime green leaves turn a remarkable showy yellow in the autumn and its pyramidal habit makes it a genuinely robust urban tree.

It is not best suited on heavier soils but thrives on well drained ones and usefully it is very tolerant of drought once established. It also copes well with reflected heat and light bouncing off pavements and buildings making it a fine prospect for inner city planting.

12|17 Mature height: 12-17m	Shape of mature tree	Urban trees

GLEDITSIA triacanthos Sunburst

Although originally from moist and even swampy areas, the Honey Locust does well in much drier and free draining soils. Introduced in the mid 1950s it won the Award of Garden Merit in 2002. It is one of the best yellow foliaged trees on the market.

This medium to large cultivar has the advantage of being thornless. It has a rounded, rather spreading form and its yellow foliage, which appears late, is retained for most of the summer. We recommend it as a very good substitute for the more brittle Robinia pseudoacacia Frisia.

12|17 Mature height: 12-17m | Shape of mature tree | Yellow foliage

GYMNOCLADUS dioica
Kentucky Coffee Tree

The Kentucky Coffee Tree is surely one of the most handsome of all trees. The seeds were used as a substitute for coffee beans by the early settlers in North America but are thought to be poisonous if not roasted first. The exact introduction date is vague but it is thought to have been planted in the UK since the 1750s.

This slow growing tree of medium to large size has large, compound leaves, which are pink tinged in spring and clear yellow in autumn. The young twigs are pale grey, almost white, and particularly noticeable in winter. A wonderful choice for parks.

12|17 Mature height: 12-17m | Shape of mature tree | Parkland trees

HAMAMELIS x intermedia Arnold Promise

Witch Hazel

Raised and introduced by the Arnold Arboretum in the USA, this clone is internationally recognised as being one of the best of the yellow flowering Witch Hazels. I have had one in my garden since 2004 and it never fails to perform.

The original plant in the States is about 7 metres high and wide. It produces magnificent clear yellow flowers contrasting against red inners that last sometimes as long as two months without fading. It is all the more beautiful for being winter flowering.

3|8 Mature height: 3-8m | Multi-stem | Autumn colour

HAMAMELIS x intermedia Jelena

Unusually we grow this as a half standard rather than the more usual bush. This beautiful flowerer, coppery red towards the base, orange in the middle and yellow at the tips, is a great addition for a garden or municipal shrubbery. Early flower is so welcome when we are all longing for Spring!

Great autumn colours of yellow through to red also distinguish this Belgium introduction that was awarded the Award of Merit by the Royal Horticultural Society in 1955. It thrives on most free draining soils and I have even got one going in a sheltered coastal location.

3|8 Mature height: 3-8m | Shape of mature tree | Autumn colour | Garden trees | Flowering trees

HIBISCUS x Resi

We have dropped all our Hibiscus syriacus clones in preference to this one, a parmutabilis and syriacus cross selected for its early flowering and superb sized lavender coloured blossoms. As Hibiscus flowers off new season's growth, it is always worth a hard winter prune to stimulate future shoot development.

This clone is hardier, stronger, more free flowering and less nutritionally demanding than syriacus types so is perfect for a small garden or urban piazza. It flowers from late July to the end of September when most other displays have quietened. Its maple shaped leaves turn to yellow in the autumn.

3|5

Mature height:

Shape of

Flowering

ILEX x altaclerensis Golden King

One of the very best golden variegated hollies. It was derived from a cutting of Ilex x Hendersonii in Edinburgh in 1884. It won the First Class Certificate in 1898 and the Award of Garden Merit in 2002.

Tolerant of coastal conditions and air pollution, this medium, slow growing tree of pyramidal form has vivid golden margins to its virtually spineless leaves. Very good for gardens, female, with reddish-brown fruits.

3|8			
Mature height: 3-8m	Shape of mature tree	Variegated foliage	Evergreen trees

ILEX aquifolium Common Holly

One of the most evocative and best loved of all trees; the Common Holly is beautiful in its simplicity and brings cheer at the darkest time of year. It is very tolerant of shade and prefers well drained soils.

This native of Britain is a small, conical, evergreen tree which provides year-round interest, but is particularly attractive in autumn and winter. Great for gardens, it only retains its spiky leaves within the first ten feet of height in the tree, as after this point it suffers no predation so has no need for a thorny defence.

3|8			
Mature height: 3-8m	Shape of mature tree	Native trees	Evergreen trees

ILEX aquifolium Alaska

A great clone of common Holly with spiky, dark, glossy foliage. We grow this variety as a single stemmed full standard tree ideal for either specimen planting or for spot screening. Female.

The dark evergreen foliage contrasts well with the vivid red berries that are produced in the autumn. It retains an upright pyramidal habit and is a useful tree for screening in gardens. Tolerant of shade and prefers well drained soils.

3|8 Mature height: 3-8m | Shape of mature tree | Evergreen trees

ILEX aquifolium Argentea Marginata

Broad-Leaved Silver Holly

This lovely clone won the Award of Garden Merit in 2002. Ideal for hedging or specimen planting, it prefers free draining soils and is tolerant of shade.

It is a most dramatic small tree with spiny leaves, edged with white, and plenty of berries for winter and wildlife interest. Young growth is tinged pink. Slow growing and female.

3|8 Mature height: 3-8m | Shape of mature tree | Variegated foliage | Evergreen trees

ILEX aquifolium J C Van Tol

This self pollinating Holly is in our opinion one of the best green leaved bush Hollies on the market. It won the Award of Garden Merit in 2002 and for those of you who like making up Christmas wreaths this is the clone for you!

This vigorous cultivar has very dark, shiny, almost spineless leaves and a good show of autumn berries. It remains a small tree with a good pyramidal form. Excellent for gardens, it prefers well draining soils and is tolerant of shade.

3|8 Mature height: 3-8m | Shape of mature tree | Evergreen trees

ILEX aquifolium Pyramidalis

This fast growing Holly has apically dominant growth and is self pollinating. A winner of the Award of Merit in 1989 and the Award of Garden Merit in 2002, it makes a great evergreen tree for gardens where space is restricted.

This clone has smooth leaves and retains a pyramidal shape if the leader is sustained. Plenty of red berries in the autumn compliment its bright green evergreen leaves. It is tolerant of shade and prefers free draining soils.

3|8 Mature height: 3-8m	Shape of mature tree	Evergreen trees

ILEX castaneifolia
Sweet Chestnut-Leaved Holly

A great favourite at Barcham, this female Holly is a vigorous grower and won the Award of Garden Merit in 2002. It is a form of Ilex x koehneana and is thought to be of French origin.

Its thick green leaves are large and resemble the shape and form of Castanea sativa from which it derives its name. Its good apical dominance produces a medium to large tree of conical habit. Red berries are produced in abundance in the autumn and it is tolerant of shade. Like all hollies it will thrive on most soils so long as they are well drained.

3|8 Mature height: 5-10m	Shape of mature tree	Privacy raised screening	Evergreen trees

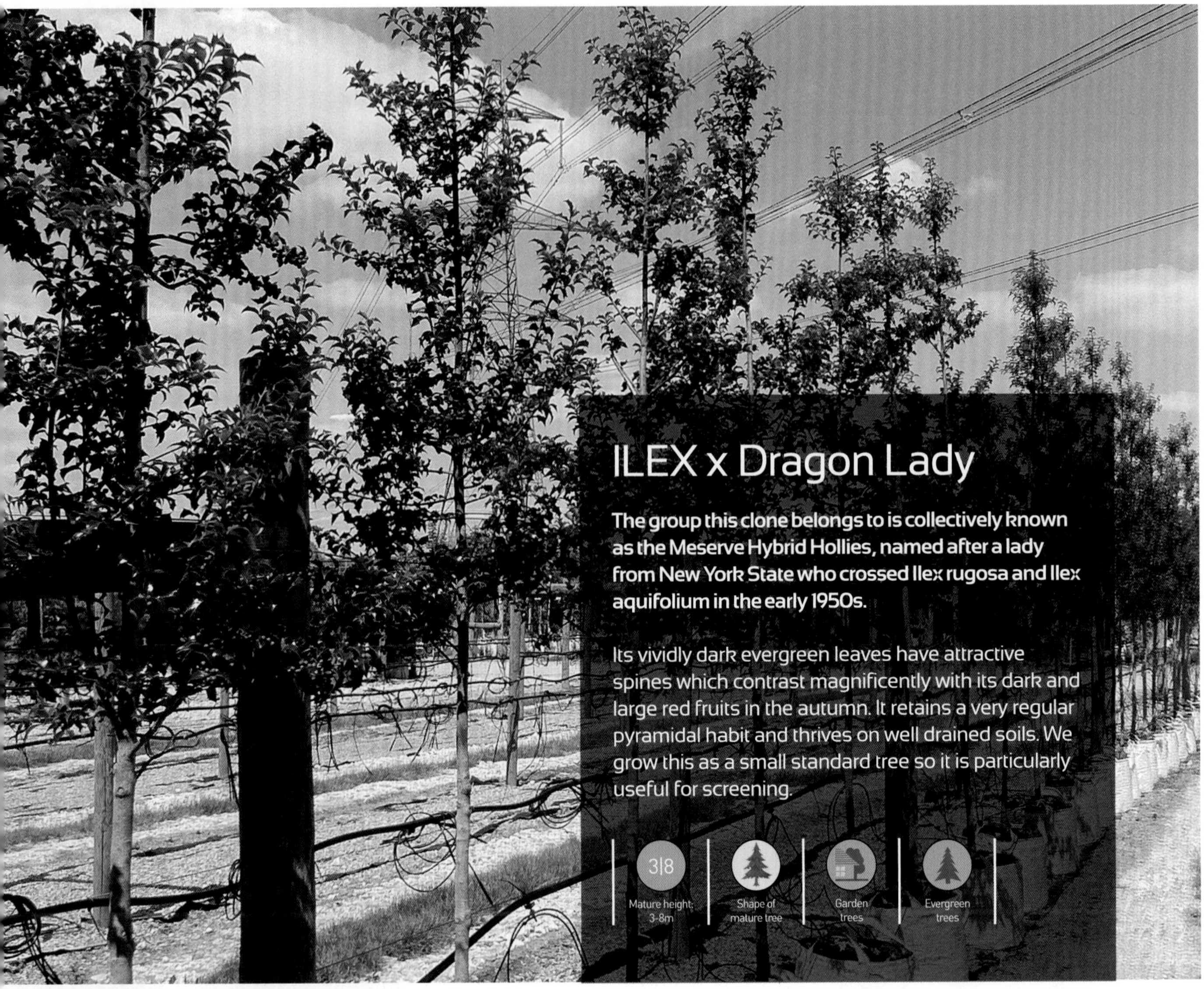

ILEX x Dragon Lady

The group this clone belongs to is collectively known as the Meserve Hybrid Hollies, named after a lady from New York State who crossed Ilex rugosa and Ilex aquifolium in the early 1950s.

Its vividly dark evergreen leaves have attractive spines which contrast magnificently with its dark and large red fruits in the autumn. It retains a very regular pyramidal habit and thrives on well drained soils. We grow this as a small standard tree so it is particularly useful for screening.

3|8			
Mature height: 3-8m	Shape of mature tree	Garden trees	Evergreen trees

ILEX x Nellie Stevens

This clone was derived from a seed source collected by Ms Stevens in 1900 from the US National Arboretum. It is a hybrid between Ilex aquifolium and Ilex cornuta and is exceptional for its vigour and readiness to make a small single stemmed tree.

Smooth dark glossy leaves contrast well with the orange-red berries in autumn and we supply this cone as a feathered bush or as a clear stemmed standard at semi mature. Ideal for spot screening and it tolerates most free draining soils. Female.

3|8			
Mature height: 3-8m	Shape of mature tree	Privacy raised screening	Evergreen trees

JUGLANS nigra
Black Walnut

Introduced from native central and eastern America into Europe in 1629, this fast growing tree won the Award of Garden Merit in 2002. The national US champion stands at 44 metres high by 47 metres wide in Oregon so not one to be planted in restricted places.

It makes a large tree with a broadly pyramidal crown and is a very good choice for parkland settings. It produces an abundance of nuts over a long period, but they are rather difficult to extract from their very hard shells. Rough barked from a young age so easily distinguished from the smooth barked Juglans regia. It grows on most soils but thrives on deep loam.

17|22		
Mature height: 17-22m	Shape of mature tree	Edible nuts

JUGLANS regia
Common Walnut

A native of South Eastern Europe, Himalaya and China, this well known tree is highly prized for its timber. It makes a splendid and stately subject for parkland and avenue plantings, developing a broad crown at maturity and preferring full sun. Thought to have been in cultivation in the UK since Roman times.

Slow growing and of medium to large stature, this rounded Walnut has delightfully aromatic young foliage, from which a wine can be made, followed by a good crop of delicious nuts. Smooth barked when young, it thrives on most soils but does not favour waterlogged conditions.

12|15		
Mature height: 12-15m	Shape of mature tree	Edible nuts

JUNIPERUS communis Hibernica

Irish Juniper

Introduced in the late 1830s, this is an excellent choice of small conifer, ideal for gardens and large rockeries. It won the Award of Garden Merit in 2002.

Its slender and dense form imposes a sense of architectural formality to a garden and it requires little or no maintenance. It tolerates most soils but does not thrive on waterlogged ground.

3|8			
Mature height: 3-8m	Shape of mature tree	Narrow trees	Evergreen trees

JUNIPERUS scopulorum Blue Arrow

From the same stable as the better known clone 'Skyrocket' this very upright conifer is ideal for small gardens. It was introduced in the 1980s and is an improved form with intense blue foliage and wonderful 'pencil' habit.

I've always had a problem with Skyrocket as it starts off lovely but gets grottier with age and sparse at its base. Blue Arrow is definitely the way to go! Thriving on any well drained fertile soils, this family of Junipers originated from the Rocky Mountains of the USA.

3|8			
Mature height: 3-8m	Shape of mature tree	Narrow trees	Evergreen trees

KOELREUTERIA paniculata
Pride of India

Also known as the Golden Rain Tree, this was introduced from China in the 1760s but it is also a native of Japan and Korea. It is a much tougher tree than people think.

A most attractive, rounded tree of medium height, it deserves to be more widely grown as it has much to recommend it. The clusters of small yellow flowers which it produces in July and August are followed by lantern shaped fruits in the autumn. It does best in dry, calcareous soils and in a reasonably sunny position.

3|8			
Mature height: 3-8m	Shape of mature tree	Flowering trees	Bee friendly trees

I have seen this tree thriving on a narrow soil strip of central reservation in south London taking all urban pollution can throw at it. For such a pretty tree it can tolerate locations where our native trees would soon succumb to failure.

KOELREUTERIA paniculata Fastigiata

A columnar form of Pride of India. Raised by Kew Gardens from seeds received in 1888 from Shanghai, this botanical oddity is a must for plant collectors.

A good choice for restricted spaces and excellent as a specimen tree in a park. The clusters of small yellow flowers which it produces in July and August are followed by lantern shaped fruits in the autumn. It does best in dry, calcareous soils and in a reasonably sheltered position, such as an urban courtyard garden.

3|8 Mature height: 3-8m | Shape of mature tree | Narrow trees | Bee friendly trees

LABURNOCYTISUS Adamii

This remarkable tree, a graft chimaera, is thought to have been fluked when a nurseryman from M Adam nurseries near Paris in 1825 turned his attention to grafting purple flowered broom after finishing with Laburnum.

Whether intentional or not the result was extraordinary! The plant looks more like laburnum than anything else until it flowers when some branches bear the anticipated yellow flowers of Laburnum while others bear dense clusters of the purple flowered Cytisus. Just to confuse matters further most branches also produce intermediate flowers of coppery pink! There is a particularly good specimen at Kew gardens. It tends to thrive on most soils though dislikes water logged conditions. As it is so rare it is best planted as an individual specimen in a tree collection.

3|8 Mature height: 3-8m | Shape of mature tree | Flowering trees

LABURNUM x watereri Vossii

A most floriferous cultivar that won the Award of Garden Merit in 2002. Selected in Holland late in the 19th century, it has remained very popular over the years and is readily seen in gardens up and down the UK.

This small tree produces a wealth of yellow racemes up to 50cm long in spring. All parts of the plant are highly poisonous as it contains an alkaloid called cytosine. It thrives on most soils and is particularly effective when grown as an arching avenue.

One of the very best examples of this is at Bodnant Gardens in North Wales where the abundant flowers droop down above you and fill the air with their fragrance.

3|8 Mature height: 3-8m | Shape of mature tree | Flowering trees

Much is made of its black seeds being fatal if eaten and rightly so, but occurrences of laburnum poisoning are extremely rare. Educating children to keep away from this genus is the key.

LAGERSTROEMIA indica Rosea

Crape Myrtle

This selection of the Crape Myrtle is best grown in south facing and sheltered locations. Native of both Korea and China, it was introduced into the UK in 1759 and won the Award of Garden Merit in both 1924 and 2002.

A beautiful small tree with a rounded, somewhat flat-topped growth. The bark is most attractive, being mottled with grey and pink, while the small, dark green leaves turn flame red in autumn. The deep rose pink flowers, with their crimped petals, are borne late summer but are only initiated after warm summers.

Much has been made of climate change over the last decade and I find it interesting that we have routinely been able to get our Lagerstroemia to flower in recent years. When I first started growing trees in the late 1980s this tree was treated as half hardy and flowers were not even considered!

3|8 Mature height: 3-8m | Shape of mature tree | Flowering trees

LAGERSTROEMIA indica Violacea

Similar in every way to the cultivar 'Rosea' this lovely small tree produces clusters of violet flowers from late August onwards so long as the summer gives enough heat. Flowers are often initiated in even the dullest summers but do not fully emerge unless we have decent weather in September and October. It is well worth taking the risk!

A beautiful small tree with a rounded, somewhat flat-topped growth. The bark is most attractive, being mottled with grey and pink, while the small, dark green leaves turn flame red in autumn.

3|8 Mature height: 3-8m | Shape of mature tree | Flowering trees

LARIX decidua Common Larch

A lovely deciduous conifer and underused in amenity plantings. Being coniferous it has very good apical dominance, so retaining a lovely pyramidal habit through to maturity. Not a native tree but introduced into the UK in the early 1600s. It won the Award of Garden Merit in 2002.

Ideal for verges, as a specimen tree for parkland, or for woodlands, its crown is slender and conical when young. At maturity the older branches droop. Glorious green foliage heralds the spring and the autumn colour of yellow-orange provide good contrast. It thrives on most soils. We supplied some for the A47 coming into Leicester in 2001 and they are romping away!

17|22 Mature height: 17-22m | Shape of mature tree | Urban trees

LARIX x eurolepis
Dunkeld Larch, Hybrid Larch

Discovered at Dunkeld, Perthshire, around 1904, this hybrid is particularly robust and is a cross between Larix decidua and Larix kaempferi. In truth all the Larch we grow have very similar attributes and are difficult to distinguish. I would choose this cultivar for its toughness.

It is a large and fast growing tree with good timber and amenity value. Ideal for street verges or parkland, this deciduous conifer is, in my opinion, greatly underused. There is something primeval about Larch, a wonderful relic to an age before us.

17|22 Mature height: 17-22m | Shape of mature tree | Parkland trees

LARIX kaempferi
Japanese Larch

This deciduous conifer was introduced from its native Japan in the early 1860s by the well known plant enthusiast JG Veitch. It thrives on most soils and is great for verges, parkland or large gardens. Unfortunately in recent years the Forestry Commission have seen huge swathes of this tree suffer a swift demise from Phytophthora ramorum, sudden oak death, so beware!

A fast growing and large tree of conical form, the bright green leaves turn yellow in autumn. Its twiggy growth is tinged red, and when seen as a plantation against a setting sun in the winter the effect of this is quite dramatic.

17|22		
Mature height: 17-22m	Shape of mature tree	Parkland trees

LAURUS nobilis
Bay Laurel

We grow this as a clear stemmed full standard tree. A native of the Mediterranean, it was introduced in the early 1560s though it's foliage probably hit these shores a lot earlier when Julius Caesar visited with a wreath of it on his head! It won the Award of Garden Merit in 2002.

A very useful evergreen tree that reacts well to pruning to form a dense pyramidal tree well suited for screening or specimen planting. The aromatic foliage can be added to bolognaise sauce for extra flavour. Suitable for most free draining soils. It prefers to be planted in areas of semi-shade and is also coastal tolerant.

Often considered as a half hardy plant when young, it proves to be tougher when mature and combats the vagaries of UK winters very well. However the harsh winter of 2010/11 accounted for many new plantings so beware! When it is used as a potted plant in a garden the soil volume may freeze in winter making it impossible for the plant to access water. Drought is the killer here, not hardiness.

3|8		
Mature height: 3-8m	Shape of mature tree	Garden trees

LIGUSTRUM japonicum
Japanese Tree Privet

Introduced in 1845 by PF von Siebold from its native Japan, this is often used as a stilted hedge above the fence line so is a favourite in urban gardens where privacy is needed.

It can be planted very close to buildings without fear of subsidence and is compliant as such with the building regulation code. It is very useful in a small garden as its trunk below the fence line takes up little garden space.

3|8			
Mature height: 3-8m	Shape of mature tree	Privacy raised screening	Evergreen trees

A small semi-evergreen tree, it is generally regarded as an evergreen in the south of England. It has a rounded habit, long, pointed leaves and white flowers, which are borne in autumn. Very good in restricted areas and it thrives on most soils. There are some fine examples of this maturing in London, transforming winter streets with their evergreen canopy.

There are many occasions when screening above fence height, sometimes referred to as stilted screening, is needed to secure privacy from neighbouring windows. Ligustrum japonicum retains its leaves year round in all but the coldest of winters with new leaves pushing off the old in April and May. It is easy to prune and doing this every March promotes a bushy vibrant crown for the rest of the year.

It is the most popular tree we grow for screening as it is tough and great value for money for the instant height it can bring to an overlooked garden.

The 'before' and 'after' photos to the right demonstrate quite clearly how views between neighbouring properties can change in one day for the benefit of both parties!

LIGUSTRUM lucidum Variegata

A variegated form of Chinese Privet and a good choice for urban settings. Sometimes listed as 'Superbum', it won the Award of Garden Merit in 2002. We grow this as a full standard so it is an ideal candidate for planting close to a fence line to provide screening cover over the fence height. I saw some planted in a street in London whilst walking to our stand at the Chelsea Flower Show and they were performing admirably.

A most striking, top worked form with a rounded habit. A small semi-evergreen tree, it is generally regarded as an evergreen in the south of England. It has long, pointed gold margined leaves and white flowers, which are borne in autumn. Very good in restricted areas and it thrives on most free draining soils.

3|8			
Mature height: 3-8m	Shape of mature tree	Urban trees	Evergreen trees

LIGUSTRUM ovalifolia
Hedging Privet

Introduced from Japan in the late 1880s, this great hedging plant makes a fantastic evergreen screen. What is more, if it runs away through neglect a privet hedge can be absolutely butchered in March back to bare wood only to spring back into life and vigour in one season to get the screen back in order.

It will lose leaves in extremely cold winters but thrives on most soils and aspects. It has almost gone out of fashion with the introduction of laurel and photinia but remains the most straightforward and easily maintained hedging plant on the market. As it is easy to grow it is also often the most economical option to buy!

1|3			
Mature height: 1-3m	Hedging trees	Urban trees	Evergreen trees

LIQUIDAMBAR acalycina

A fast growing form of Sweet Gum introduced from China in the 1980s. Its three lobed leaves and general habit are very similar to Liquidambar formosana but it is much hardier and it grows with a tough vigour.

Unlike most other Sweet Gum clones, it is better known for its spring and summer foliage effect than its autumn colour.

12|17	Shape of mature tree	Parkland trees
Mature height: 12-17m		

Of pyramidal form and medium height, it produces bronze-purple foliage that is retained with flushing new growth throughout the growing season. It turns to yellow in autumn and leaves are often retained until well into winter. Suitable for streets, avenues and parks, it does best in fertile, well drained soils. It does not thrive in chalky soils.

LIQUIDAMBAR styraciflua
Sweet Gum

The Sweet Gum is one of the finest trees for autumn colour. Introduced from its native Eastern USA in the 17th century, it won the equivalent of the Award of Garden Merit in 1975.

Sometimes confused with maple on account of its similar leaves, this makes a large tree with a broad, pyramidal crown if its central leader is retained. Its attractive, corky bark is a feature at all times of the year, but it is at its magnificent best in autumn when it simply seems to burn with crimson and gold. Suitable for streets, avenues and parks, it does best in fertile, well drained soils. It does not thrive in chalky soils.

12|17			
Mature height: 12-17m	Shape of mature tree	Avenue trees	Autumn colour

LIQUIDAMBAR styraciflua Lane Roberts

This sweet gum cultivar is particularly reliable in Britain and won the Award of Garden Merit in 2002. Like many of the styraciflua cultivars, the bark is smooth rather than corky. When planted en masse the autumn effect is both sensational and long lasting.

The autumn colour of the foliage is a highly dramatic dark crimson to red. A medium size tree, it has a tighter conical habit and larger leaves than the species. A good choice as a street or garden tree, it does best in fertile, well drained soils, but does not thrive in chalky soils.

12|17			
Mature height: 12-17m	Shape of mature tree	Garden trees	Autumn colour

LIQUIDAMBAR styraciflua Slender Silhouette

With a leaf akin to Stella or Worplesdon, the shape of this tree is Liquidambar's equivalent of Cupressus sempervirens! Extremely columnar, it develops a ratio of height to width of 5 to 1. This American introduction also has good autumn colour with leaves turning yellow, orange and red before leaf fall.

Thriving on most free draining soils this narrow form is ideal for small gardens or restricted streets. Autumn colour is more reliable on acid soils and like many clones of Liquidambar styraciflua, its bark is smooth when young unlike its parent.

7|12		
Mature height: 7-12m	Shape of mature tree	Autumn colour

LIQUIDAMBAR styraciflua Stella

This Sweet Gum with deeply cut star-like leaves resembles a semi dwarfing clone of Liquidambar Worplesdon. Prized for its autumn colour, this is a wonderful tree for a medium to large garden. Its bark is smooth rather than corky.

The bright green foliage of spring and summer turns from golden yellow through to crimson as autumn progresses. Stella is a medium to large tree of pyramidal habit; its leaves are similar to, but slightly smaller than, Worplesdon.

12|17		
Mature height: 12-17m	Shape of mature tree	Autumn colour

LIQUIDAMBAR styraciflua Thea

This lovely Sweet Gum is broad leaved and late to colour in the autumn, starting with the top third of the tree which turns a remarkable purple. A recent introduction, selected in the Netherlands.

Thea is in many respects similar to Lane Roberts, but as a medium to large tree, is a little taller. It has a good, conical form and distinctive purple foliage in the autumn. A good choice as a street or garden tree, it does best in fertile, well drained soils, but does not thrive in chalky soils.

12|17		
Mature height: 12-17m	Shape of mature tree	Autumn colour

LIQUIDAMBAR styraciflua Manon Variegata

This Sweet Gum is a must for those who like their variegated trees. The striking foliage is best in summer and can provide excellent contrast against a dark evergreen background.

This medium size cultivar, with its horizontal lateral branches, has a very regular, pyramidal form. It is of medium height and resistant to both pests and disease. Its blue-green foliage, with a creamy white margin, turns pink in autumn. Suitable for streets, avenues and parks, it does best in fertile, well drained soils. It does not thrive in chalky soils.

7|12			
Mature height: 7-12m	Shape of mature tree	Variegated trees	Garden trees

LIQUIDAMBAR styraciflua Worplesdon

Unlike most other Sweet Gums, this clone often bears fruit in British conditions. A winner of the Award of Garden Merit in both 1987 and 2002, this is our favoured clone of Liquidambar for both autumn colour and form. I have one thriving in my garden on a very thin and slightly alkaline soil. It is also the hardiest clone, thriving on our exposed Fen field unit where other clones and even the parent can fail to cope in some winters.

Its foliage is delightful and more deeply lobed than other clones and its pyramidal habit is both reliable and architecturally pleasing. However its real beauty lies in its autumn colour starting in September when some leaves turn yellow through to orange before falling but the outermost leaves gradually turn to magnificent claret red. A great tree for any urban aspect where space allows.

12|17		
Mature height: 12-17m	Shape of mature tree	Autumn colour

LIRIODENDRON tulipifera
Tulip Tree

Introduced from America in the late 1680s this stately tree is known as Whitewood in North America, where the timber is widely used in house interiors.

There are some tremendous specimens in the States that have grown to over 60 metres in height. As an aside, if you ever prune the young wood, take time to breathe in the sweetly fragrant sap.

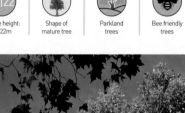

17|22			
Mature height: 17-22m	Shape of mature tree	Parkland trees	Bee friendly trees

A large and fast growing tree, it has a broad, pyramidal crown. The tulip shaped flowers, which appear only on older trees, are produced in June and July and are yellow-green with a band of orange at the base. It is deep rooted and wind resistant, and does well on most fertile soils. A splendid subject for parks and large gardens. Apparently, excellent honey is derived from bees harvesting its flowers.

LIRIODENDRON tulipifera Aureomarginatum

This form of the Tulip Tree has yellow variegation to its leaves and was introduced in the early 1900s. The British champion I have heard is in Stourhead and stands at over 25 metres tall. The foliage is at its most striking in the spring.

Growing rather smaller than the species, this is a medium tree with a pyramidal habit. The bright yellow variegation tends to turn greenish-yellow by the end of the summer. It is deep rooted and wind resistant, and does well on most fertile soils. Lovely for parkland settings.

12|17			
Mature height: 12-17m	Shape of mature tree	Garden trees	Bee friendly trees

LIRIODENDRON tulipifera Fastigiatum

This very upright form tends to flower earlier than its parent and we regularly see a decent floral display on 12-14cm girth crop. Like fastigiate hornbeam it can be prone to a bit of middle aged spread so allow for a bit more room around it at planting than you think. I saw a maturing specimen in Rutland and it was pretty much as wide as it was tall!

Its stiffly ascending branches are very effective if kept as a feathered tree, eventually competing with the leader to become a fat tear drop shape at maturity. It is best planted as a specimen tree in medium sized gardens or parks and thrives in most fertile free draining soils.

7|12			
Mature height: 7-12m	Shape of mature tree	Garden trees	Bee friendly trees

MAGNOLIA x brooklynensis Elizabeth

Raised in New York by Eva Maria Sperbes in the 1970s, it is a cross between Magnolia acuminata and denudata. One of the finest yellows. The jury is still out on its ultimate shape and vigour as it is so recent an introduction.

This lovely small conical tree produces clear, pale primrose-yellow cup shaped flowers in the spring that are nicely fragrant. The flowers tend to be a deeper yellow the cooler its position, but make sure it is well placed for spring viewing as its show can be breathtaking.

3|8 Mature height: 3-8m | Shape of mature tree | Multi-stem | Garden trees | Flowering trees

MAGNOLIA x brooklynensis Yellow Bird

We grow this clone as a tree rather than a bush. It is a hybrid of Magnolia acuminata and was raised at the Brooklyn Botanic Garden before being introduced in 1981. The glorious flowers are yellow with a greener tinge held at the base of the outer petals and are borne in April / May.

Its leaves are nice and large to carry on the interest throughout the summer. Yellow Bird is quite a tidy looking tree with a pyramidal habit making it a good choice for medium size gardens and urban areas. It will grow on most well drained soils, preferably acid and is better without grass competition.

3|8 Mature height: 3-8m | Shape of mature tree | Multi-stem | Flowering trees

MAGNOLIA chameleon
Chang Hua

A very pretty cultivar that is known to flower three times in a single year in its native China. We grow this on a single stem to be raised as a standard specimen tree and its last flowering can be as late as the autumn.

The flower is beautifully upright, tulip shaped, and nicely fragrant. The outside of the flower is flushed pink, particularly at the base of the cup. Like all magnolias, give a newly planted tree no competition from other plants for the first couple of years to quicken establishment.

3|8 Mature height: 3-8m | Shape of mature tree | Flowering trees

MAGNOLIA denudata
Yulan

Introduced from China in 1789, this tree won the First Class Certificate in 1968 and won the Award of Garden Merit in 2002.

Fragrant pure white flowers emerge cup shaped in spring, opening with heavy duty petals. Fruits, seldom produced away from its native land, can be 10cm in length and turn rose red when ripe. This is a beautiful tree in flower, when the weather permits, but is rarely seen in the UK.

3|8		
Mature height: 3-8m	Shape of mature tree	Flowering trees

MAGNOLIA denudata
Yellow River

A lovely addition to our deciduous Magnolia range, producing large canary yellow flowers in April and May. The flowers are beautifully fragrant, sweet melon comes to mind! It is difficult to tell apart from another yellow clone 'Yellow Lantern'.

Wonderful as a specimen plant in a garden or park, we grow this cultivar as a standard tree as well as a multi-stemmed bush. It is vigorous and has an ascending habit when young, broadening with age.

3|8			
Mature height: 3-8m	Shape of mature tree	Multi-stem	Flowering trees

MAGNOLIA Galaxy

This Magnolia was bred in the US National Arboretum in 1963 and is a cross between Magnolia lilliflora and Magnolia sprengeri 'Diva'. It is a seedling sister of 'Spectrum'.

Such a glamorous tree, we once supplied them in full flower to a private house in London and a day later the neighbouring property ordered some as well.

Galaxy is a medium sized tree of conical habit formed by its ascending branches that broaden at maturity. A good choice for gardens or parkland, it produces stunning, purple-pink to red, tulip-shaped flowers, which are lightly scented.

7|12		
Mature height: 7-12m	Shape of mature tree	Flowering trees

MAGNOLIA grandiflora
Southern Magnolia

Introduced in 1734, this is a well known native of the USA, naturally ranging from North Carolina to Florida, Arkansas and Texas.

From being associated with south facing wall plantings, this wonderful evergreen has crept into the wider landscape in southern England in recent years with the advent of warmer summers and not so punishing winters. Capable of becoming a medium to large tree if given full sun and a sheltered position, it is a magnificent, round headed specimen. The large, cream flowers, which are delicately scented, are borne through summer and into autumn, set against dark green, almost leathery leaves. It does best in rich, fertile soil and, given this, will tolerate lime.

7|12			
Mature height: 7-12m	Shape of mature tree	Urban trees	Evergreen trees

MAGNOLIA grandiflora Gallissonière

This Magnolia was being grown in France prior to 1750 so is more in tune with European winters. It is difficult to tell apart from its parent and is now a popular choice for urban gardens in southern Britain.

A very hardy, evergreen clone, it produces large flowers, while the large, green leaves are tinted reddish brown underneath. It is of medium stature and broadly oval habit. We offer it as a standard well-suited to urban planting.

7|12			
Mature height: 7-12m	Shape of mature tree	Privacy raised screening	Evergreen trees

MAGNOLIA Heaven Scent

A member of the Swelte Brunettes Group of Magnolias this lovely variety won the Award of Garden Merit in 2002. We grow it as a standard tree with an oval crown that broadens at maturity.

A superb small tree with heavily scented, rather narrow, cup shaped flowers in April. It has pale pink petals, flushed with a deeper pink towards the base, and a cerise stripe on the back. It makes an ideal tree for a medium sized garden and a showy urban tree. The conditions of the 2015 Spring gave an unrivalled flowering display that had arborists buzzing on social networks!

7|12 Mature height: 7-12m

Shape of mature tree

Flowering trees

MAGNOLIA kobus

Introduced in 1865 from Japan, this sturdy Magnolia is both very hardy and versatile. Unlike the other magnolias we supply, this only flowers at its full potential after about 15 years but as we supply them well over five years old it isn't too long to wait! In between time you will have a decent display rather than a sensational one.

We grow this medium size, round headed tree as a full standard, and recommend it for planting on verges and in parkland. It does well in most soils, including chalky ones. The very large, white flowers are produced as early as March and can reach up to 10cm across. This is definitely the best choice for neutral to high ph soils.

Interestingly, recent research named this tree as the candidate best equipped to gobble up urban pollution so it is now being widely used in inner cities to perform this valuable service and help out all those with respiratory problems associated with exhaust fumes.

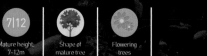

7|12 Mature height: 7-12m

Shape of mature tree

Flowering trees

MAGNOLIA x loebneri Leonard Messel

A chance cross between Magnolia kobus and Magnolia stellata Rosea, originating at Colonel Messel's Nymans garden in Sussex. Often sold as a shrub, we also grow this as a single stemmed small tree that would grace any garden.

One of the prettiest and delightful Magnolias, it produces abundant dainty white-lilac flowers in spring. It only makes a small tree so is perfect for a garden and it is reasonably lime tolerant.

As many as 12 to 15 petals adorn a single glorious flower and in the spring the tree is smothered with velvety cased buds waiting to burst. In my opinion this is the pick of 'garden' Magnolias and even the oblivious register this beauty when it is in full swing.

I planted the multi stem version of this tree in my garden in 2009 and even though it is only about 2 metres tall it produces well over 100 flower buds that furnish its limbs with bloom in March. This spectacular tree is one of the first plants in my garden to register the spring.

1|3 Mature height: 1-3m	Shape of mature tree	Multi-stem	Garden trees

MAGNOLIA x loebneri Merrill

An outstanding American selection, raised at the Arnold Arboretum, Boston, in the late 1930s and the winner of more horticultural awards than you can shake a stick at! Very numerous velvety flower cases become noticeable after Christmas suggesting the promise that spring is around the corner.

This Magnolia does well in all soils, including chalky ones. Small and of rounded habit, it has large, fragrant white flowers in spring that are produced in great abundance. Very attractive in both parks, hard areas and in my garden. Normally a banker for Mothering Sunday, which gets my two out of gaol!

Mature height: 3-8m | Shape of mature tree | Flowering trees

MAGNOLIA x soulangeana

The most popular form of Magnolia, widely planted in parks and gardens. It has a long history, originating from Japan but was developed in France early in the 19th century. It has almost become synonymous with urban gardens in England.

Usually grown as a large shrub with a broad, round habit, the large, white, purple tinted, tulip-like flowers appear in April and May before the arrival of foliage. It tolerates heavy clay soils and is also moderately lime tolerant. Again, we buck the trend and grow this as a single stemmed tree as well as a multi-stem.

Mature height: 3-8m | Shape of mature tree | Multi-stem | Flowering trees

MAGNOLIA Spectrum

This Magnolia was bred in the US National Arboretum in 1963 and is a cross between Magnolia lilliflora and Magnolia sprengeri 'Diva'. It is a seedling sister of 'Galaxy' and one of our customers routinely sends us an emailed photo of his every spring when it is in full flower.

A medium sized tree of conical habit formed by its ascending branches that broadens at maturity. A great choice for gardens or parks, it produces most attractive, dark purple, tulip-shaped flowers, which are lightly scented. Flowers emerge before the foliage. It does best on moist, but free-draining, fertile soils and in sheltered or partially shaded positions.

7|12 Mature height: 7-12m | Shape of mature tree | Flowering trees

MAGNOLIA Susan

A lovely small deciduous tree that tolerates alkaline soils. One of the so called 'Little Girl Hybrids' developed between 1955 and 1956 at the US National Arboretum, it is renowned for its profuse floral display.

Abundant deep pink-purple flowers are produced in April-June and its erect habit makes this clone a lovely addition for a small garden. We grow this variety as a tree rather than as a bush and although growth is slow the flowers never fail to disappoint. I've recently placed one within view of the coast in Cornwall but within shelter of a conifer to protect it against the strongest winds and it's romping away.

3|8 Mature height: 3-8m | Shape of mature tree | Garden trees | Flowering trees

3|8

Mature height: 3-8m

Multi-stem

Garden trees

MAGNOLIA Star Wars

A great name for any plant and probably sold on this basis more than any other. Introduced from Blumhardt of New Zealand and won the Award of Garden Merit in 2002 as well as the Award of Merit in 1991. The 'force' is certainly carried within this clone!

We grow this variety as a multi-stem bush. It is a campbellii x lilliflora cross and produces vigorous growth with large thick leaves after a glorious display of rich pink large goblet flowers in the spring. It is worth planting for its tremendous foliage alone.

MALUS baccata Street Parade

This is a cultivar of the Siberian crab which is widely distributed throughout Southern Asia and was introduced into the UK in 1784.

This small crab has a tight, columnar habit and is a good choice for small gardens, street plantings or where space is limited. Plentiful, single, white flowers emerge from salmon pink buds. Shiny, purple-red fruits are produced from August onwards. Street Parade has the added advantage of being scab and mildew resistant.

3|8			
Mature height: 3-8m	Shape of mature tree	Garden trees	Bee friendly trees

MALUS Bramley Seedling

A superb and well known cooking apple that produces large green fruits. It has been in cultivation for over 200 years and many a house buyer inherits one with their new purchase as it had been widely planted during this period.

The original tree resides in Nottinghamshire. The white, pink blushed, flowers in spring provide a lovely display and like other Malus, this variety is best suited to heavier but well drained soils. The abundant fruit crop can be harvested by autumn and when combined with blackberries makes my favourite fruit pie.

3|8			
Mature height: 3-8m	Shape of mature tree	Edible fruits	Bee friendly trees

MALUS Cox's Orange Pippin

The nation's favourite eating apple, available from us as a clear stemmed full standard and grown on the robust M16 rootstock. An ideal spring blossom specimen for any garden with the added bonus of autumn fruit.

Profuse white flowers lead to good sized eating apples by late summer. A round headed tree that thrives on most soils, including clay, and a must for any garden orchard. Autumn colour of yellow tinged with red, is an attractive ornamental attribute.

3|8			
Mature height: 3-8m	Shape of mature tree	Edible fruits	Bee friendly trees

MALUS Director Moerland

A round headed variety notable for its distinctive large red / purple maple like leaves. It was bred as a disease resistant form of Malus Profusion.

Slightly fragrant wine red flowers are borne profusely in spring which complements emerging red leaves making this a stunning little tree for the first few growing months of the year. Best suited for gardens and parks and tolerant of most soils and conditions.

3|8 Mature height: 3-8m | Shape of mature tree | Flowering trees | Bee friendly trees

MALUS Discovery

Introduced from Essex in 1949, this rosy red tinged fruiting desert apple is a firm favourite with its agreeable sharp flavour. If no other Malus is around, it is best to include a crab apple such as Malus John Downie or Evereste as pollinator.

It will thrive on most soils including heavy clay but will benefit from keeping competition at bay around it, especially grass, to fulfil fruiting size potential. Lovely white flowers are borne in the spring and these produce the lush fruit for use in August / September which can be stored with success.

3|8 Mature height: 3-8m | Shape of mature tree | Flowering trees | Edible fruits | Bee friendly trees

MALUS Donald Wyman

A tried and tested performer raised by the late Donald Wyman at the Arnold Arboretum in the USA. Satisfactorily resistant to both apple scab and mildew it develops a rounded habit at maturity and is ideal for parks and gardens.

The spring flower is red to pink in bud, opening to white when in full glory. The fruit matures to a glossy vivid red and can be profuse so it is best to plant away from paved areas to avoid cleaning up. The leaves are dark green by summer.

3|8 Mature height: 3-8m | Shape of mature tree | Flowering trees | Bee friendly trees

MALUS Egremont Russett

First recorded in 1872, this lovely eating apple is thought to have originated in Sussex. It rose to popularity in Victorian times and is still a favourite today, only behind Cox's Pippin and Bramley Seedling in terms of commercial production acreage. The yellow / green russet apples are sweet with a hint of pear flavour and can store well.

Where no other Malus is in the vicinity it is always worth planting with a Malus John Downie or Evereste to pollinate. It is a tough tree, thriving on most soil types, light and heavy, as well as taking on more northerly aspects of the UK with ease. Pink tinged flower buds open to white in the spring and apples can be harvested from August onwards.

3|8 Mature height: 3-8m	Shape of mature tree	Flowering trees	Edible fruits	Bee friendly trees

MALUS Elstar

A cross between Golden Delicious and Ingrid Marie, this flavoursome eater is a recent addition to our range of harvest apples. Grown at Barcham as a full standard on the vigorous rootstock M16.

Pale pink flowers in the spring are an attractive aside before the fruits take shape for the autumnal bonanza. Although it prefers full sun it will tolerate semi shade but either way it tends to thrive best if the soil is free draining.

3|8 Mature height: 3-8m	Shape of mature tree	Edible fruits	Bee friendly trees

MALUS Evereste

We recommend three crab apples in particular, one white, one red and one upright and this is one of them! A winner of the Award of Garden Merit in 2002, it was introduced in the early 1980s.

This rounded tree of medium height has flowers that are red in bud before turning white - and the blossom is borne in profusion. The small fruits look like miniature 'Gala' and are held onto until they are taken off by birds after Christmas. On the continent they are used in displays as the little fruits hold their form so well. The orange-yellow autumn foliage also holds well. Good for gardens, parks and verges.

5|7			
Mature height: 5-7m	Shape of mature tree	Flowering trees	Bee friendly trees

MALUS floribunda
Japanese Crab

A most elegant crab, introduced from Japan in the early 1860s, but prone to suffer badly from Apple Scab after flowering rendering the crown to look rather threadbare from June onwards. This popular variety has been superseded by more disease resistant clones such as Malus Rudolph and Evereste in recent years so as a result it is seen less and less in commercial production.

Very early to flower, the crimson buds open to reveal white or pale blush blossom, making this one of the most attractive crabs. The plentiful and long lasting fruits are greenish-yellow with a hint of red to them. Good for gardens, verges and parks.

3|8 Mature height: 3-8m | Shape of mature tree | Flowering trees | Bee friendly trees

MALUS Golden Delicious

Always derided by the purists as a tasteless French import, getting anything green and organic down my kids is a godsend in my book! Crunchy and sweet is the main criteria for my two and Golden Delicious fits the bill.

Grown at Barcham on M16 vigorous rootstock and as a full standard, my old Writtle fruit lecturer would not be amused to hear we were growing this clone! The abundant autumnal fruit is best eaten straight off the tree as it doesn't store too well.

3|8 Mature height: 3-8m | Shape of mature tree | Edible fruits | Flowering trees | Bee friendly trees

MALUS Golden Hornet

This well known garden crab has been in cultivation since the 1940s and is highly regarded for its profuse display of yellow marble sized fruits. A winner of numerous awards including the First Class Certificate in 1961.

A small tree which produces white blossom and yellow fruits, which are retained for many weeks. It has a good, oval habit and is a reliable "all-rounder", well suited to parks, verges and gardens.

3|8			
Mature height: 3-8m	Shape of mature tree	Flowering trees	Bee friendly trees

MALUS Howgate Wonder

This rosy tinged cooking apple has been eclipsed in popularity by Bramley Seeding but should not be overlooked! For those of you who can take a sharp taste, this apple can be enjoyed straight from the tree as well as being the basis for pies, crumbles and juices.

Introduced in the early 1900s, this apple is best planted with a Malus John Downie or Evereste to enhance pollination if no other Malus are within sight. It thrives on most soils and produces a lovely floral display in the spring. The apples are generally ready from August onwards and are suitable to store.

3|8				
Mature height: 3-8m	Shape of mature tree	Edible fruits	Flowering trees	Bee friendly trees

MALUS hupehensis

A lovely crab introduced to Britain from the Far East by Ernest Wilson in 1900. Rarely planted but never forgotten if seen in full cry in the late spring.

A fine choice for gardens and parkland plantings, the ascending branches of this small tree give it a broadly columnar appearance. The fragrant flowers are pale pink while in bud, opening to white, while the small fruits are generally dark red..

3|8 Mature height: 3-8m | Shape of mature tree | Flowering trees | Bee friendly trees

MALUS James Grieve

A classic addition to our eating apple range and one that is particularly popular with our despatch lads in the autumn!

Pale pink flowers in spring are followed by sweet edible fruits in late autumn to early winter. It prefers a fertile and moist free draining soil in full sun or partial shade. For best fruiting results keep the ground fallow a metre radius from the trunk and top dress this area with bark mulch. This cuts down weed competition which in turn increases fruit size.

3|8 Mature height: 3-8m | Shape of mature tree | Edible fruits | Bee friendly trees

MALUS John Downie

Raised in 1875, this is thought by many to be the best fruiting crab. It won the updated Award of Garden Merit from the Royal Horticultural Society in 2002.

A small tree with an irregular, oval crown, it makes a splendid tree for gardens with limited space. The white flowers are followed by relatively large, conical orange-red fruits, which have a good flavour if required for preserves or jelly. Like all crab apples, it thrives on most soils.

3|8 Mature height: 3-8m | Shape of mature tree | Flowering trees | Bee friendly trees

MALUS Jonagold

This American apple is a cross between Jonathon and Golden Delicious. Grown on the tough M16 rootstock its white flowers in spring are attractive in their own right. Not the best on its own for pollination, it is always recommended to plant this within a varied mix of Malus to aid fertilization.

A vigorous small tree with a rounded habit, it bears an excellent crop of crisp, juicy fruits, which are full of flavour. The apples are large, greenish-yellow, lightly flushed with red, can be picked from mid October and will store well until the following spring.

3|8 Mature height: 3-8m | Shape of mature tree | Edible fruits | Bee friendly trees

MALUS Mokum

A beautiful crab for small gardens, parks and verges that is often overlooked by people favouring the more well known varieties.

The leaves of this small, oval headed tree are an eye-catching dark red and its rosy-red flowers emerge by late spring. The autumn fruits are also red giving this clone a very long season of interest. Like most crab apples, it thrives on most ground including heavier clay soils.

3|8			
Mature height: 3-8m	Shape of mature tree	Flowering trees	Bee friendly trees

MALUS Profusion

A fast growing and well known crab from the late 1930s. It can occasionally get clobbered by both apple scab and mildew in the summer so it is best to avoid if replacing other Malus that may carry these pathogens.

This lovely cultivar is just about the best of those with wine red flowers. It is a small tree with a rounded crown, well suited to gardens and parks. The young, copper-crimson foliage turns bronze-green at maturity, while the rich, purple flowers, which are lightly fragrant, turn pink as the season progresses. Its fruits are small and blood red in colour.

3|8			
Mature height: 3-8m	Shape of mature tree	Flowering trees	Bee friendly trees

MALUS Red Sentinel

Brought into cultivation in 1959, this profusely fruiting crab is a favourite for gardeners who are looking for winter interest. In some years the fruits are so numerous that the branches can weigh too heavily with them so that the crown loses its shape.

The red leaves of this small, round headed tree contrast well with its white flowers. These are followed in autumn by clusters of dark red crabs that often stay on the tree right through the winter. Good for gardens and parks.

3|8 Mature height: 3-8m	Shape of mature tree	Flowering trees	Bee friendly trees

MALUS Royalty

An upright crab, bred in Canada in the early 1950s. The foliage is so dark it is always canny not to overdo the numbers on this one. A dark foliaged tree always focuses the eye in a landscape so too many can make a garden quite dark.

Its ascending branches give Royalty a broadly columnar form. A small tree, it has shiny, rich purple foliage, which turns a vivid red in autumn. Large, purple-crimson flowers give rise to dark red fruits. Like most crabs, this is suitable for parks and gardens.

3|8 Mature height: 3-8m	Shape of mature tree	Flowering trees	Bee friendly trees

MALUS Rudolph

Another Canadian crab developed in the 1950s. I have mentioned before that we recommend one white, one pink and one upright apple, well this is the pink. The autumn colour of clear yellow is an added bonus but the main reasons we rate it so highly is its resistance to pest and disease as well as its glorious floral display.

A tree of medium size, it is rather columnar when young, but the crown becomes rounded at maturity. The leaves gradually turn from copper-red to bronze-green, and rose pink flowers are followed by numerous elongated fruits, which last well. Rudolph is resistant to scab, and is particularly good as both a garden tree and for urban verge plantings.

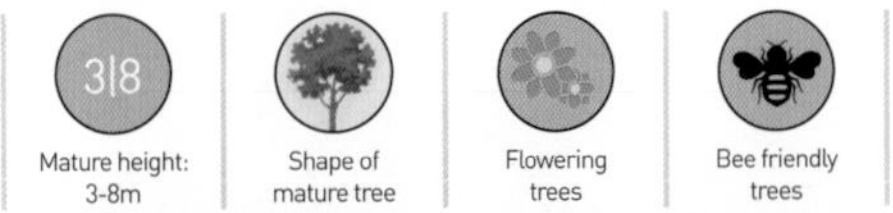

MALUS sylvestris

Arguably one of our prettiest native trees, this small crab apple provides profuse white, tinged pink in bud, flowers in the spring and a good yellow autumn colour. Yellow / green and occasionally red flushed fruits are a favourite for birds in the autumn.

Most suited to heavy and clay soils, this small tree is rarely seen above twenty feet in height and is the parent of numerous crab and eating apple varieties. Ideal for native mixed planting or shelterbelts that provide great low cover for wildlife.

3|8 Mature height: 3-8m | Shape of mature tree | Native trees | Bee friendly trees

MALUS toringo

A delightful little dainty Japanese crab that is rarely seen but never forgotten. Its leaves are attractively lobed and it is otherwise known as Malus sieboldii, a Japanese type introduced in 1856.

This semi-weeping, very small tree has flowers that are pink in bud, fading to white and small red or yellow fruits. Perfect for even the smallest gardens and thrives on most soils, its distinctive growth habit makes it easily identifiable even during dormancy. Like all crabs, it thrives on even heavy soils so it is a useful inclusion for inhospitable gardens where space is restricted.

3|8 Mature height: 3-8m | Shape of mature tree | Flowering trees | Bee friendly trees

MALUS toringo Scarlet Brouwers Beauty

Beauty by name and nature! This glorious new introduction looks like a cross between Malus toringo and Malus Director Moerland with purple / red foliage and pink to faded pink / white flowers in the spring giving way to small dark red fruits in late summer.

A great tree for giving contrast within a garden, it thrives on most soils, light and heavy, and is one of the last crab apples to lose its leaves on the nursery in the autumn. Malus toringo has such a pretty leaf and this also shows through in this variety. It is a good pollinator for culinary apples whilst providing stunning interest in its own right.

3|8 Mature height: 3-8m | Shape of mature tree | Flowering trees | Bee friendly trees

MALUS trilobata

A rather rare crab from the Mediterranean, so distinct it is sometimes classed as a separate genus, Eriolobus. We doggedly keep it under the Malus section and it is our recommended upright form for restricted spaces. It is a wonderfully symmetrical tree and gives a formal structure to any garden or street.

A medium size tree with an upright habit, this is a good choice for parks and gardens. Its deeply lobed leaves are maple-like and take on attractive burgundy tints in autumn.

3|8			
Mature height: 3-8m	Shape of mature tree	Flowering trees	Bee friendly trees

It produces large, white flowers and green fruits, which are sometimes flushed red. The fruits only usually appear following hot summers.

MESPILUS germanica
Medlar

The Medlar has been in cultivation since early times, having been grown in the Emperor Charlemagne's garden. The small brown fruits it produces are only edible when "bletted" or left to turn half-rotten.

A small, gnarled, wide spreading tree which is at home in a garden, where it produces a rounded form. It has large, hairy leaves, which turn a russet brown in autumn, and large, white flowers borne in May and June.

There are some particularly interesting specimens in the Kitchen Garden at Grimsthorpe Castle in Lincolnshire that are mushroom shaped and well worth a visit in the summer.

METASEQUOIA glyptostroboides
Dawn Redwood

This Redwood is of great botanical interest. It was discovered in China in the 1940s, before which the genus consisted only of fossilised forms. A deciduous conifer, it has rapidly established itself as a huge urban and rural favourite. Often confused with Taxodium, it is quite different if they are seen together at close quarters.

Very large and statuesquely pyramidal, it makes a grand park or specimen tree, but is also good for streets and avenues with a clear stem.

17|22 Mature height: 17-22m | Shape of mature tree | Avenue trees

It has spongy, shaggy bark, and its pale green, feathery foliage turns brown in autumn. The Dawn Redwood is tolerant of air pollution, but needs a moist soil in its first year to establish successfully.

METASEQUOIA glyptostroboides
Goldrush

I first saw this as a maturing specimen at Uppingham School arboretum in Rutland and its golden foliage bounced back against a darker backdrop. It is smaller growing than the green Dawn Redwood but apart from its yellow foliage is similar in every other way.

Importantly, its delicate yellow foliage doesn't seem to scotch under the intense summer sun but this tree does thrive best in damp soils like its parent. Its lovely pyramidal habit makes it suitable for medium gardens and parkland alike. There aren't many yellow deciduous trees on the market and this one is one of the best for intensity of colour that is sustained all summer long.

12|17 Mature height: 12-17m | Shape of mature tree | Yellow foliage

MORUS alba Platinifolia
White Mulberry

A large leaved form of the White Mulberry. I first saw this at maturity near to the coast in Brittany and its lush large foliage gives it an outstanding feeling of health and vigour.

This is a most beautiful, small, architectural tree, perfect for parks and gardens, with a rounded habit. The white fruits, from which it takes its name, can turn pink or red and they are both sweet and edible. The leaves of the White Mulberry are the main food of the silkworm.

3|8		
Mature height: 3-8m	Shape of mature tree	Edible fruits

MORUS alba Fruitless

This male clone has maple like foliage and is an ideal form to pleach or 'roof top' where a flat frame is installed above head height for the foliage to colonize and provide a green umbrella to shade patios of urban piazzas. Its tough leaves make it a good tree to take windy conditions and I have seen this plant thriving within view of the coast but not as the first line of defence.

It thrives on most free draining soils and enjoys full sun and reflected heat bouncing up from surrounding hard areas such as paving or adjacent buildings. Its lustrous foliage display gives it a healthy disposition.

3|8		
Mature height: 3-8m	Shape of mature tree	Garden trees

MORUS alba Pendula

Awarded with several accolades over the years from the Royal Horticultural Society, this weeping tree is ideal for a medium sized garden. This fruiting clone has cascading branches that mushrooms as it matures to form a dense dome of lush foliage in the summer. The leaves turn to yellow in the autumn.

It thrives on most free draining soils and prefers full sun. There aren't many weepers like this to go at in the tree world as most are contrived man made affairs that structurally implode over time but this tree is the real ticket!

3|5		
Mature height: 3-5m	Shape of mature tree	Garden trees

MORUS alba Pyramidalis

An upright clone taking up little room so well suited for a small garden or restricted urban piazza. Lush foliage develops in the spring that gives the tree a healthy look all summer long. It thrives best in full sun but would not stand up well to severe winds as its shape will not diffuse air flow efficiently.

Thriving on most free draining soils this unusual tree is rarely seen but gives a great architectural look to a garden with its ascending limbs more akin to Populus nigra Italica than a gnarled round headed mulberry.

3|8 Mature height: 3-8m	Shape of mature tree	Garden trees

MORUS nigra
Black Mulberry

Brought to Britain by the Romans and widely planted by James I, who wished to establish a silk industry only to find that silkworms feed exclusively on the White Mulberry! People commonly mistake white and black mulberry and they are not defined by the colour of their fruit. Rough stems and rough leaves for black, smooth stems and smooth leaves for white!

A medium tree of great dignity and beauty, it has a gnarled, rugged trunk and most attractive, heart

shaped leaves. The deep purple fruits, which look like large loganberries are tasty and have a variety of culinary uses. It has a domed, rounded habit, giving it a most architectural appeal. Very long-lived, but not as slow growing as is often supposed.

3|8 Mature height: 3-8m	Shape of mature tree	Multi-stem	Edible fruits

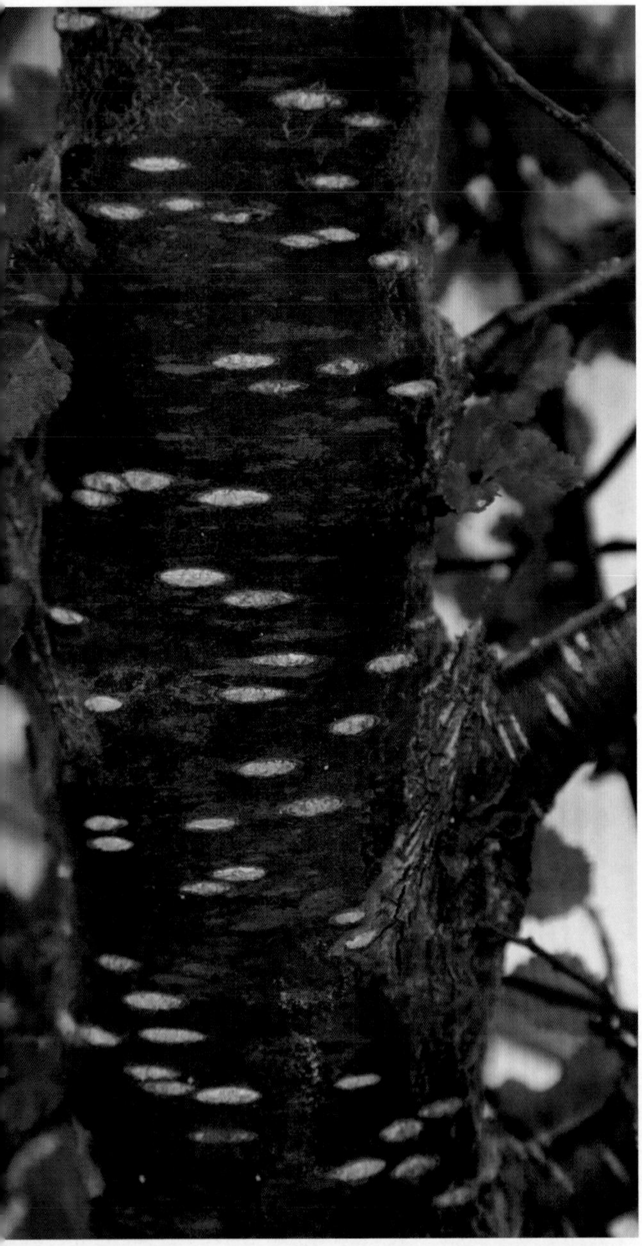

NOTHOFAGUS antarctica
Antarctic Beech

A native of Chile and introduced to Britain in the early 1830s, this beech is a fast grower. Many see this in leaf and take it for an evergreen tree but it is deciduous. Its bark is dark and covered with attractive white lenticels.

Of rounded habit and medium to large size, this has small, heart shaped leaves which turn yellow as the year progresses. Very good for parks and public spaces, it does best in a sunny position and fairly fertile soil. It will not tolerate planting in calcareous soils.

12|17 Mature height: 12-17m | Shape of mature tree | Parkland trees

NYSSA sylvatica

Introduced from America in 1750, this is widely regarded as the most attractive of all the native trees from the States. It won the Award of Garden Merit in 2002.

Pyramidal when young it can resemble Quercus palustris in shape and habit, and certainly rivals it for autumn colour when its foliage turns magnificent reds, oranges and yellows. The dark glossy green leaves are narrowly oval and can reach 15cm in length. They do not tolerate lime soils so please bear this in mind if you choose one.

12|17 Mature height: 12-17m | Shape of mature tree | Autumn colour

OLEA europaea
Olive

3|5 Mature height: 3-5m | Shape of mature tree | Edible fruits

Surely the quintessential tree of the Mediterranean and cultivated virtually since the beginning of time, the Olive is only really hardy in the milder areas of Britain. I have one thriving in my garden in Rutland but I have yet to reap a harvest. However, it is worth growing for its evergreen foliage alone.

A small tree with a rounded form, it can take on an attractively gnarled appearance as it develops. It has small, leathery grey-green leaves and small, white, fragrant flowers. We grow olive as both half standard, in the classical Tuscan shape, and full standard. Olive can benefit greatly by a severe biannual prune in April and can also withstand southern coastal conditions if in full sun.

OSMANTHUS armatus

Native of Western China and introduced into the UK back in 1902, this evergreen tree produces fragrant flowers in the autumn. Its thick dark evergreen leaves are excellent for screening and it grows happily in shade or sun.

It thrives in most free draining soils and as it is such a small tree it can be planted very close to a house without any worry about disturbing foundations or compromising building regulations. Although hardy enough for Southern and middle England, winters in the rest of the UK may prove too much for it to endure.

3|8			
Mature height: 3-8m	Shape of mature tree	Privacy raised screening	Evergreen trees

OSTRYA carpinifolia
Hop Hornbeam

The Hop Hornbeam is so-called because it looks like a Hornbeam and its creamy white flowers resemble hops. Introduced in 1724 from Southern Europe and Western Asia it won the Award of Merit in the hot summer of 1976.

This medium to large tree is good for parkland settings, verges and many urban locations. It looks particularly good in spring with its display of yellow-green catkins. A really tough tree, which will tolerate most conditions.

The wood produced by Ostrya carpinifolia is extremely hard and its name is derived from the Greek word 'ostrua' which literally means 'like bone'. It is also dense and heavy so bare this in mind if you are ever considering some for your log burner for the winter! Typically growing to less than 20 metres, this lovely tree is often overlooked for UK planting but thrives on most free draining soils so is worthy of being far more widespread.

12|17 Mature height: 12-17m | Shape of mature tree | Clay soils

PARROTIA persica
Persian Ironwood

Persian Ironwood is usually grown as a large shrub, and was formerly classified as a species of Hamamelis.

It takes its name from the well known German horticulturalist, FW Parrot and is a native of Iran. There are some particularly nice specimens at the Westonbirt Arboretum near Stroud.

7|12		
Mature height: 7-12m	Shape of mature tree	Autumn colour

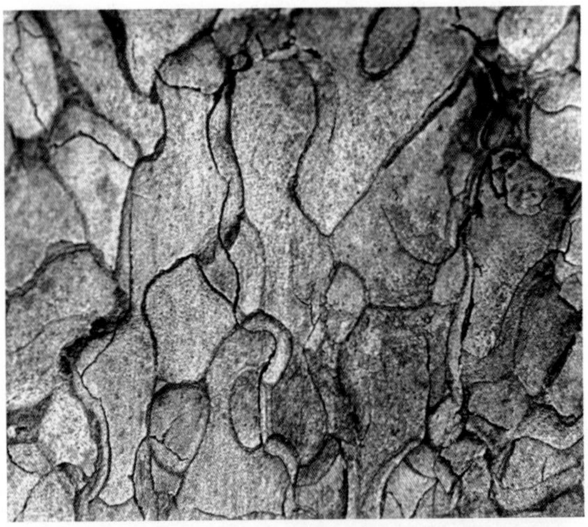

A beautiful, small, rounded tree with grey-brown bark which becomes attractively mottled with yellow. This really is one of the finest small trees for autumn colour, giving a display of crimson, purple, red and gold. A splendid choice for gardens and parks, it does well on most soils, including chalk.

PARROTIA persica Vanessa

Vanessa has a more tree-like form than the species, and was selected as a seedling in the Netherlands in the mid 1970s. A great favourite at Barcham, it produces small but vivid red flowers at maturity.

A small tree with a broad, oval crown. Vanessa gives a stunning display of autumn colour and is ideal for specimen planting in a park or large garden. Prior to that, it displays red shoots and bronze edges to its deep green leaves. It does well on most soils and will tolerate chalk.

7|12 Mature height: 7-12m | Shape of mature tree | Autumn colour

PAULOWNIA tomentosa
Foxglove Tree

One of the most spectacular of ornamental flowering trees, the Foxglove Tree takes its name from the foxglove-like flowers, which are formed in autumn, but do not open until the following spring. Introduced from China in 1834, its wood is much prized in Japan for furniture making.

Amazingly, a mature tree in its native environment can produce up to 20 million seeds per year which converts to over 85,000 seeds per ounce. The tree was named after Anna Pavlovna, daughter of Czar Paul 1 and wife of Prince Willem of the Netherlands.

It is so quick to grow in its younger years that its growth rings have been recorded at three every inch. However, our more temperate climate slows it down and any growth under pencil thickness generally succumbs to winter frosts which contribute to its overall broadness. The flower cases are formed in the autumn so if the temperature dips below 5 degrees Celsius for too long, no flower will develop the following spring.

12|17 Mature height: 12-17m | Shape of mature tree | Flowering trees

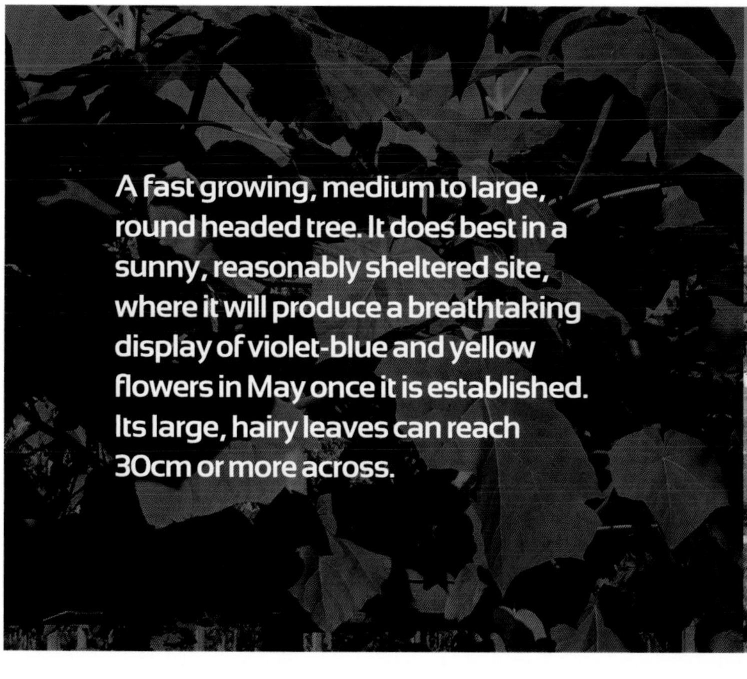

A fast growing, medium to large, round headed tree. It does best in a sunny, reasonably sheltered site, where it will produce a breathtaking display of violet-blue and yellow flowers in May once it is established. Its large, hairy leaves can reach 30cm or more across.

PHELLODENDRON amurense
Amur Cork Tree

A small genus from East Asia, resembling Ailanthus that was introduced into the UK in 1885. It is more suited to rural rather than urban settings but is rarely seen in Britain.

Large leaves, over 25cm in length, and silver, hairy winter buds distinguish this tree from others but it is the corky bark of mature trees that is its most impressive feature. An unusual tree for arboricultural collectors.

12|17		
Mature height: 12-17m	Shape of mature tree	Parkland trees

PHOTINIA x fraseri Red Robin

This beautiful clone was bred in New Zealand and won the Award of Garden Merit in 2002. Much is made of its foliage but more mature plants give a profuse display of white flower in the spring that contrasts magnificently with emerging red leaves.

This small, evergreen tree is often grown as a shrub. As a tree, it develops a rounded crown; its new leaves open to red before hardening to green as they age. Frequent pruning encourages glorious red foliage and makes it every bit as beautiful as Pieris formosa. Lovely in gardens and parks. It is mostly grown as a shrub but we grow it as a standard tree, mainly for stilted screening.

3|8		
Mature height: 3-8m	Shape of mature tree	Privacy raised screening

PHYLLOSTACHYS aurea
Golden Bamboo

In the Far East the canes of this Bamboo are used for walking sticks and umbrella handles, while in America they are turned into fishing rods. Introduced from China in the 1870s it won the Award of Garden Merit in 2002.

This Bamboo forms clumps of canes which are bright green at first and then mature to a pale creamy yellow. The young shoots, which it produces in spring, are edible but beware, this plant is not for the faint hearted as it is extremely vigorous!

If it ever gets out of hand you can decimate it to an inch or two above ground level and it will sucker up good as new. Being evergreen, it is a very useful plant to achieve dense screening from ground level to fence height.

3|5 Mature height: 3-5m | Multi-stem | Evergreen trees

PHYLLOSTACHYS nigra
Black Bamboo

Black Bamboo is surely the most dramatic of all. It is less vigorous than the golden equivalent but that didn't stop me reducing mine to 5cm off ground level in the Spring to stimulate a fresh display only three months later.

This stylish Bamboo has a gracefully arching habit and does best in a sunny position. The canes begin as green before becoming mottled with brown and then black. The shoots which it produces in spring are edible.

3|5 Mature height: 3-5m | Multi-stem | Evergreen trees

PICEA abies
Norway Spruce

Introduced into the UK in about 1500, this well known spruce is common over most of Northern and Central Europe. For many of us its fragrance is very familiar as it was the Christmas tree of choice when we were kids and its foliage litter over carpets up and down the country before Twelfth Night must have clogged up many a vacuum cleaner. Needle holding varieties like the Nordman Fir have since balanced its numbers but it still remains one of the most common conifers around.

Quick to grow and thriving on most free draining soils its stiff ascending branches are clothed with 2cm dark green needles. It is a pyramidal tree producing brown cones when older and it can outgrow a small garden as many have found out after trying to rescue their Christmas tree in January.

PICEA omorika
Serbian Spruce

The Serbian Spruce was widely distributed through much of Europe before the onset of the Ice Age. It was not, however, introduced to Britain until the late 1880s. Similar in looks to a traditional Christmas tree when young, its branches adopt a graceful pendulous habit when mature.

Certainly one of the most beautiful of Spruces, this is a medium to large, slender columnar tree which grows quickly. It tolerates air pollution, calcareous soils and is good as an evergreen street or avenue subject. If planting in a public area my advice is to install after Christmas and not before!

PICEA pungens Hoopsii

This form of Colorado blue spruce is slow growing but highly ornamental. Introduced in the mid 1950s it won the Award of Garden Merit in 2002 and like most conifers it prefers free draining soils.

Vividly glaucous blue leaves and dense conical habit make this small tree a real contrast in a garden or parkland setting. It is so slow to grow that it is perceived as expensive for its size supplied but it offers a unique colour to a garden.

3|8 Mature height: 3-8m | Shape of mature tree | Evergreen trees

PINUS nigra Austriaca
Austrian Pine

Sometimes referred to as 'Black Pine' or 'Pinus nigra nigra' this tough two needled evergreen was introduced in the mid 1830s. Its needles are much greener and longer than Scots Pine and its growth more solid giving it a denser habit than our native pine. Stand behind a maturing Austrian Pine on a windy day and be amazed how the wind is diffused by the needles to calm the air flow.

A first rate choice for coastal areas and exposed, windswept sites, it thrives even in very chalky soils. This large evergreen has a pyramidal form, but retains its bushy, juvenile appearance much longer than Scots Pine. It is from ancient genera, so its toughness is based on a very solid track record.

PINUS maritima
Corsican Pine

Introduced way back in 1759 from Southern Italy,this large tree is a great wind diffuser for coastal sites. Its long green needles are distinctive and it is generally a little quicker to grow than the Austrian Pine, sometimes throwing up a 60cm whorl of new growth in early summer.

Thriving on most free draining soils, this large broadly pyramidal tree can be too big for a small garden but is ideal for parkland and southern coastal sites where shelter is needed to get other species in play.

17|22 Mature height: 17-22m | Shape of mature tree | Evergreen trees

PINUS mugo Mops
Swiss Mountain Pine, Mugo Pine

Introduced in the early 1950s, this clone of the dwarf shrub pine is considered by many to be the finest. Pinus mugo can be very variable in size and habit with recorded mature heights of between 1 metre and 15 metres but 'Mops' rarely gets larger than 1.5 metres.

This is a new addition to our range and should be online in containers by September 2012. It is a very versatile garden or landscape plant, mimicking a bonsai effect of traditional pine and requiring minimal maintenance. It is tough and is suited to most soil types including shallow chalk.

1|2 Mature height: 1-2m | Multi-stem | Evergreen trees

PINUS pinaster
Bournemouth Pine, Maritime Pine

A highly useful introduction from the Western Mediterranean. Introduced in the 16th century it thrives on light sandy soils and tolerates coastal conditions. It won the Award of Garden Merit in 2002. Commonly planted on England's South coast from which it derives its common name.

Sparsely branched, it can get quite large and develops a dark reddish brown patchwork bark at maturity. Shiny brown cones are produced about 18cm long which compliment the long leaves that are grown in pairs. It is very important in Western France where it supplies industry with large quantities of turpentine and resin. Also referred to as Pinus maritima.

12|17 Mature height: 12-17m | Shape of mature tree | Evergreen trees

PINUS pinea
Italian Stone Pine

The Stone Pine is sometimes also known as the Umbrella Pine. Its seeds, which when roasted, are an essential ingredient of the well known Italian pesto sauce. Unlike other Pines we grow, this one is produced as a half standard or standard tree with a well developed rounded crown.

A distinct and rather picturesque medium tree, this Pine does well in coastal locations and on light, sandy soils. Its bark is gorgeously craggy, flaking off easily when disturbed. A native of the Mediterranean, it won the Award of Garden Merit in 2002.

12|17 Mature height: 12-17m | Shape of mature tree | Evergreen trees

PINUS radiata
Monterey Pine

This makes a large tree with a deeply fissured bark and a dense crown of branches supporting needles in threes up to 15cm in length. Introduced in 1833 by David Douglas from California, it won the Award of Garden Merit in 2002.

Cones are borne in whorls along the branches and often remain intact for several years. A very useful subject for coastal areas as it is quick to grow and able to withstand strong salt laden winds.

17|22 Mature height: 17-22m | Shape of mature tree | Evergreen trees

PINUS strobus
Weymouth Pine, Eastern White Pine

Introduced from Eastern North America in the early 1600s, when I first saw this Pine in a nursery setting I mistook it for Pinus Wallichiana as it had similar long, soft and slightly glaucous needles.

The leaves are in 5's and last for two seasons before falling. It is a very touchy feely plant and incredibly graceful, especially when young when its pyramidal habit flows beautifully in the breeze. Thriving on most well drained soils it makes a wonderful specimen parkland tree. It is not for urban planting as it is not tolerant of pollution and especially salt so it is best placed in our countryside.

17|22 Mature height: 17-22m | Shape of mature tree | Evergreen trees

PINUS sylvestris
Scots Pine

The Scots Pine is the only Pine native to Britain. A familiar sight in bleak and inhospitable landscapes, it can be grown as a tall stemmed or a low, spreading subject.

Its paired needles can be very variable in colour from green to almost blue, especially when juvenile. It is very quick to develop a symbiotic relationship with mycorrhiza which helps sustain vigorous growth..

17|22 Mature height: 17-22m | Shape of mature tree | Evergreen trees | Native trees

This large evergreen tree is distinctive by its tall, bare trunk and broadly pyramidal crown. It is best suited in parks, gardens, heathland and woodlands. It is tolerant of most soils but never reaches its true potential in areas prone to flooding. As a cautionary note, it is worth sticking with Austrian Pine for coastal conditions as Scots Pine rarely seems to thrive near the coast.

PINUS sylvestris Fastigiata
Sentinel Pine

A wonderfully columnar form of Scots Pine, so tight in habit that one has to get quite close to indentify it. There are some nicely maturing specimens in the conifer garden at the Harlow Carr arboretum. The needles appear almost blue when young giving it a highly ornamental feel.

Introduced circa 1856, it is naturally occurring in Europe. It can reach over 10 metres tall if it isn't hampered by snow and ice build up which can cause it to fracture. However, there are no such problems in the UK making this a fabulous choice for many aspects.

7|12		
Mature height: 7-12m	Shape of mature tree	Narrow trees

PINUS wallichiana
Bhutan Pine

A native of the Himalayas, this wonderfully attractive soft needled pine was introduced to Britain in the early 1820s and is also known by many as Pinus griffithii. A winner of the Award of Garden Merit in 2002 and the Award of Merit in 1979, it is a worthy subject for any large garden.

Elegant and most ornamental, this large, rather conical tree has blue-green foliage and pendent cones which become covered in resin. It is moderately lime tolerant but shallow chalk soils should be avoided. It offers a unique softness to a large garden and so easily draws the eye.

17|22 Mature height: 17-22m | Shape of mature tree | Evergreen trees

PLATANUS x hispanica (acerifolia)

London Plane

First recorded in the early 1660s, the London Plane was extensively planted as a street tree in the capital due to its tolerance of air pollution and of pruning. It is believed that it was significantly responsible for clearing up the smog laden air resulting from the industrial revolution.

A large, fast growing tree with a broadly oval crown. One of its main features is the trunk, which flakes to reveal a patchwork of green, white and cream. The leaves are large, deeply lobed and palmate. The rounded fruit clusters, produced in strings, resemble little baubles, which hang from the branches for much of the year. Still a good choice for urban plantings, it is also great for parkland.

17|22 Mature height: 17-22m	Shape of mature tree	Urban trees

Reputedly the oldest Plane tree in England is in the Bishops Palace Garden at Ely. Planted by Bishop Gunning more than 300 years ago it is one of the most impressive trees in Britain, and just a stones throw from Barcham.

PLATANUS orientalis Digitata

One of the most striking of Planes, it is also known as the Chennar Tree, and often provides shaded meeting places in southern European villages. There is a wonderful example of its parent, Platanus orientalis, in the Bishops Palace garden in Ely not too far from Barcham.

This has similar, attractively flaking bark to the London Plane, but has deeply cut five lobed leaves.

A large tree with a generally rounded habit, it can attain a very great age. Magnificent in parkland and large estates as well as gracing the main arterial roads of central London.

17|22 Mature height: 17-22m | Shape of mature tree | Urban trees

PLATANUS orientalis Minaret

Similar to 'Digitata' this clone was planted along the pavement avenues of O'Connell Street in Dublin to great effect. Very neat in habit when young, it develops a broad crown much the same as its parent, Platanus orientalis, when maturing.

Lovely cut leaves and a good pyramidal habit makes this a good choice for urban streets and parkland. Reputed to have good resistance to anthracnose, but I have not seen it for long enough to make judgement.

17|22		
Mature height: 17-22m	Shape of mature tree	Urban trees

POPULUS alba
White Poplar

The fast growing White Poplar is ideal for exposed and coastal plantings. Long naturalised in the UK, it was first introduced from South Eastern Europe. Its vivid foliage is most spectacular on a bright sunny day against a cloudless sky.

Ultimately a large tree of fairly rounded form, it has green leaves, the undersides of which are silver-white, turning yellow in autumn. It is a tough tree, but it needs to be given plenty of space for its extensive root system to develop. A good choice for calcareous soils.

17|22		
Mature height: 17-22m	Shape of mature tree	Coastal sites

POPULUS alba Raket

This cultivar of White Poplar was raised in Holland in the 1950s for urban use. It is a particularly useful choice for coastal settings where the sea breezes constantly flicker the silver white leaves to provide splendid contrast.

It is notable for its columnar and slender habit when young but it still makes a formidable tree when mature so care should be taken to give it enough space to colonise. It thrives on most soils and is quick to grow.

17|22		
Mature height: 17-22m	Shape of mature tree	Coastal sites

POPULUS x candicans Aurora

Given the Award of Merit in 1954, this highly showy tree is both vigorous and instantly recognisable. Universally used as a substitute by the trade for Populus serotina Aurea, which is totally different, so beware!

The leaves are randomly variegated, especially when young, with coloured creamy white leaves that are also often tinged pink. Older leaves turn green and mysteriously newly transplanted trees show no sign of variegation either until they settle down in the second year. For best results, hard prune the shoots in winter and you will be rewarded by a magnificent display the following growing season.

12|17 Mature height: 12-17m | Shape of mature tree | Variegated trees

POPULUS nigra
Black Poplar

The Black Poplar, a native of Europe and Western Asia, is rarely found these days. We propagate native Black Poplar trees, originally from parent trees in Thurrock, Essex, so can supply the true type instead of relying on hybrid lookalikes from continental imports.

Cultivated for a long time and prized for its timber, this makes a large,rounded and heavy-branched tree, characterised by its burred trunk and glabrous twigs. Very good for parks and woodland, this tough tree is also great for getting trees going in exposed areas by giving much needed shelter.

17|22 Mature height: 17-22m | Shape of mature tree | Native trees

POPULUS nigra Italica
Lombardy Poplar

The Lombardy poplar is a male clone, propagated from cuttings taken in Lombardy in the 1700s. It is a particularly tough tree even coping with coastal exposure. Introduced to the UK in 1758 it won the Award of Garden Merit in 2002.

These are the trees that line mile after mile (or should that be kilometre after kilometre?) of French roads. Very tall, tightly columnar and of uniform habit, they make a fine windbreak or screen, and are also good for specimen planting in parks. One of the very best for verges and avenues.

POPULUS serotina Aurea
Golden Poplar

Derived from a sport taken at Van Geert's nursery in Ghent in 1871, this won the Award of Garden Merit in 2002.

Large and fast growing, this tree is also known as Populus x canadensis serotina Aurea. It sometimes produces a rather uneven crown so it is best for parkland. Its leaves, coppery red when young, are late to show and its catkins have conspicuous red anthers. Like all Poplars, it thrives on most soils.

POPULUS tremula
Aspen

The shimmering of Aspen leaves, set in motion on even the most gentle of breezes, provides a wonderful rustling sound in the landscape reminiscent of slow cascading water. Thriving on most soils, light or heavy, this tough tree can also cope with wet land so is an ideal candidate for exposed and difficult sites.

Grey catkins appear in early spring, while the serrated leaves turn clear yellow in autumn and often remain on the tree for many weeks. The Aspen is a medium to large tree with a rounded habit. Well suited to verges and parkland.

17|22 Mature height: 17-22m | Shape of mature tree | Parkland trees | Native trees

POPULUS tremula Erecta

Widely used as a street tree in the USA this underused tree was first discovered in a Swedish woodland and still bears the name 'Swedish Upright'. Similar in shape and habit to the Lombardy poplar it offers far more ornamental interest with bronze foliage emerging in April once the long catkins have finished.

We rate this highly as a tightly columnar tree that is very suitable for planting within an urban environment. The trembling leaves turn a lovely orange yellow in the autumn and this clone requires very little maintenance. The architectural shape of this tree is very striking within a landscape and tends to draw the eye with its symmetry. In Italy they have the evergreen pencil cedar to define their rolling Tuscan hills but we are restricted to this deciduous version in the UK to achieve a similar effect. Usefully, this variety is also suited to coastal planting, though not as the first line of defence.

12|17 Mature height: 12-17m | Shape of mature tree | Narrow trees

PRUNUS Accolade

This Flowering Cherry is a cross between Prunus sargentii and Prunus x subhirtella and so inherits the best features of both, namely profuse pink flowers in spring as well as a smattering in the winter. This great clone is well proven, winning the First Class Certificate in 1954, the Award of Merit in 1952 and the updated Award of Garden Merit in 2002.

An outstandingly fine small tree with a rounded and spreading habit, its semi-double pink blossoms are hard to rival. Tolerant of most soils, including calcareous ones, this is a good choice for streets, parks and gardens.

3|8			
Mature height: 3-8m	Shape of mature tree	Flowering trees	Bee friendly trees

PRUNUS Amanogawa

This late April and early May blossoming Japanese Cherry is also known as Prunus serrulata Erecta Miyoshi. A well used and recognised variety, it won the Award of Garden Merit in 2002.

Perfect as a street tree or garden tree where space is at a premium, this tightly columnar cultivar is often grown as a feathered tree to maximise the number of semi-double, shell pink flowers it produces. The young leaves are a copper-bronze. Tolerant of most free draining soils.

3|8			
Mature height: 3-8m	Shape of mature tree	Flowering trees	Bee friendly trees

PRUNUS avium
Wild Cherry

The red-brown wood of the Wild Cherry is used in cabinet making and for musical instruments and pipes. Although its own fruits tend to be bitter, it is one of the parents of most European cultivated Cherries.

One of the most attractive of our native, woodland trees, this becomes a medium to large tree with a broadly rounded form. Its white flowers in spring are followed by foliage which often shows good autumn colouring of red and gold. A good tree for parks and woodlands that thrives on most free draining soils.

12|17				
Mature height: 12-17m	Shape of mature tree	Native trees	Flowering trees	Bee friendly trees

PRUNUS avium Kordia

For fresh cherries straight off the tree this one is hard to beat! Lush black fruits are produced by August and their tough shiny skins make them resistant to splitting when growing with summer rain. White flowers in the spring add to the garden interest.

It will thrive on most free draining soils but benefits greatly from a fertilizer in the spring and a one metre mulch strip around the stem to keep other plant competition at bay. With no VAT on edible fruit trees, if you like cherries look no further! Combine with Prunus Early Rivers to get early and late fruit.

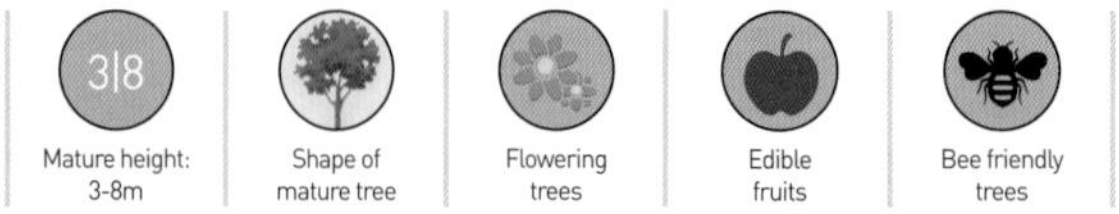

PRUNUS avium Plena

This wonderful double flowering version of our native Wild Cherry has been in cultivation since the early 1700s and is still a favourite today. Its mass of double white flowers are absolutely superb when in full swing.

Although it is best suited to parkland / woodland planting it is also a very useful urban tree, coping well with reflected heat and light bouncing back from hard surfaces.

It often retains a strong apically dominant leader making the trunk easy to crown lift over time. Given the right conditions the autumn foliage can also be glorious, and like most cherries it thrives on most free draining soils. Being a native derivative it is easily placed within the UK landscape and is probably one of our prettiest indigenous clones. If it is grown on avium rootstock it may cause damage to hard areas so it is safer to plant trees that have been budded onto colt.

12|17 Mature height: 12-17m | Shape of mature tree | Flowering trees | Urban trees | Bee friendly trees

PRUNUS cerasifera Nigra
Purple-Leaved Plum

Introduced in the early 1900s this form of the Cherry Plum (or Myrobolan) usually sets only a few red fruits. A popular tree, often planted in city streets or verges, it is easy to maintain in a garden as it reacts well to very severe winter pruning. I once decimated an overgrown specimen in a friend's garden by reducing the crown by about 60%. They were pretty sceptical but now always comment on its regrowth and apply the same treatment every five years of so!

A small tree with a rounded form, it is most notable for its purple leaves and stems. Early pink spring flowers fade to white before the leaves take full effect. This is a robust performer, thriving on most free draining soils.

3|8 Mature height: 3-8m	Shape of mature tree	Red/purple foliage	Bee friendly trees

PRUNUS cerasifera Crimson Point

A great clone of Purple Leaf Plum for smaller gardens and restricted areas. The branches are stiffly ascending, resembling the habit of a Prunus amanogowa rather than its rounded parent. At maturity it broadens but still retains an oval habit with leaves that have more hints of red and dark green rather than solely purple.

Thriving on most free draining soils this tough tree is great for formal avenues or tree lined streets where little maintenance is required. Discovered amongst a batch of Prunus ceriasfera seedlings in 1983 in the USA, it flowers well in the spring with a good covering of small white blooms that contrast well with emerging bronze foliage.

3|8 Mature height: 3-8m	Shape of mature tree	Garden trees	Flowering trees	Bee friendly trees

PRUNUS
Cheals Weeping

This well known garden tree has been oversold by garden centres for years but still represents one of the best weeping cherry cultivars in production. It requires very little maintenance, thrives in most free draining soils and never fails to perform.

Rather similar to Prunus Kiku-shidare Sakura, this has a more steeply weeping habit. It is a small tree, and is stunning in spring when it bears double pink flowers. An excellent choice for gardens where space is limited.

3|5 Mature height: 3-5m | Shape of mature tree | Garden trees | Bee friendly trees

PRUNUS domestica
Early Rivers

Bred by the well known Rivers Nursery in Hertfordshire in the 1860s, this edible cherry produces dark red fruits by July. Buying cherries from the supermarket can be expensive so getting them from your own tree may be a better option. Classified as fruit, this tree has no VAT attributed to it.

White flowers in the spring add to the general interest and this round headed tree thrives in most free draining soils. It is always beneficial to keep competition away from its base and to top dress with a general purpose fertilizer each spring to enhance fruiting.

3|8 Mature height: 3-8m | Shape of mature tree | Garden trees | Edible fruits | Bee friendly trees

PRUNUS domestica
Hauszwetsche

This dark blue damson / plum has green tinged flesh and is great eaten straight from the tree or as the ingredient for a crumble or pie. As it is classified by the Government as food, there is no VAT when buying this tree which makes it even more palatable!

Thriving on most free draining soils, its fruit size and flavour can be enhanced by keeping completion, especially grass, at bay within a metre radius of its trunk. Attractive white flowers in the spring should not be forgotten as a reason to include this round headed tree into a garden.

3|8 Mature height: 3-8m | Shape of mature tree | Garden trees | Edible fruits | Bee friendly trees

PRUNUS domestica Reine-Claude d'oullins Greengage

Raised in France, greengages are less common than plums in the UK but I think that means we have missed out! Green plum-like fruits mature to green / yellow when ripe and are sweet and juicy eaten straight from the tree. They are also a fantastic ingredient for a crumble or pie.

There is no VAT on this tree making it even better tasting! Thriving on most free draining soils a spring fertilizer is recommended to power fruit size and flavour. Keeping grass competition away from the base of the trunk is also beneficial, based on many a commercial fruit trial.

3|8 Mature height: 3-8m | Shape of mature tree | Garden trees | Edible fruits | Bee friendly trees

PRUNUS domestica Victoria
Victoria Plum

The nation's favourite eating plum, grown on a colt rootstock here at Barcham as a full standard. The small white flowers that emerge in the spring are superseded by good sized red blushed fruits that beckon to us, birds and insects alike.

Our despatch teams tend to gorge themselves with the plums prior to autumn delivery so don't be surprised to take delivery of baron plants! Nutritious free draining soils free from grass competition within a metre radius from the trunk provide best results for your fruiting harvest.

3|8 Mature height: 3-8m | Shape of mature tree | Edible fruits | Bee friendly trees

PRUNUS dulcis
Common Almond

I was shown a lovely painting of Hampstead Garden Suburb depicting a Victorian tree-lined avenue of Almonds in full flower which prompted me to bring back this old favourite into our range. However it is fraught with difficulty as they tend to attract every insect pest and fungal mildew under the sun so beware!!

Its pink, single and double flowers can reach up to 5cm across before the foliage emerges to create a lovely effect. It is always best to plant on free draining soils where no other Prunus have been to try and avoid pest and disease build up.

3|8 Mature height: 3-8m | Shape of mature tree | Edible nuts | Bee friendly trees

PRUNUS fructosa Globosa

This man-made tree has its uses in urban environments where space is limited. Small white flowers in spring are replaced by a dense canopy of small vivid green leaves that turn a glorious orange / red in the autumn.

A top worked, dwarfing clone which forms a compact and rounded crown. Budded onto Colt rootstock, Prunus avium is used as the inter-stock, with fructosa Globosa top grafted to form the crown. The avium inter-stock gives the height, while the Colt rootstock prevents pavement heave. It requires virtually no maintenance, and is an admirable urban tree.

3|8 Mature height: 3-8m | Shape of mature tree | Urban trees | Bee friendly trees

PRUNUS x gondouinii Schnee

A most attractive form of Duke Cherry with lustrous and large green leaves that give a good autumnal display of gold and orange. It is a cross between Prunus avium and Prunus cerasus and although not commonly planted it has considerable merit.

This small, rounded tree is perfect for gardens, parks and street plantings. The large, white, single flowers are borne in late April and early May. It thrives best in free draining soils and there is a historic avenue of them in Battersea Park, London.

3|8 Mature height: 3-8m | Shape of mature tree | Garden trees | Bee friendly trees

PRUNUS x hillieri Spire

A cross between Prunus sargentii and Prunus yedoensis raised in the late 1920s. The original tree now stands at 10 metres high and its autumn colour can be a joy to behold. It has had many accolades over the years and won the Award of Garden Merit in 2002.

This ranks as one of the finest of small street trees, and it is also excellent in gardens and parks. With its tight, upright habit and profusion of pink flowers, it is ideal for most sites where space is limited. Rather slow growing and not suited to the north of Scotland where the winters are too wet and cold.

3|8 Mature height: 3-8m	Shape of mature tree	Narrow trees	Bee friendly trees

PRUNUS Hokusai

With stiffly ascending branches when young, this elegant garden tree broadens with age to become vase shaped at maturity. Its flowers emerge semi double and light pink in May before fading to a lovely white. Bronze spring foliage contrasts well with its floral display before hardening to summer green.

Like most cherries, it doesn't thrive on wet soils and is intolerant of waterlogged land. Its autumn colour is good, sometimes turning to orange and reds before leaf fall. It is a relatively small tree so great for restricted areas and small gardens.

3|8			
Mature height: 3-8m	Shape of mature tree	Flowering trees	Bee friendly trees

PRUNUS Joi-nioj

This spreading ornamental cherry has an abundance of slightly scented white flowers in the spring and seldom sets fruit. Its crown flattens at maturity giving it a classic Japanese Cherry feel. Ideal for medium sized gardens and parks, this lovely cultivar must have a free draining soil as it doesn't suffer wet land.

Its leaves emerge bronze in the Spring like Tia Haku, before hardening to green in the summer. Autumn colour is generally good depending on the season with leaves turning to yellow, orange and sometimes red.

3|8			
Mature height: 3-8m	Shape of mature tree	Flowering trees	Bee friendly trees

This cherry has stiffly ascending branches forming a columnar crown when young before becoming more rounded at maturity. It is of medium height and reliably produces plenty of very showy, dark pink flowers in the spring. Sometimes rather too vigorous for paved areas, it is, nevertheless, good in parks.

PRUNUS Kanzan

A very widely planted and most popular Flowering Cherry. Introduced in the early 1900s, it has won numerous awards culminating in the Award of Garden Merit in 2002.

Its large green leaves can turn to a glorious display in the autumn but first emerge a coppery red. It is more vigorous but otherwise similar to 'Pink Perfection'.

3|8 Mature height: 3-8m | Shape of mature tree | Flowering trees | Bee friendly trees

PRUNUS laurocerasus Novita

A tree form of laurel, grown as a standard. White flowers in the spring and year round evergreen leaves marks this clone as very useful for those requiring privacy. Another clone, Novita, is also an option but too similar to merit a separate listing!

Hedging laurel often takes as much horizontal space as vertical space in a garden, and with small areas this can be problematic. This clone of laurel has thinner leaves than that of Prunus Rotundifolia and also runs up as a standard plant so the screening is effective beyond the fence line without encroaching into valuable garden space at ground level.

5|7			
Mature height: 5-7m	Shape of mature tree	Privacy raised screening	Bee friendly trees

PRUNUS laurocerasus Rotundifolia
Laurel

Cherry laurel was introduced from its native Eastern Europe in 1576 and is now naturalised over much of the UK. It relies on the trace element magnesium so if your hedge is yellowing you now know what to apply! It does not thrive on shallow chalky soils.

A particularly bushy, rounded form, this cultivar is ideal for hedging and screening. It is a very versatile plant as it can be savagely pruned back to bare wood and still only takes a few months to regain its screening use.

3|8			
Mature height: 3-8m	Multi-stem	Hedging trees	Bee friendly trees

PRUNUS angustifolia Lusitanica
Portugal Laurel

Portugal Laurel is widely used for hedging, but also makes a fine, specimen tree if required. It is prettier than common laurel with red stems and narrower leaves but it is just as durable. White flowers in the spring are an added bonus.

We offer them as half-standards. Grown as a tree, it remains small and has a good rounded habit, and it does well on most soils, including shallow chalk. Very attractive as a hedge, giving year-round interest and cover to many small birds. Ideal for gardens and parks.

3|8 Mature height: 3-8m | Shape of mature tree | Privacy raised screening | Hedging trees | Bee friendly trees

PRUNUS maackii Amber Beauty

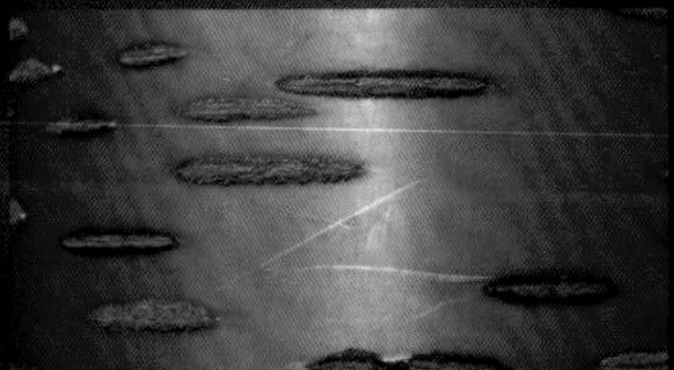

A Dutch selection of the Manchurian Cherry. Thriving on most free draining soils the white flowers in spring are more akin to Bird Cherry than anything else and their effect is lovely against a clear blue sky.

Stunning in winter with its smoothly polished, golden stems, this cultivar of medium height and rounded form is early into leaf in spring. It is a stout and vigorous grower tolerating the harsher aspects of our urban environments. I have seen this clone planted as a street tree in Portsmouth and it makes a fantastically stocky tree with a rounded crown as it drifts into maturity.

3|8 Mature height: 3-8m | Shape of mature tree | Bark interest | Bee friendly trees

PRUNUS Okame

This very pretty cherry is derived from Prunus incisa and was raised by Captain Collingwood Ingram in the 1940s. A winner of the Award of Garden Merit in 2002, its dainty foliage produces a great autumnal display of orange and reds.

A small rounded tree, Okame produces a mass of profuse rich pink flowers in late March and early April. It is a splendid choice for gardens and parks. Like most of its type it is not suited to waterlogged soils.

3|8 Mature height: 3-8m	Shape of mature tree	Garden trees	Bee friendly trees

PRUNUS padus
Bird Cherry

The Bird Cherry, a native of Britain as well as the rest of Europe, is a relatively late flowerer. It is a tough tree, withstanding the rigours of the urban environment but like other cherries does not thrive on waterlogged ground.

The white flowers of the Bird Cherry are produced in May in hanging racemes. The black fruits in late summer are edible but rather bitter. Luscious and large green leaves turn yellow to bronze in autumn. This is a rounded tree of medium height, and is good in parks, gardens and woodlands.

7|12 Mature height: 7-12m	Shape of mature tree	Native trees	Bee friendly trees

PRUNUS padus Albertii

This clone of Bird Cherry has been cultivated since the 1900s and is probably the best clone for urban plantings where space is more restricted. The crown is very ascending when young before developing into an oval to rounded shape at maturity.

A rather good choice for garden, street and verge planting, this very free flowering form has an excellent track record for requiring little maintenance. It thrives on most soils but is best suited to free draining sites.

7|12 Mature height: 7-12m	Shape of mature tree	Urban trees	Bee friendly trees

PRUNUS padus Watererii

Sometimes referred to as Prunus padus Grandiflora, this clone of Bird Cherry was introduced slightly after 'Albertii' in the early 1900s. It won the Award of Garden Merit in 2002 and is a popular choice for amenity planting.

Remarkable for its long white racemes up to 20cm long this cultivar is of medium height and with a rounded, rather spreading habit. A good selection for parks and other open spaces but is too vigorous for streets. Quick to grow in the first few years it tolerates most soils.

7|12 Mature height: 7-12m	Shape of mature tree	Parkland trees	Bee friendly trees

PRUNUS Pandora

This wonderful Prunus yedoensis cross is a great choice for an urban garden or street. It won the Award of Merit in 1939 and the updated Award of Garden Merit in 2002. It has relatively small leaves for a cherry and requires very little maintenance for so much ornamental interest.

Pandora makes only a small tree, but its ascending branches, which give its broadly columnar habit, become smothered by pale pink blossom in March and early April. The bronze-red leaves in autumn also provide a wonderful show. It thrives best on free draining sites.

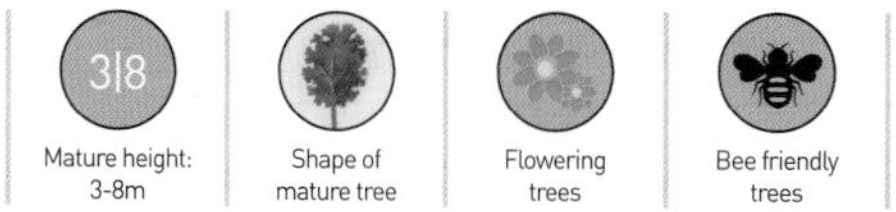

PRUNUS
Pink Perfection

A British-bred form of flowering cherry that started its commercial origins in about 1935 and won the Award of Garden Merit in 2002. It prefers free draining soils and will generally suffer if waterlogged.

Similar in some ways to Kanzan, which we believe to be one of its parents, Pink Perfection is less vigorous. Its double flowers, dark pink in bud, opening slightly paler, are borne in long clusters. It has a broadly oval crown and is of medium to large form. Suitable for verges, broad streets and parks.

3|8			
Mature height: 3-8m	Shape of mature tree	Flowering trees	Bee friendly trees

PRUNUS
Royal Burgundy

This Flowering Cherry is rather like a purple-leaved equivalent of the well known Prunus Kanzan. Fairly new to our range, it gives wonderful contrast to a garden with its spectacular foliage and flower display.

Historically Prunus cerasifera Nigra is thought of as the choice for purple leaf interest but this clone provides real competition.

3|8				
Mature height: 3-8m	Shape of mature tree	Multi-stem	Red/purple foliage	Bee friendly trees

A small tree with ascending branches, it forms an oval to rounded crown at maturity. Its double, shell pink flowers are set against beautiful, wine-red foliage to create an eye-catching effect. Lovely in parks and gardens but like most cherries it prefers a free draining soil.

PRUNUS sargentii

Introduced from its native Japan in 1890 this is widely regarded as one of the loveliest of flowering cherries and with the advantage of its blossom usually being ignored by bullfinches. A winner of numerous accolades culminating in the Award of Garden Merit in 2002.

A superb, small tree of rounded habit, and a great choice for gardens, parks and streets. It bears abundant, single, pink flowers in March and April, and is one of the first to take on its autumn tints of orange and crimson, which complement its chestnut-brown bark so effectively.

3|8			
Mature height: 3-8m	Shape of mature tree	Flowering trees	Bee friendly trees

PRUNUS sargentii Rancho

Sometimes too close to call from straight forward Prunus sargentii, this flowering cherry was raised in the USA in the 1950s and came across to be grown by European nurseries shortly afterwards.

A broadly columnar form of the species, it is of similarly low height, and is just the job where space is rather restricted. It bears abundant, single, pink flowers in March and April, and is one of the first to take on its autumn tints of orange and crimson. Its bark is noticeably darker than most cherries and it thrives best on free draining soils.

3|8			
Mature height: 3-8m	Shape of mature tree	Flowering trees	Bee friendly trees

PRUNUS x schmittii

This Prunus avium cross originates back to 1923 and can grow more than 15 metres given suitable conditions. Sometimes too vigorous for streets, it is better placed on green verges or gardens where it needs little or no maintenance.

It is most remarkable for its polished, red-brown bark that improves with every passing year. Fairly quick growing, it's stiffly ascending branches form a narrow but large conical crown even at maturity. It shows fine autumn colours and thrives best on free draining soils.

7|12			
Mature height: 7-12m	Shape of mature tree	Bark interest	Bee friendly trees

A fast growing, but small tree of rounded form. It has really shiny, mahogany-brown bark that just keeps on getting better and more sensational with age which makes it worth growing for this reason alone. It has narrow, willow-like leaves and small, white flowers, which are produced in April. Like most cherries it thrives best on free draining soils.

PRUNUS serrula Tibetica

Tibetan Cherry

This lovely cherry was introduced from Western China in 1908 by Ernest Wilson and is surely one of the best trees available for bark interest.

Available as single stemmed or multi- stemmed this wonderfully dramatic tree can provide great contrast within a garden or urban environment. Its many horticultural honours culminated in the Award of Garden Merit in 2002.

3|8 Mature height: 3-8m | Shape of mature tree | Multi-stem | Bark interest | Bee friendly trees

PRUNUS Shimidsu Sakura

This dainty Japanese Cherry, introduced very early in the 1900s is also known as Shôgetsu. It is remarkably pretty in flower and in my opinion the most attractive flowering cherry on the market although Prunus Shirofugen comes a close second! A First Class Certificate winner in 1989 it also won the Award of Garden Merit.

A small tree with a broad, rounded habit, this is one of the most outstanding Japanese Cherries, and one we strongly recommend for verges, parks and gardens. The pink buds open to reveal large, white, petals sharply toothed at the fringe, which clothe the branches in long stalked clusters.

3|8 Mature height: 3-8m | Shape of mature tree | Flowering trees | Bee friendly trees

PRUNUS Shirotae

This cherry is sometimes referred to as Mount Fuji and was introduced to Britain in the early 1900s. Like most weeping varieties it gets better with age and at maturity it can be overwhelmingly stunning when seen in full flower against a blue spring sky. It won the Award of Garden Merit in 2002.

Gently weeping is perhaps the best way to describe the habit of this small, but vigorous tree. Green fringed foliage is followed by very large single and semi-double pure white flowers. Very good for verges, parks and gardens.

3|8 Mature height: 3-8m | Shape of mature tree | Flowering trees | Bee friendly trees

PRUNUS Shirofugen

A late and long lasting flowerer introduced in the very early 1900s by Ernest Wilson that won the Award of Garden Merit in 2002. Considered by many as the best flowering cherry on the market, it is hard to disagree with them. A superb garden tree, it also thrives within an urban environment.

A rather spreading tree with a rounded crown, Shirofugen remains small. Its large, double, white flowers finish pink, contrasting well with the young, copper coloured foliage.

3|8			
Mature height: 3-8m	Shape of mature tree	Flowering trees	Bee friendly trees

Excellent for verges, parks and gardens it is a wonderful sight when in full flow.
It thrives best on free draining soils. Its floral display is incredibly long lasting.

PRUNUS x subhirtella Autumnalis
Autumn Cherry

The Autumn Cherry brings cheer at the darkest time of year. Introduced in 1894 it won the Award of Merit in 1930 and remains a favourite for planting in the UK. Often top grafted on the continent, we strongly recommend base grafted trees for structural longevity.

This small, rounded tree produces its semi-double, white flowers intermittently from November through to March a welcome sight on a bleak, winter's day. Autumn foliage is orange-yellow.
A lovely tree for streets, parks and gardens that thrives best on well drained soils.

3|8 Mature height: 3-8m | Shape of mature tree | Flowering trees | Bee friendly trees

PRUNUS x subhirtella Autumnalis Rosea

An alternative form of the beautiful Autumn Cherry that won the Award of Garden Merit in 2002 after it received the Award of Merit in 1960. Prized by inventive flower arrangers in winter for its woody flowering stems.

This small, rounded tree produces its semi-double, pink flowers sporadically from November through to March, a welcome sight in the dark, winter months. Autumn foliage is orange-yellow.
Ideal for streets, parks or gardens but it does not care for waterlogged ground.

3|8 Mature height: 3-8m | Shape of mature tree | Flowering trees | Bee friendly trees

PRUNUS Sunset Boulevard

This relatively new introduction was bred at the Arboretum Kalmthout, Belgium, in the late 1980s for urban use. Many state it is extremely columnar but we reckon broadly oval would be more appropriate a description.

Its young coppery foliage turns green in summer and golden yellow in autumn and its large, white, single flowers are edged with pink. This durable tree is very good for parks and street plantings and thrives best on free draining soils.

The more I have seen of this tree the more I like it and once it develops a good crown the floral display is lovely, especially against a blue sky. I think this may become an urban favourite for its durability and aesthetics.

7|12 Mature height: 7-12m	Shape of mature tree	Flowering trees	Bee friendly trees

PRUNUS Tai haku
Great White Cherry

The Great White Cherry makes a magnificent specimen. The famous cherry enthusiast, Captain Collingwood Ingram, reintroduced this fine tree back to its native Japan in 1932 after he found a specimen growing in a Sussex garden. A winner of numerous awards including the First Class Certificate in 1944, the Award of Merit in 1931 and the Award of Garden Merit in 2002.

One of the finest of all Cherries, and probably the best of the "whites", it bears its large, single flowers profusely, contrasting beautifully with its young, copper coloured foliage. Very good for urban plantings, streets, parks and gardens, but in our experience it does not thrive in very wet soils. It is of medium height and rounded habit.

7|12			
Mature height: 7-12m	Shape of mature tree	Flowering trees	Bee friendly trees

Like many flowering cherries its best moments are demonstrated mainly in the spring and early summer but this relatively short display still makes planting this clone well worth the endeavour. Its foliage can turn to a beautiful yellow / orange in the autumn. Never accept a top grafted plant as they are prone to a shorter life expectancy.

PRUNUS Ukon

Introduced in the early 1900s this unusual cherry won the Award of Garden Merit in 2002. Sometimes imported as top grafted from the continent. This is a false economy in the long term, as the top can outgrow the bottom. We would advise base grafted trees.

A vigorous, rounded, medium size tree with a rather spreading crown, it has unusual pale yellow flowers, tinged with green and occasionally flushed with pink. They are semi-double and work well with the young bronze foliage. Its large green leaves produce a great autumn display of red and purple.

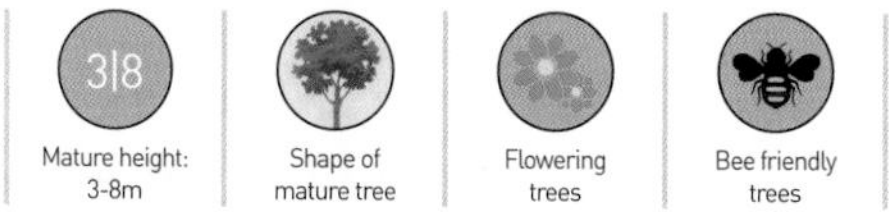

PRUNUS Umineko

This Flowering Cherry is a cross between Prunus incisa and Prunus speciosa. Sometimes also referred to as 'Snow Goose' it won the Award of Merit in 1928 and represents a very good tree for the urban environment.

Umineko has a narrow, columnar form, which broadens with age and is a very good choice for streets, parks, gardens and other restricted areas. It makes a medium size tree, and its white, single flowers are produced in April, along with the foliage, which colours very well in autumn. It is a robust and vigorous tree that thrives best on free draining soils.

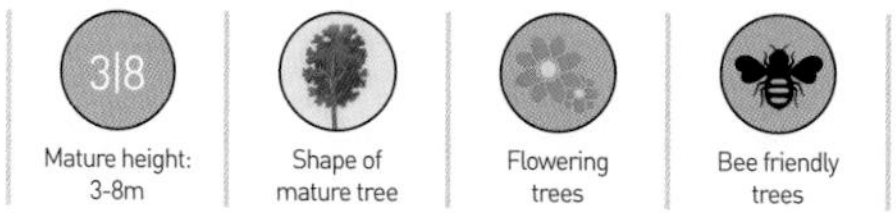

PRUNUS x yedoensis

Yoshino Cherry

3|8 Mature height: 3-8m | Shape of mature tree | Flowering trees | Bee friendly trees

The Yoshino Cherry is a cross between Prunus speciosa and Prunus x subhirtella. It came from Japan around 1902 and won the Award of Garden Merit in 2002. This superbly pretty tree is hard to beat when in full flow and there is a particularly nice specimen to behold at Kew Gardens.

A broad, flat crowned tree, its arching branches create an almost weeping effect. It is of medium height and puts on a wonderful display of almond-scented, blush-white blossom in late March and early April. The fruits are dark red, almost black. Lovely as a park tree and also very good on broad verges.

PTEROCARYA fraxinifolia Wing Nut

The Wing Nut, a relative of the Walnut originating from Iran, was introduced into the UK way back in 1782. It is a brute of a tree with some specimens reaching over 38 metres high with a crown diameter of 35 metres so be sure to give it enough room!

A fast growing, large and broadly oval tree, which does well in most fertile, moisture-retentive soils, but is especially good for use close to rivers and lakes in parkland setting. It has deeply furrowed bark and very long summer catkins, which produce two-winged nut fruits. Its deciduous dark green leaves can be up to 60cm in length and separated by numerous toothed leaflets.

17|22 Mature height: 17-22m | Shape of mature tree | Parkland trees

PYRUS Beurre Hardy

A strong growing pear, grown at Barcham as a full standard and a vigorous cropper that is particularly valued by our staff in September!

This small, rounded tree does best in a warm, sunny, sheltered position, such as a courtyard garden. The large fruits, greenish yellow flushed with red, are juicy and have a distinctive flavour. They are best picked while still hard and allowed to ripen in store. The foliage turns bright red in autumn.

3|8 Mature height: 3-8m | Shape of mature tree | Edible fruits | Bee friendly trees

Abundant blossom is produced as early as March, followed by glossy foliage which is late to fall in autumn, when it turns orange and red and even golden. It has rapidly established itself as a fine street tree, and is tolerant of air pollution and even salty, coastal winds. An excellent choice for the urban or rural environments

PYRUS calleryana Chanticleer

This Ornamental Pear was selected in the USA and named after the cockerel in Chaucer's Canterbury Tales. Bred by Edward Scanlon and patented in the States in 1965, it is often referred to as the 'Bradford Pear' which is in fact slightly broader, denser and unlike Chanticleer is prone to crown collapse at maturity.

It won the Award of Garden Merit in 2002 and as its green lush foliage is so early to appear in spring and so late to fall in autumn it has excellent screening uses.

It is one of the very best Ornamental Pears with much to recommend it. It is of medium height, generally rather columnar, becoming more oval when mature.

PYRUS calleryana Redspire

Patented by Princeton Nursery in America in 1975, this seedling of Bradford Pear is happily less vigorous than its parent which has been known to break apart when older due to tight branch angles. As the foliage is so late to fall in autumn it is also great for screening.

medium height, generally rather columnar, becoming more oval when mature. Profuse white blossom is produced in spring, followed by glossy foliage which becomes orange and red. An excellent choice for urban conditions and very good in streets and gardens.

12|17 Mature height: 12-17m	Shape of mature tree	Autumn colour	Bee friendly trees

PYRUS communis Beech Hill

Many nurseries describe this as a splendid upright variety requiring little maintenance but most fail to mention the volume of fruit produced by late summer that weigh the stiffly ascending branches down. The small fruits are not edible and very hard so not ideal for urban plantings.

This medium size tree has a columnar form when young, but opens out as it matures. It provides good spring interest with its white flowers and shiny green leaves that turn to attractive shades of orange and red in autumn. Best suited to gardens.

7|12 Mature height: 7-12m	Shape of mature tree	Garden trees	Bee friendly trees

PYRUS communis Conference
Conference Pear

First introduced in 1885, this well known eating pear variety won the Award of Garden Merit in 2002. Grown at Barcham as a full standard tree for garden planting.

Juicy and sweet green / yellow fruits are generally ready October through to November. This cultivar partially self pollinates and is a good pollinator of other varieties. It tolerates most soil conditions and is still the nation's favoured edible pear.

3|8 Mature height: 3-8m	Shape of mature tree	Edible fruits	Bee friendly trees

PYRUS Doyenne du Comice
Comice Pear

Introduced from France in 1849 this tasty pear requires a pollinator and produces yellow / green rotund fruits that can be harvested from late September.

Not as well cultivated as Conference, it has more flavour but less storage longevity. It won the Award of Garden Merit in 2002 and is worth planting alongside Pyrus communis Beech Hill which can act as the pollinator. Like most fruit trees we recommend a metre radius mulch ring round each tree to promote fruit size and to avoid planting in soils with poor drainage.

3|8			
Mature height: 3-8m	Shape of mature tree	Edible fruits	Bee friendly trees

PYRUS salicifolia Pendula
Willow-Leaved Pear

This very popular garden tree won the Award of Garden Merit in 2002. Its dainty foliage can provide lovely contrast and the tree is very adaptable in that I have seen it pruned in a variety of shapes and sizes.

This small, weeping and rather broad tree produces its creamy white flowers and willow-like silvery grey foliage at the same time in spring. Its weeping branches are silver grey, giving good winter interest. A very good subject for parks and gardens tolerating urban conditions well. It reacts well to severe pruning in the early spring, just before the leaves emerge to prevent the crown getting too woody.

3|8			
Mature height: 3-8m	Shape of mature tree	Garden trees	Bee friendly trees

QUERCUS bimondorum

This alba x robur cross is a native of the North Eastern USA and has a crisp vibrant seven to nine lobed leaf that marks it as different to our native oak. Its name is Latin for 'Two Worlds', Quercus robur representing the old world and Quercus alba representing the new and it has been a naturally occurring hybrid for over 100 years.

Preferring lighter soils its acorn has a hint of red about it as it matures. Ideal for estates and parks, this botanical oddity is rare in the UK so is a must for those with collections and arboretums.

Mature height: 12-17m	Shape of mature tree	Parkland trees

QUERCUS castaneifolia
Chestnut-Leaved Oak

The Chestnut-leaved Oak was introduced from the Caucasus and Iran in the mid 1840s but is rarely seen in the UK. A must for any plant collector who has the space to plant one.

Similar to Quercus cerris in appearance, this medium to large, oval shaped tree has oblong leaves, tapered at both ends. It is a magnificent tree for parks, arboretums and woodlands where there is space for its superb crown to mature.

Mature height: 17-22m	Shape of mature tree	Parkland trees

QUERCUS cerris
Turkey Oak

The highly durable Turkey Oak was introduced into the UK in 1735. A magnificent specimen can be seen at the National Trust's Knightshayes Garden in Devon, where it imposes itself on the field in which it stands.

This large, rounded tree is probably the fastest growing Oak grown in Britain. It does well even in chalky soils and in coastal areas. The dark green, lobed leaves are resistant to mildew, which affects some others of the genus. A tough tree, good for wide verges and parks, but also a host of the Knopper Gall Wasp which can migrate to Quercus robur and distort the acorn.

Mature height: 17-22m	Shape of mature tree	Parkland trees

QUERCUS coccinea
Scarlet Oak

This superb autumn colourer was introduced from its native South Eastern Canada and Eastern USA in 1691. The USA national champion in Kentucky is over 40 metres tall by 31 metres wide but trees of this stature are only seen on dry sandy soils which suits it best.

It requires a slightly acidic soil to perform at its best so select the more robust Quercus palustris if in doubt. The overall effect is very similar.

A large and impressive subject, with a broad and rounded habit. The summer's dark, glossy, green leaves turn, branch by branch, to a flaming scarlet as autumn progresses. Its acorns are carried in shallow cups. A magnificent specimen forplanting in parkland but it is often confused in the UK with Quercus palustris.

12|17			
Mature height: 12-17m	Shape of mature tree	Parkland trees	Autumn colour

QUERCUS frainetto
Hungarian Oak

This stately tree was introduced from South East Europe in the late 1830s. There are some magnificent specimens at the National Trust's Anglesey Abbey in Cambridgeshire which coincidentally is a garden not to be missed if you are in the vicinity!

This is a large tree with a broad, rounded crown. Its fissured bark and large, dark green leaves, which are boldly cut and regularly lobed, makes this a most striking subject for parks and woodlands.

We also recommend it as an avenue tree. It does best on moist soils, but will tolerate chalky ones. The clone "Trump" retains a slightly improved shape at maturity.

17|22		
Mature height: 17-22m	Shape of mature tree	Parkland trees

QUERCUS hispanica Wageningen

This rarely seen tree is thought to be a hybrid between Quercus Castanefolia and Quercus Lucombeana and is furnished with green glossy leaves that are beyond 10cm in length and 5cm across.

An interesting addition to parkland planting as this clone generally hangs onto its leaves until the spring. It has an upright habit when young and broadens with age to develop into a large tree with a rough bark at maturity. It thrives on most fertile soils.

12|17 Mature height: 12-17m	Shape of mature tree	Parkland trees

QUERCUS hispanica Fulhamensis

A botanical oddity in the UK, this semi evergreen oak holds most of its leaves winter long unless it gets very cold in which case they are jettisoned and re-flush the following Spring. It will tolerate chalky soils but is ideally placed on fertile well drained loamy soils where it forms a graceful and stately crown.

Formally known as Dentata, it is a hybrid between Quercus cerris and Quercus suber. Ideal for parkland or estates, avoid exposed situations as prolonged cold winter winds can significantly reduce leaf coverage over winter. Similar in many ways to Quercus Lucombeana, it develops a fissured corky bark when older.

12|17 Mature height: 12-17m	Shape of mature tree	Parkland trees

QUERCUS ilex
Holm Oak

The Holm Oak is a native of Mediterranean countries, but it has been grown in Britain since the 1500s, and is now thought to be a native of Southern Ireland. The timber is hard and long-lasting, used for joinery, vine-props and for charcoal. It won the Award of Garden Merit in 2002 and is surely one of the most majestic of evergreen trees grown in the UK. They seem to be more intensely silver on the coast and can quickly be mistaken for Olive when the tree is juvenile.

If left to its own devices it forms a large tree with a densely rounded habit, fine examples of which can be seen within the Holkham Hall Estate on the North Norfolk coast. The avenue there is so impressive that I obtained permission to harvest acorns for our production. Many thanks to the Estate for this.

17|22
Mature height: 17-22m
Shape of mature tree
Evergreen trees

Quercus ilex is surprisingly versatile, being suitable for coastal planting, hedging, topiary and stilted screening. It also tolerates shade and air pollution. Suitable for parks and gardens but thriving best on free draining soils.

QUERCUS imbricaria
Shingle Oak

The Shingle Oak was introduced from North America in the 1780s. Its name derives from its use for roof tiles "shingles" in its native land. The USA national champion is in Ohio and stands at over 35 metres in height with a crown at over 23 metres across, so it is not for the faint-hearted!

A medium to large vigorous tree, it has a pyramidal habit, and shiny dark green leaves, which turn golden in the autumn. Splendid for parks or estates, it thrives best on moist but well drained deep fertile acid soils and prefers full sun.

17|22 Mature height: 17-22m | Shape of mature tree | Parkland trees

QUERCUS palustris Pin Oak

More pyramidal at maturity than the similar Quercus coccinea, this magnificent tree was introduced into the UK from its native North America in 1800. It is a relatively tough tree and can withstand limited periods of waterlogging even though it prefers free draining slightly acidic soils. The USA national champion is in Tennessee and stands at 37 metres tall and broad. It won the Award of Garden Merit in 2002.

This large, pyramidal tree is one of the most graceful of Oaks, with its slender branches gently drooping at their tips. Its autumn colour is simply stunning.

20+ Mature height: 20m+ | Shape of mature tree | Parkland trees | Autumn colour

QUERCUS palustris Green Pillar

An introduction from the USA, where it is referred to as 'Pringreen'. It is an exceptional tree with ascending branches forming a very columnar crown, akin to our Quercus robur Fastigiata. Its leaves are lustrous and shiny, particularly pleasing in the summer when the sun shines on them. However, its real glory is in its autumn colour which can turn to vivid scarlet when supported by a free draining soil without alkalinity.

Great for urban areas where space is restricted, this clone is also a good choice for medium sized gardens. This clone was spotted within a seedling bed in New Jersey in the 1990s and was raised by a nurseryman working for the famous Princeton Nursery. A good find! We are sure this clone will be used more in the UK in the years to come as it ticks many of the boxes for urban planners.

12|17			
Mature height: 12-17m	Shape of mature tree	Urban trees	Autumn colour

QUERCUS palustris Helmond

The first time I saw this variety I thought it was my ideal urban Quercus palustris, not knowing it was a clonal variation. Large shiny leaves and a very regular ascending habit that forms a symmetrical broadly oval crown, this tree also has a stunning autumn display of reds and scarlet.

Like its parent, it can take wet soil but those soils prone to waterlogging should be avoided. The best autumn colour comes from trees planted in neutral to acid land. Best in full sun it can also toerate partial shade. An ideal urban tree where space allows but also great for a large garden.

12|17			
Mature height: 12-17m	Shape of mature tree	Parkland trees	Autumn colour

QUERCUS petraea
Sessile Oak

One of our two native Oaks, the Sessile Oak is long-lived and was extensively used in ship-building. A winner of the Award of Garden Merit in 2002 it is more often seen on the west side of the UK where rainfall is higher.

A good choice for coastal locations, this large, oval shaped tree will also tolerate acid soils. Similar in many respects to Quercus robur, it tends to have a greater degree of apical dominance so developing a more pyramidal crown. A wonderful choice for wildlife, this tree supports a host of animals.

17|22 Mature height: 17-22m | Shape of mature tree | Parkland trees | Native trees

QUERCUS phellos
Willow leaved Oak

Introduced from the Eastern USA in 1723, this distinctive oak has willow shaped leaves and is best established on neural to acid free draining soils even through it can tolerate wetter soils later on. It forms a broad crown at maturity so is best suited to parkland and estates to show off its autumn tints of orange and yellow.

Its slender green leaves make it difficult for the uninitiated to identify but autumn acorns that mature in their second year give it away. A great tree for plant collectors, this tree remains rare in the UK and is often restricted to arboretums.

12|17 Mature height: 12-17m | Shape of mature tree | Parkland trees

QUERCUS Regal Prince

Selected from acorns in 1974 from a mother plant in Illinois, this magnificent clone is thought to be a Quercus robur Fastigiata x Quercus bicolor cross. Its upright habit makes it a great urban tree but its resistance to powdery mildews gives its leaves a lustrous and clean look that makes Quercus robur Fastigiata look positively dowdy! Its leaves are two toned, dark green above and silvery green beneath and the tree has great hybrid vigour.

Thriving on most free draining soils, its wonderful summer foliage display turns to yellow and orange in the autumn. Not as fastigiate as 'Koster' it is nevertheless still very narrow and even through I haven't seen one at full maturity I expect it to grow to be a quarter of its width to height and this view is supported by the ongoing evidence from 30 year old plants in the States.

12|17 Mature height: 12-17m | Shape of mature tree | Urban trees

QUERCUS robur
Common Oak, English Oak

Perhaps the most majestic of our native trees, the English or Common Oak was once the predominant species in English lowland forests, and has become virtually a national emblem. Very long-lived, its hard timber has been used to produce the finest furniture, from ships through to coffins.

Many superb specimens exist in our countryside but perhaps the most famous is the Major Oak in Sherwood Forest which is estimated to be some 1000 years old and weigh over 23 tonnes. Whether Robin Hood actually took refuge in it is of debate!

A large, imposing, broadly oval tree, heavy-limbed and long-lived. Its deeply grained bark gives year-round appeal, and its expansive root system does best on deep, heavy soils. A wonderful choice for parkland and large estates, it is also good in avenues and wide verges. It is a great host for supporting wildlife and its acorns are hidden and distributed by forgetful Jays. Given the right conditions one can expect between three and four summer flushes of growth.

A wonderful choice for parkland and large estates, it is also good in avenues and wide verges. It is a great host for supporting wildlife and its acorns are hidden and distributed by forgetful Jays. Given the right conditions one can expect between three and four summer flushes of growth.

Mature height: 17-22m | Shape of mature tree | Native trees

QUERCUS robur Fastigiata (Koster)

Cypress Oak

The Cypress Oak used to be seed grown, which resulted in variability in its form, so now the industry standard is the uniformly narrow clone 'Koster' which is grafted onto Quercus robur rootstock. It won the Award of Garden Merit in 2002.

Common Oak is such a wonderful tree for wildlife, that for restricted areas this clone makes it possible to plant one. It thrives best in more rural environments where soil volumes are greater to support its growth.

12|17 Mature height: 12-17m | Shape of mature tree | Narrow trees

QUERCUS rubra

Red Oak

Introduced from its native North America in 1724, this well known stately tree won the Award of Merit in 1971 and the updated Award of Garden Merit in 2002. The bark of the Red Oak is rich in tannin essential for tanning leather.

This large, broadly oval tree does best in deep fertile soils, but tolerates most others. It is a fast grower and seems to tolerate polluted air well. Young growth emerges almost yellow in the spring before expanding into large broad green and lobed leaves by May. These in turn go a wonderful red in autumn before turning a red / brown and falling. Best suited for planting in parks and large gardens.

17|22 Mature height: 17-22m | Shape of mature tree | Parkland trees | Autumn colour

QUERCUS suber
Cork Oak

Introduced in the late 1690s, the Cork Oak is a native of southern Europe and North Africa so in the UK it is best suited to the warmer south. Until it gets beyond semi-mature it is often buoyed up by a thick bamboo cane by nurseries to support the weak stem. Our advice is never accept one unless it is strong enough to support itself.

Widely grown in Spain and Portugal for the wine industry it is resistant to British frosts. It is a short stemmed, wide, rounded, evergreen tree. Its thick and craggy bark can provide outstanding interest in a garden and it tends to thrive better on free draining soils.

3|8		
Mature height: 3-8m	Shape of mature tree	Garden trees

QUERCUS turneri x Pseudoturneri
Turners Oak

Raised by Spencer Turner of Essex way back in the 18th century, this rare collector's item is a must for any specialist arboretum. Thriving on most calcareous soils, this semi evergreen tree slowly develops into a broad headed medium sized tree with distinct dark green leaves.

During very severe winters the tree sometimes defoliates completely before new leaves emerge in April and May. Sheltered gardens in southern England generally sees it keep most of its leaves through the winter period. It prefers free draining soils and will not tolerate waterlogged ground.

7|12		
Mature height: 7-12m	Shape of mature tree	Garden trees

RHUS typhina
Stag's Horn Sumach

Stag's Horn Sumach can be grown as a small tree or as a shrub. A native of North America, it was introduced into the UK in the late 1620s and won the Award of Garden Merit in 2002. It may surprise you that the national champion in the States is over 20 metres tall but I have not seen one much over 5 metres over here.

3|8 Mature height: 3-8m | Multi-stem | Garden trees

This small tree has an irregular wide spreading and rather architectural habit. It provides superb autumn colour, and the conical red fruit clusters last for much of the winter. Very good for gardens and parks. It can be prone to suckering so allow for this when planning its position.

ROBINIA pseudoacacia
False Acacia

The False Acacia was introduced to France from America in 1601, and is now naturalised through much of Europe. It produces large epicormic thorns and can be prone to suckering so it can be used as a stout defence against unwelcome visitors.

A large irregular crowned tree with soft, green, pinnate leaves that emerge early May. Racemes of sweetly scented white flowers in June are replaced by purple tinged seed pods in autumn. It thrives on any soil, and tolerates urban pollution, but is not good in windy, exposed locations due to its rather brittle branches.

12|17 Mature height: 12-17m | Shape of mature tree | Parkland trees

ROBINIA pseudoacacia Bessoniana

This thornless clone, in cultivation since the 1870s, can be seen at its mature dimensions in the Royal Horticultural Garden at Wisely. It seldom flowers and its foliage is a paler but more vibrant green that its parent.

Of only medium height, this clone is probably the best Robinia cultivar for street planting. It has a compact, rounded crown of virtually thorn-free branches and pale green leaves. It thrives on any soil, and tolerates urban pollution, but its brittle and twiggy growth is not suited to windy sites.

Robinia and its clones are generally high maintenance but this clone is without doubt the pick of them. Its soft green spring growth is particularly attractive.

7|12 Mature height: 7-12m | Shape of mature tree | Urban trees

ROBINIA pseudoacacia Casque Rouge

This delightful cultivar of False Acacia makes a particularly fine garden, verge or parkland tree as its profuse flowers emerge in June after the Cherries, Crab Apples and Thorns have all finished.

This tree of medium height and broadly rounded habit, it is greatly prized for its showy and highly ornamental lilac-pink flowers that are richly appreciated by all those who notice. It thrives on any soil, and tolerates urban pollution, but is not good in windy, exposed locations due to its rather brittle branches. It should be noted that its scruffy form makes it a highly unsatisfactory urban tree.

7|12 Mature height: 7-12m | Shape of mature tree | Flowering trees

ROBINIA pseudoacacia Frisia

This superb yellow clone has been very popular over the past 25 years and can now be seen in most urban areas in the UK. It is tolerant of dry conditions and is well suited to cope with reflected heat and light from buildings and pavements. It won the Award of Garden Merit in 2002. Beware, however, in recent years it has been proven to be very susceptible to disease and decline.

Raised in the Netherlands in the mid 1930s, this medium tree of rounded habit only rarely flowers, but displays its beautiful golden yellow foliage from spring through to autumn. It thrives on any soil, and tolerates urban pollution.

7|12		
Mature height: 7-12m	Shape of mature tree	Garden trees

ROBINIA pseudoacacia Umbraculifera

In cultivation since the early 1800s this top grafted clone forms a rounded and compact crown ideal for urban piazzas and town gardens. It is more regularly seen in French and German cities than here in the UK.

This small, mop-headed tree seldom flowers and requires very little maintenance. The largest tree of this clone I have heard of is about 6 metres in diameter. It is best to have them top grafted between 1.8-2 metres from ground level so they can easily be walked under. It thrives on most soils and is tolerant of urban conditions.

3|8		
Mature height: 3-8m	Shape of mature tree	Garden trees

SALIX alba
White Willow

Our native White Willow is a lovely subject for water-side plantings. Very prominent in our fenland landscape surrounding the nursery, it reacts well to regular pollarding where size becomes an issue.

A fast growing, large, conical tree with slender branches which droop at the tips. The leaves give a characteristically silver appearance from a distance. Catkins are borne in spring. Although it is good in wet soils and will tolerate temporary flooding, it thrives in most soils, and is a fine choice for coastal areas.

17|22 Mature height: 17-22m | Shape of mature tree | Native trees

SALIX alba Chermesina
Scarlet Willow

This clone is also known by the cultivar name of Britzensis. A winner of the Award of Garden Merit in 2002, it has been known to extend over 3 metres of growth in a single growing season from a coppice.

A medium to large tree with a rather pyramidal crown, its young branches are a brilliant orange-red in winter, especially if severely pruned every other year to produce a multi-stemmed tree. It makes a very good park tree and thrives on most soils including those prone to flooding.

17|22			
Mature height: 17-22m	Shape of mature tree	Multi-stem	Wet soils

SALIX alba Liempde

This male clone has been planted extensively in the Netherlands, where it was selected in the late 1960s. As with all willows it reacts well to pruning if its ultimate size is too much to handle and this work is best undertaken in the winter months.

This vigorous tree has upright branches which form a narrow, conical tree. The slender, silvery green leaves turn clear yellow in autumn. It does particularly well in wet soils, and is suited to coastal areas.

17|22		
Mature height: 17-22m	Shape of mature tree	Wet soils

SALIX alba Tristis (x sepulcralis Chrysocoma)
Golden Willow

The beautiful and much admired Weeping Willow has several botanical names including Salix babylonica and Salix vitellina Pendula but in fact is a hybrid of the two with a bit of Salix alba thrown in for good measure.

A winner of the Award of Garden Merit in 2002 this is surely one of the most graceful weeping trees grown in the UK.

17|22		
Mature height: 17-22m	Shape of mature tree	Wet soils

It is a large, weeping and wide spreading tree, often seen close to water as it does so well in wet soils. The narrow, pale green leaves are early to flush in the spring and slow to fall in the autumn. A fast grower well suited to parks. It reacts well to severe crown pruning sending the glorious golden stems and light green foliage plunging towards the ground.

SALIX caprea
Pussy Willow

The Pussy Willow has been loved by generations of children, and is often associated with Easter. Sometimes referred to as Goat Willow, it is a tough prospect for industrial areas that need rapid greening.

One of our native Willows, this makes a small, rounded tree and is often found by rivers and streams, as it thrives in damp soil. It is particularly noted for its silver-white, furry catkins, which open to yellow in spring.

3|8 Mature height: 3-8m	Shape of mature tree	Wet soils	Native trees

SALIX caprea Pendula
Kilmarnock Willow

The weeping form of Pussy Willow that is top grafted onto a Salix caprea stem. It was discovered by the side of the River Ayr in Scotland in the mid 1850s and was granted the Award of Merit in 1977.

This small male weeping tree, which does best on moist soils, is perfect for gardens, producing an ultimate shape resembling an umbrella. Its yellow shoots are followed in spring by attractive, grey catkins.

3|5 Mature height: 3-5m	Shape of mature tree	Garden trees

SALIX daphnoides
Violet Willow

Native to Northern Europe, Central Asia and the Himalayas, this lovely tree was introduced into the UK in the late 1820s and won the Award of Merit in 1957. The Violet Willow is an excellent choice for coppicing to show off its sensational purple-violet shoots overlaid with a white bloom.

Catkins are an attractive feature in spring. This is a medium, fast growing tree with a rounded habit that thrives on most soils including wet ones. The male clone 'Aglaia' is often grown by nurseries for ease of propagation but its properties are the same.

7|12 Mature height: 7-12m	Shape of mature tree	Wet soils

SALIX matsudana Tortuosa
Dragon's Claw Willow

Introduced from its native China in 1905, the fondly known 'Wiggerly Willow' is otherwise known as Salix babylonica Pekinensis, the Pekin Willow.

A weird and wonderful sight in winter when its framework of contorted and twisted branches can be best appreciated. It is a fast growing, medium to large tree with a rounded habit. Good for parks, garden and for waterside plantings, it is also prized by flower arrangers and by my wife to hang Easter decorations.

Very early to leaf in spring, this vigorous tree can outgrow a small garden so beware! Its contorted branches can cost a fortune from florists so it is always nice to harvest your own when the need arises.

7|12 Mature height: 7-12m | Shape of mature tree | Garden trees

SALIX pentandra
Bay Willow

The native Bay Willow is sometimes found growing wild in northern areas of Britain and developed its name from the Norwegians who use it as a substitute for tender Laurus nobilis as its foliage is pleasantly aromatic when crushed.

A most beautiful, medium size tree with a rounded crown at maturity. Catkins are produced at the same time as the leaves in late spring.

Very good for parks and wetland areas, it is both vigorous and vibrant. It is often overlooked by specifiers but is a lovely native tree that could be used more often. This tree is always a good one to throw into the mix on a plant identification competition as it tends to catch a lot of people out.

7|12 Mature height: 7-12m | Shape of mature tree | Wet soils | Native trees

SAMBUCUS nigra
Black Lace

Even though many wouldn't classify this as a tree we have chosen to refute this so we can include it in our listing. Given time this wonderful multi-stem shrub can grow to over three metres making it a tree and giving us a perfect excuse to grow it. Fantastic fern like dark purple to black leaves contrast beautifully with the clusters pink/white elder flowers in June.

Growing well on most free draining soils, this tough plant provides superb summer contrast within a garden or municipal border. It can be vigorously pruned each winter or left alone to become a small tree. It grows well in full sun but it doesn't perform so well in exposed windy locations.

3|5 Mature height: 3-5m | Multi-stem | Garden trees

SEQUOIADENDRON giganteum
Wellingtonia

The Wellingtonia is a native of California, where it grows incredibly tall on the western slopes of the Sierra Nevada and can live for more than 3000 years. It holds the distinction of being the largest living thing on Earth.

Introduced into the UK in the early 1890s, it is quick to grow and there are a number of fine examples growing today including the collection at Wakehurst Place in Sussex. The USA national champion is in Sequoia National Park and stands at a staggering 92 metres tall by 36 metres wide.

17|22		
Mature height: 17-22m	Shape of mature tree	Evergreen trees

**A large, evergreen conifer, it has a densely branched, conical habit while young, but the branches become more widely spaced and distinctly down swept as it ages. Its deeply furrowed, red-brown bark is another of the hallmarks of this magnificent specimen, which is suited to large country estates and parklands.
It thrives on most soils and romps away when young given enough water.**

SEQUOIA giganteum Glauca

First introduced in the early 1860s this stunning clone is narrower and generally smaller that it's green parent. Sequoias can grow very quickly when young and this blue clone is no exception. Its lovely foliage is a subtle blue and really stands out when compared to a green equivalent nearby.

It thrives on most free draining soils but needs plenty of moisture to get it established. Lifting Sequoia from the field to transplant them is a very hit and miss affair but once they are established in their containers they are much more straight forward. Best planted in either large gardens or parkland, this majestic conifer forms a symmetrical pyramidal shape at maturity.

12|17		
Mature height: 12-17m	Shape of mature tree	Evergreen trees

SEQUOIA sempervirens
Coastal Redwood

The Coastal Redwood first came to Europe (St Petersburg) from California in 1840. You cannot help but be touched by the majesty of these trees as you head through California to Oregon on the coastal road into the Valley of the Giants. Even my young children were awestruck at the beauty and sheer magnitude of these trees!

A large, conical evergreen, it has a thick, fibrous, red-brown outer bark, which is soft and spongy to the touch. The slightly drooping branches bear two-ranked, linear-oblong leaves. A wonderful choice for large areas of parkland, they prefer the cleaner air of rural sites and plenty of water to get them going.

17|22		
Mature height: 17-22m	Shape of mature tree	Evergreen trees

SOPHORA japonica
Japanese Pagoda Tree

Introduced in 1753 this heat loving tree won the Award of Garden Merit in 2002 but truthfully is only worth while in the warmer parts of Southern England on south facing sites. Despite its specific and common names, this medium to large, rounded tree is actually a native of China, although widely planted in Japan.

Once mature, panicles of yellow-white, pea like flowers are borne in August, followed by long grey seed pods in autumn. The clone 'Princeton Upright' is so like its parents to be of any consequence. Recently it's changed name to Styphnoiobium japonica but I struggle to pronounce this so am keeping it listed as before!

7|12 Mature height: 7-12m | Shape of mature tree | Garden trees

SORBUS aria Lutescens

This outstanding clone is most attractive in spring and won the Award of Merit in 1952 and the Award of Garden Merit in 2002. A very popular choice for urban gardens, it requires little maintenance and tolerates chalk soils.

The young leaves emerge silvery-white from purple shoots in spring, before hardening to grey-green in summer. This is a small, compact, rounded tree, producing white flowers in April and May and, in good years, orange-red, cherry like fruits in autumn. A very good choice for streets, gardens and parks.

This lovely compact tree is stunning when its spring canopy is contrasted with a clear blue sky. We generally take this variety to The Chelsea Flower Show each year as it is at its best in May and June.

3|8 Mature height: 3-8m | Shape of mature tree | Garden trees | Bee friendly trees

SORBUS aria Magnifica

Introduced into general nursery cultivation in the early 1920s, this urban clone has ascending branches and is well equipped to cope with the rigours of reflected heat and light common to developed areas. Although it is not as stunning in the spring as 'Lutescens' it will keep going for longer in the late summer and autumn.

This medium size tree is conical when young, becoming broadly oval at maturity. The large leaves are dark green on top, with silver-white undersides. It has the white flowers and red fruits characteristic of the species, and is a good choice for parks, streets and avenues.

7|12 Mature height: 7-12m | Shape of mature tree | Urban trees | Bee friendly trees

SORBUS aria Majestica

This well known variety is also known as Decaisneana and won the Award of Garden Merit in 2002. In our opinion this clone is synonymous to 'Magnifica' for its overall effect and thrives on most soils including chalky ones.

A tree of medium height with a broad, dense, conical crown, it is of symmetrical form. It has notably large leaves and fruits, and is a splendid choice for parks, streets, gardens and avenues. For further Whitebeam types, refer to Sorbus latifolia and intermedia.

7|12			
Mature height: 7-12m	Shape of mature tree	Urban trees	Bee friendly trees

SORBUS x arnoldiana Schouten

A reliable, low-maintenance Mountain Ash clone that has proved to be a very popular choice for street planting in London. Unlike many rowan types, it tolerates the reflected heat and light thrown up by hard urban areas.

Budded onto Sorbus aucuparia rootstock, this is a great choice for streets, car parks and urban plantings, because it needs next to no maintenance. It is a small tree with a dense, oval crown, and it has most attractive, green, feathery foliage with golden yellow berries from August onwards.

7|12			
Mature height: 7-12m	Shape of mature tree	Urban trees	Bee friendly trees

SORBUS aucuparia
Rowan/Mountain Ash

This wonderful native tree is often associated with Scotland. It certainly suits bird life as the profuse red autumn berries provide a lot of autumnal sustenance.

We grow this multi-stemmed rather than in standard form as they are not regular in shape and it is better to opt for a clone such as Rossica Major if uniformity is required.

7|12				
Mature height: 7-12m	Shape of mature tree	Multi-stem	Native trees	Bee friendly trees

Rowans prefer shorter day lengths and do not thrive in areas with excessive reflective heat and light such as paved and other hard surfaces. Best planted in parkland or verges, it is arguably our prettiest native tree.

SORBUS aucuparia Asplenifolia

This Rowan clone is also sometimes referred to as 'Laciniata' and has proved very popular for both urban and rural planting. There are very few cut leaf trees and their addition into the landscape provides lovely foliage contrast.

Highly recommended for streets, verges and garden planting, this medium tree forms a broad pyramid if the leader is retained. It has finely cut, fern like foliage, which turns orange-red in autumn and the red berries are loved by wild birds. Rowans readily thrive on most soils including acid ones.

7|12 Mature height: 7-12m | Shape of mature tree | Garden trees | Bee friendly trees

SORBUS aucuparia Cardinal Royal

Introduced by Michigan State University in America, their original plant stands at 12 metres tall by 6 metres wide. This makes it a very good Rowan clone for restricted areas and it is also tolerant of the reflected heat and light associated with urban planting.

The ascending branches of this medium size tree give it a columnar habit at maturity. White flowers in May are followed by red berries in September, which are readily consumed by wild birds. Very good for streets, urban plantings and rural gardens. It will thrive on most soils including acid ones.

Out of all the aucuparia types I think this and Sheerwater Seedling are the best performers for the red berried urban clones. It's uniform habit makes it a great choice where minimum maintenance is required.

7|12 Mature height: 7-12m | Shape of mature tree | Urban trees | Bee friendly trees

SORBUS aucuparia Cashmiriana

This very pretty garden tree has won a string of horticultural awards over the years including the Award of Garden Merit in 2002. Introduced into the UK in the mid 1930s from its native Kashmir, it remains the daintiest of trees but rarely seen as it is often decimated with Fire Blight, a fungal disorder that kills tree from the top down.

Soft pink flower clusters emerge in May and form good sized white berries by the autumn that often remain hanging on the tree well after the foliage has fallen.

3|8			
Mature height: 3-8m	Shape of mature tree	Garden trees	Bee friendly trees

SORBUS aucuparia Edulis

The edible berries of this Mountain Ash can be used to make Rowan jelly. Thought to have been introduced in the very early 1800s, it is sometimes also classified under the varietal names 'Moravica' or 'Dulcis'.

A vigorous and very hardy tree, which is of medium size and broadly oval at maturity. It has larger leaves than the species - and large berries too. A good choice for gardens and urban areas, it thrives on most soils.

7|12			
Mature height: 7-12m	Shape of mature tree	Garden trees	Bee friendly trees

SORBUS aucuparia Golden Wonder

Sometimes classified under the Sorbus arnoldiana group this stocky vigorous rowan makes a fine tree that requires little maintenance. Its lush leaves can turn to a decent orange/red in the autumn before falling.

This pyramidal grower is a good choice for verges, avenues and streets. It makes a medium size, large-leaved tree, which produces big bunches of golden yellow fruits from late summer onwards. It thrives on most soils but like all rowans will prefer it slightly acid.

In our opinion this is the best golden berried clone available as it doesn't suffer from the debilitating Fire Blight disease that the variety Joseph Rock can suffer badly from.

7|12			
Mature height: 7-12m	Shape of mature tree	Urban trees	Bee friendly trees

SORBUS aucuparia Joseph Rock

One of the prettiest of rowans it is both a winner of the First Class Certificate in 1962 and the Award of Merit in 1950. However, it is also the one most susceptible to fire blight which can disfigure the tree to the point of complete demise.

Small narrow green leaflets turn a fantastic red in the autumn and provide a stunning contrast to the creamy yellow berries. A small tree with ascending branches, ideal for gardens. It derives from the Chinese species, has red leaf buds and a dainty overall effect. It is ideal for small gardens and tolerant of most soils.

3|8 Mature height: 3-8m	Shape of mature tree	Garden trees	Bee friendly trees

SORBUS aucuparia Rossica Major

As trees derived from seed grown Sorbus aucuparia are genetically unique they can be quite variable in habit so if it is uniformity you are after this clone fits the bill. Otherwise it does everything you would expect of our native rowan and requires little or no maintenance.

A strong and fast growing tree, Rossica Major forms a broadly oval crown. Its dark green leaves are attached by red stalks, and it bears its dark red berries from August onwards. A good choice for both urban areas, and rural gardens.

7|12 Mature height: 7-12m	Shape of mature tree	Urban trees	Bee friendly trees

SORBUS aucuparia Sheerwater Seedling

Along with the clone 'Cardinal Royal' this variety represents the best choice for urban planting where space is restricted. A winner of the Award of Garden Merit in 2002, this well known tree has proven to be popular for a number of years.

This medium size, oval tree will also tolerate semi-shade. It thrives on most soils and its ascending branches and dominant leader makes it a tree requiring little maintenance. White flowers are followed by bird friendly red berries by September and the green leaves turn a decent yellow/orange in the autumn.

There is a marked difference on how Rowan types perform in the UK, the further north they are planted the better they are. However, Sheerwater Seedling is a good choice for southern Britain as well as is more tolerant of the occasional hot spell that can come along and its maintenance free habit makes it an ideal prospect for a small urban garden or narrow urban verge.

7|12			
Mature height: 7-12m	Shape of mature tree	Urban trees	Bee friendly trees

SORBUS aucuparia Vilmorinii

Discovered by Abbe Delavay and introduced in 1889, this dainty beauty originates from Western China. It makes a lovely little tree requiring little maintenance and giving much enjoyment.

The leaves are dark green and fern-like, turning a red-purple in the autumn. Profuse berries hang in drooping clusters, dark red at first then fading to a pink-white. Unfortunately this small tree, like Joseph Rock, is also susceptible to fire blight. Ideal for small gardens.

3|8			
Mature height: 3-8m	Shape of mature tree	Garden trees	Bee friendly trees

SORBUS commixta Embley

Chinese Scarlet Rowan

Some list this as 'Embley' and some as 'commixta' but we hedge our bets and classify it as one as there is no discernable difference to the vast majority.

Originating from Korea and Japan, it was introduced in the early 1880s and won the Award of Merit in 1979.

3|8			
Mature height: 3-8m	Shape of mature tree	Garden trees	Bee friendly trees

This small tree of broadly columnar habit is tolerant of most soils and makes a fine choice for garden planting. In autumn its glorious foliage and bright red berries makes it stand out from the rest. Its young trunk is light brown and speckled. Fluffy bunches of small white flowers are produced in the spring.

SORBUS commixta Olympic Flame

Also known as 'Dodong' this rowan originates from Japan. Its glossy green foliage is vibrant throughout the growing season and this turns to orange and red in the autumn. Dark orange berries are produced from clusters of white spring flowers by late summer.

Its young trunk is punctuated by lenticels and it thrives on most free draining soils but like all rowan types does not tolerate excessive reflective heat and light from hard areas surrounding it. Selected from seed by a Swedish botanist in 1976, this rowan looks so exotic that it is now firmly established as a favourite Europe wide.

3|8			
Mature height: 3-8m	Shape of mature tree	Garden trees	Bee friendly trees

SORBUS discolor

Introduced from its native Northern China in the mid 1880s this clone is often lumped in together with 'Commixta' even though the berry colour is different. One of the earliest rowans to flower in the spring, it makes a lovely garden tree that requires little maintenance.

Creamy-yellow fruits are borne on red stalks by late summer in the manner of 'Joseph Rock' and it forms an open crown made up from ascending branches.
It thrives on most soils although like most rowans it will prefer it slightly acid.

3|8 Mature height: 3-8m	Shape of mature tree	Garden trees	Bee friendly trees

SORBUS hupehensis

Discovered by Ernest Wilson and introduced from its native western China in 1910, this lovely rowan stands out by its flat blue tinged leaves and light brown trunk. It won the Award of Garden Merit in 2002 and forms a compact broadly oval crown at maturity.

Splendid white berries produced in large clusters and stunning red autumn colour also typifies this small low maintenance tree which thrives on most soils and can tolerate the rigours of the urban environment. Being white, the berries are the last to be taken by birds, so can remain on the tree way past Christmas.

3|8			
Mature height: 3-8m	Shape of mature tree	Garden trees	Bee friendly trees

SORBUS incana

Thought to have been bred at the Botanical Gardens of Copenhagen, this tough compact tree is incredibly hardy, thriving as an urban tree all over Scandinavia. It rarely flowers and when it does set fruit the berries are orange / red.
The foliage puts this tree into the Whitebeam family and its bushy stubby growth needs very little maintenance over its lifespan.

Thriving in most free draining soils it is happy in full sun or semi shade. This is a particularly good prospect for urban planting and gardens in the North of England or Scotland, especially where space is restricted. Its bright green summer leaves turn yellow in autumn. At maturity, its dense crown is broadly oval.

3|8			
Mature height: 3-8m	Shape of mature tree	Urban trees	Bee friendly sites

SORBUS intermedia
Swedish Whitebeam

The Swedish Whitebeam is widely planted as a street tree in northern Europe. It is a tough tree that can even thrive within view of the coast. Unlike the closely related Sorbus aria clones it is more tolerant of reflected heat and light bouncing of hard areas on urban sites.

A medium size tree with a well formed, rounded crown, its single, dark green leaves have silver-grey undersides. White flowers in May give way to orange-red fruits, produced in small bunches. It is wind resistant and tolerant of calcareous soils and air pollution, making this a really useful candidate for urban planting. We recommend it for streets and avenues.

7|12 Mature height: 7-12m	Shape of mature tree	Coastal sites	Bee friendly sites

SORBUS intermedia Brouwers

This Swedish Whitebeam clone has a more pyramidal crown than the species and is more commonly grown by nurseries as the catchall for Sorbus intermedia. Clonal variations can be very similar to their parents but crucially offer a far greater degree of uniformity.

A medium size tree with a conical crown, its single, dark green leaves have silver-grey undersides. White flowers in May produce orange-red fruits. It is wind resistant and tolerant of calcareous soils and air pollution, making this a really tough tree. It will thrive in even the harshest conditions including near the coast.

7|12 Mature height: 7-12m	Shape of mature tree	Coastal sites	Bee friendly sites

SORBUS latifolia Henk Vink

A hybrid derived from Sorbus torminalis and Sorbus aria this is a Dutch clone raised for its qualities to thrive within the urban environment. A native of Portugal through to Germany, it is a worthy alternative to the more commonly used Sorbus aria clones.

Round headed and tough, this versatile tree is ideal for streets, verges or parks. White flowers are followed by red berries in the autumn. Its leaves are grey / green and silvery grey beneath to provide a pleasing contrast in windy conditions.

7|12 Mature height: 7-12m	Shape of mature tree	Coastal sites	Bee friendly sites

SORBUS latifolia Atrovirens
Service Tree of Fontainebleau

An improved clone of the hybrid between Sorbus torminalis and aria. Native of Europe, it is seldom used due to it not being known.

Glossy lobed green leaves, grey beneath, are supported by an ascending branch network that broadens out at maturity to become rounded. White flowers in spring form orange fruits that are borne in small bunches. It is a tough tree, withstanding strong winds and coping well with urban conditions. Excellent for verge or street planting.

7|12			
Mature height: 7-12m	Shape of mature tree	Coastal sites	Bee friendly sites

SORBUS x thuringiaca Fastigiata

Sometimes referred to as Sorbus hybrida, this highly useful urban tree retains the prettiness of Sorbus aucuparia and the toughness of Sorbus aria, its parents. A winner of the Award of Merit in 1924, this tree can get to beyond 10 metres if given the space.

The best examples I have seen of this tree are at Calderstones Park in Liverpool, where they have been left long enough, and been given the space to express themselves.

7|12			
Mature height: 7-12m	Shape of mature tree	Urban trees	Bee friendly trees

This small tree is columnar when young, but becomes broadly oval as it matures. Clusters of white flowers in spring are followed by red berries in September before vivid orange autumn colour in November.

SORBUS torminalis
Wild Service Tree

The fruits of the Wild Service Tree, which are very sharp but edible when over-ripe, used to be sold as "chequers" in southern England, giving rise to its alternative name of Chequer Tree and the corresponding numbers of pubs taking the same title. The name 'Chequer' is also used to describe the pattern of its bark.

This medium native tree is columnar when young, but becomes more rounded as it ages. Its dark brown, fissured bark bears grey scales. Perfect for woodlands, it thrives best under the dappled shade of others and does not react favourably to hot urban areas prone to reflected heat and light. Its attractive green lobed leaves turn a lovely orange / yellow in autumn.

7|12			
Mature height: 7-12m	Shape of mature tree	Native trees	Bee friendly trees

SYRINGA reticulata Ivory Silk

A recent introduction from Canada, this clone was selected in 1973. It makes an excellent small tree with a dense crowned oval habit, ideal for small gardens or restricted urban areas. The wonderful thing about this clone is that it flowers in June / July when most other trees have finished their spring display so this tree can be used to lengthen the time of interest in your garden.

It produces large clusters of small, fragrant, ivory white flowers that are quite long lasting and prefers a sunny position in which to thrive. It is tolerant of most soils and its deep green leaves turn a soft yellow in autumn.

3|8		
Mature height: 3-8m	Shape of mature tree	Urban trees

SYRINGA vulgaris cultivars

There are reportedly over 900 varieties of Syringa vulgaris cultivars with many similar to each other but we major on just the four which make fine small multi stem trees. Broad oval deep green leaves are produced by buds on the extremity of the stiffly ascending branch network.

They thrive on most free draining soils and like full sun to dappled shade. Great for gardens and municipal parks, they are easy to maintain and very reliable. We favour the four classic proven varieties listed below.

3|5 Mature height: 3-5m | Multi-stem | Flowering trees | Bee friendly sites

SYRINGA vulgaris
Alice Harding

First bought to market way back in 1938, this beautiful white flowering Lilac has fragrant flowers by the end of May and into June.

SYRINGA vulgaris
Madame Lemoine

Dating back to 1890, this double white flowering Lilac blooms in mid to late May and prefers a fertile neutral to alkaline soil.

SYRINGA vulgaris
Ludwig Spath

Bred by the famous Spath nursery in Berlin, Germany, in 1883. Marvellous blue / purple scented flowers are borne on large upright spires in May / June.

SYRINGA vulgaris
Ruhm von Horstenstein

Introduced from Germany in 1928, this classic variety blooms with scented purple / blue flowers in May. A vigorous grower, perfect for tougher environments.

TAMARIX aestivalis

A native of Europe, Asia and North Africa, this ancient looking tree is incredibly useful in exposed windy areas and will thrive on pretty much any soil apart from shallow chalk. Mostly supplied as bushes, we grow our Tamarix as full standards.

A small genus well suited to coastal locations, tolerating salt laden winds and spray. This variety is virtually identical to Tamarix tetrandra but flowers about a month later, so by a mixed planting of both varieties you can look forward to about six weeks of continuous flower.

3|8 Mature height: 3-8m | Shape of mature tree | Coastal sites

TAMARIX gallica

This coastal specialist originally from South West Europe has now naturalised along many miles of the English coastline. A great tree to tolerate and diffuse wind.

Better known as a shrub, we grow it as a full standard with a clear stem of 1.8m, best suited for coastal towns or specimen planting inland. Dark brown branches support vivid green foliage and pink fluffy flowers in summer that are borne from new season's wood. Particularly useful on saline soils.

3|8 Mature height: 3-8m | Shape of mature tree | Coastal sites

TAMARIX tetrandra

The Tamarisk is so evocative of old fashioned, Mediterranean fishing villages. Introduced way back in 1821, this won the Award of Garden Merit in 2002. Although primarily thought of as a coastal plant, it can make a fine garden tree inland, so long as it is not planted on shallow chalk.

We offer this as a small standard tree with a rounded crown. Its light pink flowers are freely produced in May/June. A tough subject, which does well in light, sandy soils. Is very good for coastal locations and is also tolerant of exposed, windy sites.

3|8 Mature height: 3-8m | Shape of mature tree | Coastal sites

TAXODIUM distichum
Swamp Cypress

The Swamp Cypress is the best conifer for wet soils. A native of the Florida Everglades, it is thought of as a pyramidal grower but interestingly the national champion in the USA is 28 metres tall by 29 metres wide suggesting seed variability.

Introduced in the early 1640s by John Tradescant it won the updated Award of Garden Merit in 2002.

This large, deciduous, pyramidal conifer has fibrous, brown bark and small, round cones, which are purple when young. It does best in wet soils, and needs plenty of moisture in its first year after planting if it is to succeed. A good choice for parks and often confused with Metasequoia until seen close together.

17|22 Mature height: 17-22m	Shape of mature tree	Wet soils

Taxodium is a wonderful choice to plant near a lake as its autumn display is reflected in the water to double its impact. Its fine leaflets are less prone silt up ponds in the autumn when compared to larger leaved deciduous trees. Foliage is always late to appear in the spring, particularly after planting, but it generally starts growing at full pelt from July onwards.

TAXUS baccata
English Yew

The native English Yew is a tree of many mystical and religious associations. Incredibly long lived, the oldest reported is in Llangernyw, Wales, and is estimated to be 4000 years old with a circumference of 16 metres. The trees capacity for regeneration is outstanding; especially considering it is a conifer.

A medium tree of conical appearance, its hard wood can support this evergreen to a great age. Often used for hedging, it also makes a fine specimen tree. Very good for parks and gardens. All parts of the tree are poisonous. It can grow on highly calcareous or highly acidic soils, if there is good drainage.

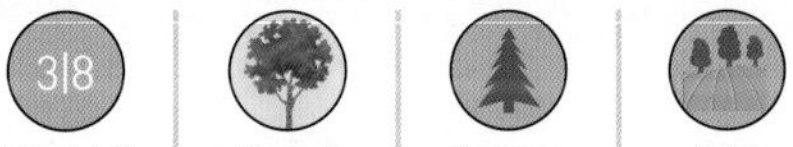

Mature height: 3-8m	Shape of mature tree	Evergreen trees	Native trees

TAXUS baccata Fastigiata
Irish Yew

Originally discovered as naturally occurring plants in County Fermanagh in 1780, this dense columnar conifer is a great favourite for garden designers wanting to instil formality within a garden. In the Mediterranean they have Cupressus sempervirens, in the UK we have this as it is more suited to our climate.

Thriving on most free draining soils this wonderful evergreen is often seen in churchyards and it requires very little pruning or maintenance. Its dark green foliage always seems unchanging but is seemlessly replaced by subsequent spring flushes. Ideal for small gardens and can be maintained within only a few metres of buildings without harm.

3|8 Mature height: 3-8m	Shape of mature tree	Evergreen trees

TAXUS baccata Fastigiata
Aurea Golden Irish Yew

A male form discovered later than its female green counterpart back in the 1880s. It forms a dense columnar tree at maturity with gold tipped margined leaves and stiffly ascending branches. Not that it needs much maintenance but Yew is a very adaptable tree to handle as unlike other conifers its shape and size can be reinstated by severe pruning back into old wood in early spring.

It thrives on most free draining soils and is a firm favourite for small gardens up and down the UK where it is planted in multiples when a structured formality is required. The spring flush of foliage is a lighter yellow than its appearance for the rest of the year and it can tolerate full sun or partial shade.

3|8 Mature height: 3-8m	Shape of mature tree	Evergreen trees

THUJA plicata Atrovirens

A form of the Western Red Cedar. It is an important timber tree in its native North America, although it is more commonly used as a hedging conifer in the UK. The national champion in the States is over 60 metres tall by 18 metres wide. Introduced in the mid 1870s, it won the Award of Garden Merit in 2002.

This large, evergreen conifer does best on wet soils and will tolerate shade. Of pyramidal form if grown as a specimen tree, it is also a fine subject for hedging. In our view superior to Leyland Cypress, but slower growing. Good for parks and gardens, its shiny, green foliage smells of pineapple when crushed.

17|22 Mature height: 17-22m | Shape of mature tree | Hedging trees

TILIA americana Redmond

This cultivar of the American Lime is of garden origin, and came from Plumfield Nurseries Nebraska, USA, in 1927. It was originally listed under Tilia euchlora but is distinctly different. It is still little known and used in the UK but should not be overlooked.

A pyramidal tree of medium size, this cultivar is barely sensitive to aphids and the associated "dripping", which makes it an ideal lime for street and avenue plantings. The super large leaves, which are a lighter green than those of the species, turn pale yellow in autumn.

12|17		
Mature height: 12-17m	Shape of mature tree	Avenue trees

TILIA americana American Sentry

Called 'McKSentry' by American growers to commemorate its breeders, Mackay nurseries in Wisconsin. Its pyramidal habit develops about half as wide as it is high making this a very popular urban tree in the USA. It's tough and has large green leaves that turn to yellow in the autumn. Young stems are a silver grey and sweetly scented flowers are borne in the spring.

This tree has a great symmetry about it so pruning is seldom necessary. It thrives best in full sun for at least six hours of the day and performs well on most free draining soils either side of neutral. Tilia americana was first introduced into the UK in 1752 but this much more recent selection is the one to go for if space is restricted or uniformity is required.

12|17		
Mature height: 12-17m	Shape of mature tree	Urban trees

TILIA cordata
Small-Leaved Lime

This well known native tree won the Award of Garden Merit in 2002 and remains a popular choice within our urban and rural landscapes. It is a good host to mistletoe for the more romantically inclined of you.

This large tree has a broadly oval crown, with small, heart shaped leaves, which are dark green on top and pale green beneath.
Its creamy white flowers are produced in July. It is a relatively sedate grower, is good for avenues and parks, and bears air pollution very well. Like most Lime, it is also a fine candidate for pollarding or pleaching.

17|22			
Mature height: 17-22m	Shape of mature tree	Native trees	Bee friendly trees

TILIA cordata Greenspire

This American clone derived from the cultivar 'Euclid'. A selection from a Boston Park, it has been in cultivation in the UK since the early 1960s. A winner of the Award of Garden Merit in 2002, it is a very popular choice for urban planting where its uniformity is preferred over the native Tilia cordata.

It maintains a strong leader and well branched crown through to maturity, which distinguishes it over other selections, as the premier clone of Tilia cordata. It thrives well on most soils and copes readily with harsh urban environments given enough soil to exploit.

At maturity I would liken it to a great example of Tilia cordata at the same size but with Greenspire you get this every time. Clonal selections give uniformity whereas seed grown trees have a significant degree of genetic variation.

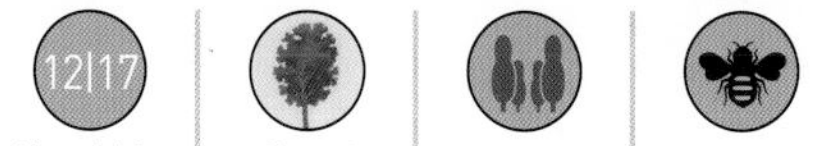

Mature height: 12-17m | Shape of mature tree | Avenue trees | Bee friendly trees

TILIA cordata x mongolica Harvest Gold

This exciting new tree to our range combines the toughness of Tilia cordata with the daintiness of Tilia mongolica. Developed in Manitoba, Canada, it makes an excellent avenue tree with spectacular yellow autumn colour. As it matures the bark exfoliates to give a pleasing patchwork effect. This clone is now used extensively in the States and is already proving its worth as an attractive and durable urban and rural tree.

A tough grower, it forms a lovely oval and ascending crown that broadens with age. From what we have seen it is a very clean tree, producing little flower or fruit, as well as importantly not attracting aphids. We started lining this clone out in our fields in 2008 from young plant material sourced direct from a specialist grower in the States. This new introduction for the UK market is now available from Barcham in our 45 litre Light Pots at 10-12cm & 12-14cm girth.

12|17 Mature height: 12-17m	Shape of mature tree	Urban trees

TILIA cordata Rancho

This often overlooked variety is of lesser overall stature than 'Greenspire' but it can be considered neater, with the added bonus of a great and fragrant floral display in early summer. Its branch angles are mechanically strong. It was introduced into the UK in the early 1960s.

Ideal for urban plantings, streets and avenues, this medium tree has a dense, conical habit, and has very shiny, small leaves. Its compact and uniform growing qualities make it ideal for avenue planting, but it is not as well known as Greenspire so rarely gets specified. We rate this clone very highly and it thrives on most soils.

12|17 Mature height: 12-17m	Shape of mature tree	Urban trees	Bee friendly trees

TILIA cordata Winter Orange

This exciting new variety was found as a seedling in the Netherlands in the 1970s. Whenever we show this tree it is widely appreciated and we never seem to have enough to go around! An ideal prospect for garden pleaching, its orange stems are most unusual.

A medium to large tree with a broadly oval crown, it is distinguished by its red buds and orange shoots in winter. Its white, sweetly scented flowers appear in July. It is a good choice for avenues and tolerates the rigours of the urban environment.

7|12 Mature height: 7-12m | Shape of mature tree | Garden trees | Bee friendly trees

It is a medium to large tree, and as aphids are not attracted to its dark green foliage, the associated "stickiness" is not a problem. Good for wide verges, parks, avenues and urban plantings.

TILIA x euchlora Caucasian Lime

The result of a cross between Tilia cordata and Tilia dasystyla, this ever popular lime can grow as broad as it is tall, so is often given the wrong sites to grow on. Its flowers can have a narcotic effect on bees, which can sometimes be found on the ground near a tree. Redeemingly, it is free of aphids, so an ideal tree for pleaching or boxing in hard areas.

This Lime reacts well to pollarding, which is a good way of controlling its broadly pendulous habit.

12|17		
Mature height: 12-17m	Shape of mature tree	Urban trees

TILIA x europaea
Common Lime

Once the most frequently planted Lime, this is a very long lived tree and commonly planted in central Europe as an urban tree. It is a hybrid between Tilia cordata and Tilia platyphyllos and has been known to reach over 50 metres tall, like the specimen at Duncombe Park in Yorkshire.

A large and impressive, broadly oval shaped tree which is widely used for avenue plantings. It is recognisable by its dense suckering, which forms burrs on the trunk. Its large lush leaves can attract aphids so care should be taken not to plant in hard areas, where the resulting sooty mould will be a problem.

17|22 Mature height: 17-22m | Shape of mature tree | Avenue trees | Bee friendly trees

TILIA x europaea Pallida
Kaiser Linden

The Kaiser Linden is the Lime of the famous Unter den Linden in Berlin and has been highly rated for many years. It is quick to grow and gives a uniform alternative against seed grown Common Lime that makes it perfect for large avenues.

A large tree of pyramidal form, its pale green leaves have attractive, green-yellow undersides. It thrives pretty much anywhere and is tolerant of most soils. Quick to grow and establish, this is one of our most popular selling limes but as with its parents, care should be taken to avoid hard areas that could be affected by aphid drip.

17|22 Mature height: 17-22m | Shape of mature tree | Avenue trees | Bee friendly trees

TILIA henryana

This rarely seen Lime was discovered in China in 1888 by Augustine Henry. It was introduced into the UK in 1901 by Ernest Wilson and for some reason is still heavily under grown. We are bucking this trend and have been bulking up production numbers, but have noticed that in young plants the growth tips can be frost sensitive, so we advise sheltered sites for final placement.

Its ovate leaves are downy to the touch on both sides, and edged with bristle-like teeth akin to the outer edges of a Venus Fly Trap. A wonderfully ornamental lime, it flowers in autumn, and is a good choice for south facing parks and gardens within the milder parts of the UK.

12|17			
Mature height: 12-17m	Shape of mature tree	Garden trees	Bee friendly trees

TILIA mongolica
Mongolian Lime

The Mongolian Lime was introduced from its homeland in the early 1880s. It is both aphid resistant and most unlike the general look of the rest of the Tilia family. Recent plantings in London have been most encouraging, and suggest this has great potential for an urban tree in the UK.

This small tree with a rounded habit has all the durability of Lime, but is of a size which makes it ideal as a street tree. It has small, serrated, glossy, green leaves, which are similar to those of ivy. A real little beauty requiring little maintenance.

It turns to a clear and delicate yellow in autumn and as the leaves are so small for a Lime in the first place, there is not much leaf litter to contend with for an urban environment.

TILIA platyphyllos
Broad-Leaved Lime

The Broad-leaved Lime is a native of Britain. A winner of the First Class Certificate in 1892, it flowers in June/July and is very tolerant of pruning. It is a compact and stocky tree, the luscious foliage always gives it a healthy demeanour.

The clonal selection 'Delft' is a European clone that forms a more pyramidal crown at maturity and could be used where uniformity is required.

17|22			
Mature height: 17-22m	Shape of mature tree	Native trees	Bee friendly trees

A large, fast growing tree with a roughly fissured bark, which remains relatively free of suckers. This is a good subject for parks and estates, and is also useful for avenue planting. The leaves are almost circular and dark green. It is well suited to urban conditions but thrives best in our countryside.

TILIA platyphyllos Rubra

Red-twigged Lime

The Red-twigged Lime is a slow grower than its parent and its fresh red twiggy growth is particularly striking when used for pleaching. It has a more ascending habit that the species and it won the Award of Garden Merit in 2002.

This reasonably columnar, medium to large tree is a great choice for avenue planting and areas which suffer from air pollution. Its young shoots are a bright brown-red, and look particularly effective in late winter. It makes a fine choice for a rural landscape and will thrive on most soils given enough room.

17|22 Mature height: 17-22m | Shape of mature tree | Avenue trees | Bee friendly trees

TILIA tomentosa
Silver Lime

The Silver Lime is a handsome tree, but with a rather variable habit. Introduced in 1767 from its native South Eastern Europe, its flowers can be toxic to bees so this should be considered if planting in a rural setting.

A large tree of generally pyramidal habit, the Silver Lime has the advantages of being resistant to both aphids and drought. It grows well in urban areas, although it requires plenty of space. Its dark green leaves have silver-white undersides, creating a beautiful effect when rustled by the breeze. Good for avenues and parks, it will also stand up well to salt-laden coastal winds.

17|22		
Mature height: 17-22m	Shape of mature tree	Urban trees

TILIA tomentosa Brabant

This Dutch clonal selection of Silver Lime was introduced into the UK in the early 1970s and won the Award of Garden Merit in 2002. It is rightly considered to be an excellent urban tree, coping with the rigours of city environments very well. The Belgium variety, 'Doornik' has very similar attributes.

Brabant has a more regularly pyramidal form than the species, but is just as large. It is very versatile, being suitable for urban settings, avenues, verges and parks. The striking silver undersides of its foliage makes it a wonderful tree for providing contrast within a landscape and the leaves turn a glorious yellow before falling in the autumn.

17|22		
Mature height: 17-22m	Shape of mature tree	Urban trees

TILIA tomentosa Petiolaris
Weeping Silver Lime

The Weeping Silver Lime is perhaps the most graceful of all large, weeping trees. Often referred to as Tilia tomentosa Petiolaris it has been recently separated to its own species but in my opinion this is too close to call so doesn't really matter anyway. There is a particularly good specimen to be seen at The RHS garden at Wisley.

Introduced in the early 1840s it won the Award of Garden Merit in 2002. It is fast growing and aphid resistant, and is an excellent subject for parks. The flowers are richly scented but narcotic to bees, while its dark green leaves have white, felt-like undersides. Autumn colour is a striking and rich yellow. It thrives on most soils.

17|22		
Mature height: 17-22m	Shape of mature tree	Parkland trees

TRACHYCARPUS fortunei
Chusan Palm

A remarkable genus of hardy palm, introduced by Robert Fortune in 1849. Slow to grow, I have one in my garden that was planted at 60cm tall, and now stands at a little over 2 metres ten years later. It won the Award of Garden Merit in 2002 and is the best hardy palm for the UK.

While it is hardy in Britain, we recommend planting it in sheltered positions to avoid wind damage to its deep green, fan shaped leaves. Its slender trunk becomes clothed in loose, dark brown fibres and small yellow flowers borne in large panicles are produced in early summer once the plant attains about 2 metres of height.

3|8		
Mature height: 3-8m	Shape of mature tree	Garden trees

TSUGA canadensis Eastern Hemlock

Introduced from the Eastern USA in 1736, this broad, often multi stemmed, evergreen conifer grows best on free draining alkaline soils. Ideal for parkland and estates, its architectural network of trunk and mature stems are very pleasing to the eye. Very hardy, its tiny thin leaves look like they are ready for the battle against mountainous climate conditions from where it came.

It thrives in both sun and shade but only where there is adequate drainage. It likes the rarefied air associated with altitude so doesn't do well in urban pollution or times of prolonged drought, so care is needed to keep it watered especially during its establishment period. It does best in the western half of the UK, away from long drying summer winds.

17|22		
Mature height: 17-22m	Shape of mature tree	Parkland trees

ULMUS carpinifolia Wredei Aurea

This rather slow growing Elm is probably protected against Dutch Elm disease as a result of its size rather than genetic makeup. A sport of 'Dampieri', it won the First Class Certificate in 1893.

A tree of small to medium size and oval habit, it tolerates pollution and salt-laden, coastal winds. Very good for parks, gardens and verges. Its luminescent yellow foliage is particularly striking if planted in a semi shaded area or against a dark backdrop.

3|8		
Mature height: 3-8m	Shape of mature tree	Garden trees

ULMUS glabra Camperdownii
Camperdown Elm

The Camperdown Elm is a form of Wych Elm. The original appeared at Camperdown House, near Dundee, in 1850. It produces clusters of attractive hop like flowers in the spring and its lustrous leaves add well to its effect.

A small weeping tree with a dome shaped head; it looks good growing in a lawn in parks and gardens. It remains neat and compact, and is generally considered to be resistant to Dutch elm disease but only because it doesn't attain the height to attract the infecting beetle.

3|8		
Mature height: 3-8m	Shape of mature tree	Garden trees

ULMUS Clusius

This Dutch hybrid was raised at Wageningen and released for general cultivation in 1983. It is derived from the same parents as Ulmus Lobel, namely Ulmus glabra Exoniensis and Ulmus wallichiana.

This large broadly oval tree is fast growing and well suited to avenue and coastal plantings. It has a resistance to Dutch elm disease but is more susceptible than 'Lutece'.

17|22 Mature height: 17-22m | Shape of mature tree | Parkland trees

ULMUS Dodoens

This Elm was seed-raised in the 1950s and eventually released for general cultivation in 1973. It has the same parentage as 'Clusius' and has moderate resistance to Dutch elm disease.

This tough large tree, which is good for verges and avenues, forms a broadly pyramidal crown. It is fast growing and a good choice for windy, exposed locations including coastal sites.

17|22 Mature height: 17-22m | Shape of mature tree | Parkland trees

ULMUS Lobel

This Elm cultivar was raised at Wageningen in the Netherlands, and was selected for its resistance to Dutch elm disease. It has the same parentage as 'Clusius' and was released for general cultivation in 1973.

Large and fast growing, this narrow, columnar tree eventually becomes broader. It will withstand exposed locations, including those on coasts, and is also good for avenues and verges.

Elm is such a versatile and tough tree and it was a tragedy when Dutch Elm Disease swept in to drastically reduce their numbers. Ulmus Lobel has been very successfully planted throughout the UK since then and is one of the better bets when planting this genus.

17|22 Mature height: 17-22m | Shape of mature tree | Urban trees

ULMUS lutece

Also referred to as 'Nanguen' this clone has a complex parentage with Ulmus minor, galbra, Exoniensis and wallichiana all present in its genetic makeup. Originally a Dutch clone, it was discarded for the unfounded fear it was susceptible to Coral Spot fungus but was adopted by the French instead who have planted extensively in Paris and surrounding cities. It rates 5 out of 5 on Dutch field tests regarding Dutch Elm Disease.

Green leaves are late to emerge in May and turn yellow in autumn. It is a tough tree and tolerates urban pollution as well as coastal locations. It is very temperature hardy and has been successfully planted in Scandinavia. It has been subject to 20 years of field trials in France before being released for general planting in 2002.

17|22 Mature height: 17-22m	Shape of mature tree	Urban trees

ZELKOVA serrata

A relative of the Elm, this is a native of Japan. Introduced into the UK in 1861, it won the Award of Garden Merit in 2002. It thrives on most soils and is well suited to tolerate the rigours of the urban environment.

This is a medium to large tree with a wide spreading and rounded habit. Its smooth, grey bark flakes attractively, and its foliage displays fine shades of red and bronze in autumn. Good for avenues and parkland. Zelkovas do best in fertile, sandy, loamy soils.

12|17		
Mature height: 12-17m	Shape of mature tree	Parkland trees

ZELKOVA serrata Green Vase

This is a recent American introduction brought into the UK in the 1980s and is widely viewed as the best clonal selection available. It is quick to grow, especially in the first ten years or so, after which it becomes more sedate.

The much tighter, columnar habit of this medium to large cultivar makes it considerably more suitable as a street tree than the species. It also tolerates air pollution and windy sites. The trunk has a soft grey bark and foliage provides very good autumn colour. It thrives on most soils.

Similar looking and related to Elm, it is very resistant to Dutch Elm Disease so represents a good and attractive alternative.

12|17		
Mature height: 12-17m	Shape of mature tree	Parkland trees

ZIZIPHUS guiggiolo
Chinese Date

We were introduced to this variety after our Sales Director saw it on his holiday in Southern Spain. Thought to have been cultivated for its fruit in China some 4000 years ago and still popular today.

Originating from China, where it is grown as a commercial fruiting crop, it makes a small dome shaped tree. Russet brown dates of about 2-3 centimetres are profusely borne by late summer, but the tree can sucker, so it is unsuitable for paved/hard areas. Being a desert species it is very tolerant of drought and its thorny stems add to a pleasing architectural effect. A collector's item!!

3|5		
Mature height: 3-5m	Multi-stem	Garden trees

Trees for a Purpose

Choosing the right tree to suit your environment

Autumn Colour

Avenue Trees

Bark Interest

Clay Soils

Coastal Sites

Dry Soils

Edible Fruits

Edible Nuts

Evergreen Trees

Extreme PH, acid or alkaline

Flowering

Garden

Hedging

Narrow Trees

Parkland trees

Red/Purple Leaves

Stilted Screening

Trees for Bees

Urban Trees

Variegated Trees

Weeping Trees

Wet Soils

Yellow Foliage

Native Trees

Planting Guide

Our trees are generally measured by girth size in centimetres. This measurement is taken one metre from ground level and is the circumference around the trunk at this point.

1. Water regularly and slowly during the first two growing seasons after planting. If the water doesn't drain away within ten minutes you are in danger of over watering.

2. All grass and weed competition around the base of the tree should be eliminated (an area of at least one metre around the base of each tree is recommended). Tree trunks will take up herbicides so take care not to spray stems.

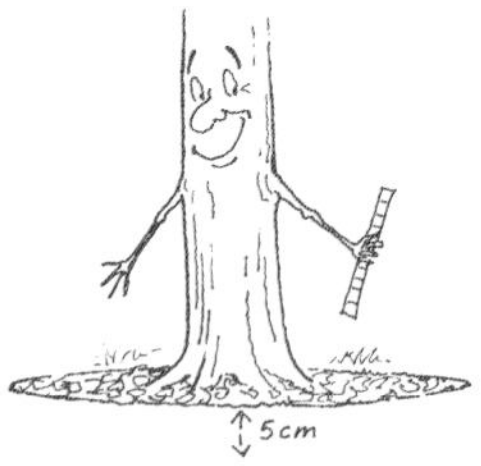

3. The area kept free from weed and grass competition can be mulched annually to a depth of five centimetres to prevent subsequent weed growth.

4. The tree can be staked either side of the container root system to avoid excess movement during establishment, and to prevent the stakes damaging the root system when they are driven into the ground.

5. All ties should be adjusted as necessary to allow the tree to grow freely, without constriction.

6. All damage from strimmers and other mowing equipment is to be avoided.

7. Trees hate to be planted deep. Once the pot has been removed for planting, the top of the compost should be at finished ground level after installation.

Girth Size	Approx Height	Pot	Height	Width	Approx Weight
8-10cm girth	= 7-9ft	20L	30cm	30cm	25kg
10-12cm girth	= 9-11ft	35L	25cm	30cm	35kg
12-14cm girth	= 11-13ft	45L	35cm	40cm	50kg
14-16cm girth	= 13-15ft	55L	35cm	45cm	55kg
16-18cm girth	= 15-17ft	65L	40cm	45cm	75kg
18-20cm girth	= 17-19ft	100L	40cm	60cm	100kg
20-25cm girth	= 19-21ft	150L	55cm	60cm	155kg
25-30cm girth	= 20ft+	250L	65cm	70cm	255kg
30-35cm girth	= 25ft+	350L	70cm	80cm	355kg
35-40cm girth	= 25-30ft+	500L	75cm	95cm	505kg
40-60cm girth	= 25-35ft+	750L	80cm	110cm	755kg
		1000L	100cm	120cm	1,005kg
		1750L	100cm	150cm	1,755kg
		3000L	125cm	175cm	3,015kg

How to find us

We are located between Ely and Soham on the A142. Disregard signposts to Barcham until you get to one saying Barcham & Eye Hill. Follow this road for a few hundred yards and our entrance is on the left. Our drive takes you to our reception where we have a cup of tea or coffee waiting for you!

If you are travelling by train, we are only 3 miles from Ely mainline train station. There are always taxis there but if you phone ahead we would be pleased to collect you. It takes about one hour to get from Kings Cross to Ely on some services so this may be a better option for those of you travelling from London.

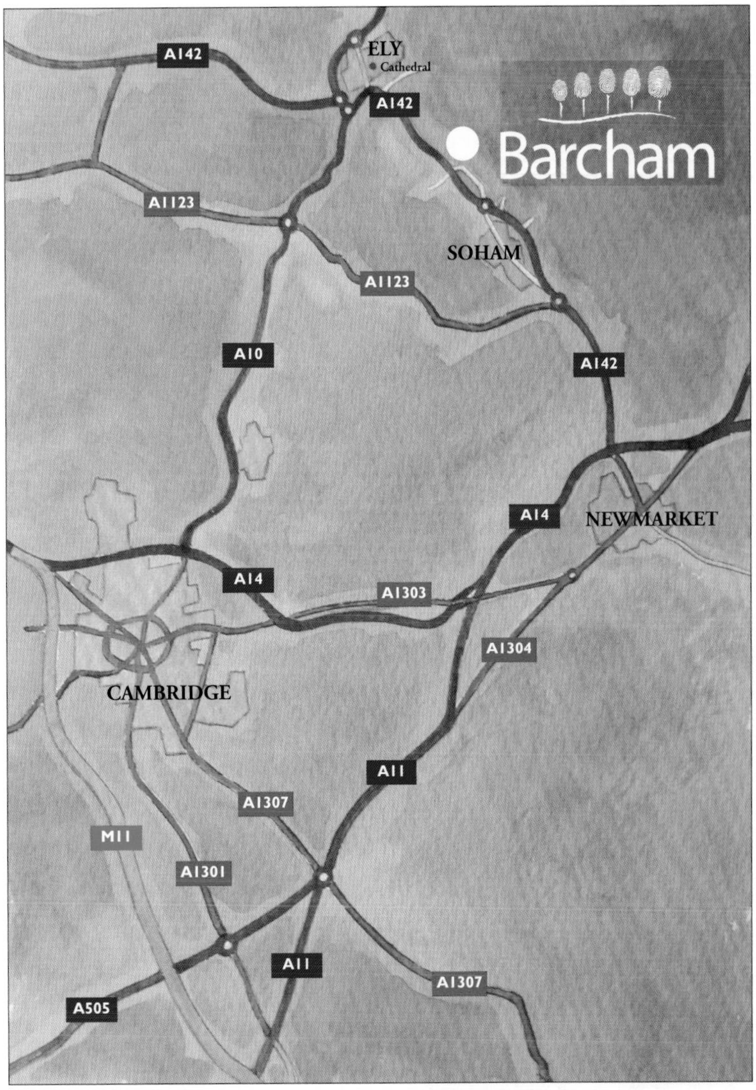

Barcham
The Tree Specialists

Barcham Trees PLC,
Eye Hill Drove,
Ely, Cambridgeshire,
CB7 5XF

Tel: 01353 720 748
Fax: 01353 723 060
Email: sales@barchamtrees.co.uk

www.barcham.co.uk
www.barchampro.co.uk

Terms & conditions

Availability
All plant material listed is offered subject to availability on receipt of order.

Prices
Barcham Trees is a wholesale business therefore all prices are ex-nursery and do not include VAT at the prevailing rate.

Ordering
Orders placed on the telephone must be confirmed in writing via email or in the post.

Credit Accounts & Invoice Terms
Barcham has its invoices credit insured by Coface UK. Accounts are vetted by our insurer and credit limits issued. If a credit limit is not issued, payment is required on a pro-forma basis. Terms are stated on the invoice and should be strictly complied with to avoid insurer collection. Until payment has been received in full, our trees are still the property of Barcham Trees Plc and can be recovered as such.

Warranty
Whilst every effort is made to keep nursery stock healthy and true to name and type, our liability for plants supplied is limited to the replacement of those plants.
No warranty expressed or implied is given as to the growth or suitability of those plants to their ultimate location. If you are not completely satisfied, contact must be made to this office within 7 days of delivery or collection, and confirmed in writing. Failure to do so will deem those goods as being accepted by the customer. No responsibility is accepted for replacements, as so much depends on the planting, soil and weather conditions. Barcham Trees Plc takes no responsibility for the cost of replanting failed trees.

Guarantee
All our container trees are guaranteed for twelve months after delivery if supplied and planted between the months of October through to March. No liability is taken for stock supplied in bud and leaf between April and September unless the concern is registered within three days of delivery. Our guarantee is subject to drought, flood, vandalism and poor practice.

These terms and conditions shall take precedence over any other that customers may attach to their orders, any variation to these terms and conditions shall not be valid unless agreed in writing. In placing an order a customer is deemed to have accepted these terms and conditions.

English to Latin translator

Alder....Alnus & varieties
Almond....Prunus dulcis
Amur Cork Tree....Phellodendron amurense
Amur Maple....Acer ginnala
Angelica Tree....Aralia elata
Antarctic Beech....Nothofagus antarctica
Apple....Malus
Ash....Fraxinus & varieties
Aspen....Populus tremula & varieties
Atlas Cedar....Cedrus atlantica & varieties
Austrian Pine....Pinus nigra Austriaca

Bamboo....Phyllostachys & varieties
Bastard Service Tree....Sorbus thuringiaca Fastigiata
Bay Laurel....Laurus nobilis
Bay Willow....Salix pentandra
Beech....Fagus & varieties
Birch....Betula & varieties
Bird Cherry....Prunus padus & varieties
Blue Spruce....Picea pungens & varieties
Bournemouth Pine....Pinus pinaster
Box....Buxus
Bottle Brush....Callistemon laevis
Box Elder....Acer negundo & varieties
Broad-Leaved Lime....Tilia platyphyllos
Bhutan Pine....Pinus wallichiana

Cabbage Tree....Cordyline australis
Camperdown Elm....Ulmus glabra Camperdownii
Canadian Maple....Acer rubrum & varieties
Candyfloss Tree....Cercidiphyllum japonicum
Cappadoci Maple....Acer cappadocicum & varieties
Cedar....Cedrus & varieties
Cedar of Lebanon....Cedrus libani
Celtic Maple....Acer pseudoplatanus & varieties
Cherry....Prunus & varieties
Chestnut-Leaved Oak....Quercus castaneifolia
Chinese Date....Ziziphus guiggiolo
Chinese Privet....Ligustrum lucidum & varieties
Chusan Palm....Trachycarpus fortunei
Coastal Redwood....Sequoia sempervirens
Contorted Willow....Salix matsudana Tortuosa
Common Lime....Tilia europaea & varieties
Cork Oak....Quercus suber
Copper Beech....Fagus sylvatica Purpurea
Cornelian Cherry....Cornus mas
Crab Apple....Malus & varieties
Crape Myrtle....Lagerstroemia indica & varieties
Cypress....Cupressus arizonica Glauca & Cupressus macrocarpa Goldcrest
Cypress Oak....Quercus robur Fastigiata & varieties

Date Plum....Diospyrus lotus
Dawn Redwood....Metasequoia glyptostroboides & varieties
Deodar Cedar....Cedrus deodara
Desert Willow....Chitalpa tashkentensis Summer Bells
Dogwood....Cornus & varieties
Dove Tree....Davidia involucrata

Elm....Ulmus & varieties
English Oak....Quercus robur
Eucalyptus....Eucalyptus & varieties

False Acacia....Robinia & varieties
Flowering Ash....Fraxinus ornus & varieties
Field Maple....Acer campestre & varieties
Fig....Ficus
Fir....Abies
Foxglove Tree....Paulownia tomentosa
Fraser Fir....Abies Fraserii

Giant Redwood....Sequoiadendron giganteum
Golden Rain....Laburnum & varieties
Golden Ash....Fraxinus excelsior Jaspidea
Great Western Cedar....Thuja plicata Atrovirens
Gum Tree....Eucalyptus & varieties

Hackberry....Celtis occidentalis
Handkerchief Tree....Davidia & varieties
Hawthorn....Crataegus & varieties
Hazel....Corylus & varieties

Holly....Ilex & varieties
Holm Oak....Quercus ilex
Honey Locust....Gleditsia & varieties
Hop Hornbeam....Ostrya carpinifolia
Hornbeam....Carpinus & varieties
Horse Chestnut....Aesculus & varieties
Himalayan Birch....Betula utilis & varieties
Hungarian Oak....Quercus frainetto

Incense Cedar....Calocedrus decurrans
Indian Bean Tree....Catalpa & varieties
Irish Juniper....Juniperus communis Hibernica
Irish Yew....Taxus baccata Fastigiata & Aurea
Italian Alder....Alnus cordata
Italian Cypress....Cupressus sempervirens

Japanese Angelica Tree....Aralia elata
Japanese Cedar....Cryptomeria
Japanese Maple....Acer palmatum & varieties
Japanese Pagoda Tree....Sophora japonica & varieties
Jelly Palm....Butta capitata
Judas Tree....Cercis siliquastrum & varieties
June Berry....Amelanchier & varieties

Katsura....Cercidiphyllum japonicum
Keaki....Zelkova serrata & varieties
Kentucky Coffee Tree....Gymnocladus dioica
Killarney Strawberry Tree....Arbutus unedo
Kilmarnock Willow....Salix caprea Pendula
Korean Fir....Abies koreana
Kusamaki....Podocarpus

Larch ... Larix & varieties
Laurel ... Prunus rotundifolia/laurocerasus
Leyland Cypress ... Cupressocyparis leylandii & varieties
Lilac ... Syringa v& varieties
Lime ... Tilia & varieties
Lobels Maple ... Acer lobelii
Lombardy Poplar ... Populus nigra Italica
London Plane ... Platanus hispanica

Magnolia ... Magnolia & varieties
Maidenhair Tree ... Ginkgo & varieties
Manna Ash ... Fraxinus ornus & varieties
May Tree ... Crataegus & varieties
Medlar ... Mespilus germanica
Mongolian Lime ... Tilia mongolica
Mountain Ash ... Sorbus aucuparia & varieties
Monkey Puzzle ... Araucaria araucana
Monterey Pine ... Pinus radiata
Mulberry ... Morus & varieties

Nettle Tree ... Celtis australis
Nordmann Fir ... Abies nordmanniana
Norway Maple ... Acer platanoides & varieties
Norway Spruce ... Picea abies

Oak ... Quercus & varieties
Olive ... Olea europaeus
One-Leaved Ash ... Fraxinus excelsior Diversifolia
Oriental Plane ... Platanus orientalis & varieties

Paper Birch ... Betula papyrifera
Paper Mulberry ... Broussonetia papyrifera
Paperbark Maple ... Acer griseum
Pear ... Pyrus & varieties
Pecan ... Carya Illinoinensis
Pencil Cedar ... Cupressus sempervirens
Persian Iron Wood ... Parrotia persica & varieties
Pin Oak ... Quercus palustris
Pine ... Pinus & varieties
Pineapple Guava ... Feijoa sellowiana
Plum ... Prunus domestica
Poplar ... Populus & varieties
Portugal Laurel ... Prunus lusitanica
Pride of India ... Koelreuteria paniculata & varieties
Privet ... Ligustrum & varieties
Purple Leaf Plum ... Prunus cerasifera Nigra
Pussy Willow ... Salix caprea

Redbud ... Cercis & varieties
Red Maple ... Acer rubrum & varieties & Acer freemanii Autumn Blaze
Red Twigged Lime ... Tilia platyphyllos Rubra
Red Oak ... Quercus rubra
Redwood ... Sequoia
River Birch ... Betula nigra
Rose of Sharon ... Hibiscus
Rowan ... Sorbus aucuparia & varieties

Rubber Tree ... Eucommia ulmoides
Scarlet Oak ... Quercus coccinea
Scarlet Willow ... Salix alba Chermesina
Scots Pine ... Pinus sylvestris
Sentinel Pine ... Pinus sylvestris Fastigiata
Serbian Spruce ... Picea omorika
Serviceberry ... Amelanchier & varieties
Sessile Oak ... Quercus petraea
Shingle Oak ... Quercus imbricaria
Silver Birch ... Betula pendula & varieties
Silver Maple ... Acer saccharinum & varieties
Silver Lime ... Tilia tomentosa & varieties
Silver Wattle ... Acacia dealbata
Small-Leaved Lime ... Tilia cordata & varieties
Smoke Tree ... Cotinus coggogria Royal Purple
Swedish Birch ... Betula Dalecarlica
Swedish Upright ... Populus tremula Erecta
Sweet Gum ... Liquidambar & varieties
Snakebark Maple ... Acer
Snow Gum ... Eucalyptus & varieties
Snowy Mespilus ... Amelanchier & varieties
Stone Pine ... Pinus pinea
Sumach ... Rhus typhina
Sugar Maple ... Acer saccharum & varieties
Swamp Cypress ... Taxodium distichum
Swedish Whitebeam ... Sorbus intermedia & varieties
Sweet Chestnut ... Castanea sativa & varieties
Sweet Gum ... Liquidambar & varieties
Swiss Mountain Pine ... Pinus mugo
Sycamore ... Acer pseudoplatanus & varieties

Thorn ... Crataegus & varieties
Tree of Heaven ... Ailanthus altissima
Trident Maple ... Acer buergerianum
Tulip Tree ... Liriodendron tulipifera
Tupelo ... Nyssa sylvatica
Turkish Hazel ... Corylus colurna
Turkey Oak ... Quercus cerris

Violet Willow ... Salix daphnoides
Victoria Plum ... Prunus domestica Victoria

Walnut ... Juglans & varieties
Wedding Cake Tree ... Cornus controversa
Weeping Birch ... Betula pendula Tristis & Youngii
Weeping Willow ... Salix alba Tristis (Chrysocoma)
Whitebeam ... Sorbus aria & varieties
Witch Hazel ... Hamamelis & varieties
White Willow ... Salix alba
Wild Cherry ... Prunus avium & varieties
Wild Service Tree ... Sorbus torminalis
Willow ... Salix & varieties
Wing Nut ... Pterocarya fraxinifolia
Western Red Cedar ... Thuja plicata & varieties

Yellow Wood ... Cladrastis kentukia
Yew ... Taxus baccata

Tree Index